RIGHTEOUSNESS IN
AMERICA

RIGHTEOUSNESS IN
AMERICA

Herman Pettiford

Charleston, SC

www.PalmettoPublishing.com

Righteousness In America

Copyright © 2022 by Herman Pettiford

First Edition

Paperback: 978-1-68515-615-2
eBook: 978-1-68515-616-9

Contents

Preface

Righteousness In America is a book about one from a very religious home who found God early. As a little boy sitting on the church bench when his feet could not even touch the floor. He asked God to come and go with him as he grew into manhood. He asked God to guide him, bless and protect him, and be with him through all the trials and tribulations that he would go through in life.

All the trouble that America would go through, from young America until the America of today, Satan would use a specific family to help carry out his sinful ways to dominate America with sin and chaos.

He tried vigorously to inflict sin into America through worldly ways. This book is fictional, and some of the people are real but recreated by adding new and different attributes to their characteristics.

Acknowledgments

Seven friends of mine have been in my life for at least sixty years or more and are familiar with my failures and accomplishments. They are also familiar with probably all the females in my life. All seven have given their time, concern, help, and support. Along with their advice and sincerity towards me at one time or another. They are John Thompson alias {Pudding}, Ronald Dorsey alias {Eggy Butch}, John Oliver Berry alias {Oliver}, Muslim name {YaYa}, William Hill alias {Tank}, Cliff Owens, Robert King alias {Byay}, and, Bassie Bell, a lifetime friend, and business associate. It is a pleasure to say that all seven of these men are presently alive doing well, in good health and strength. All seven have within their travels, time and experiences, have found God in their lives but were introduced to God Almighty as children by their parents, and God has shined on their lives and raised them whenever they were down, including me, myself, and I.

To my wife Jeannette Delores Pettiford. Who is with me in everything I do? She has taught me the functions of the computer. She has helped me with my life, and she is the one to introduce me to my book's first computer program {which was most instrumental in my writing}. She is forever arguing with me about business, but who loves me and takes good care of me, our children, our grand-children, and our dog [Lily Girl]. "Thank You, God," for sending her to me.

To Tyrese Wright, a stranger to my life who came out of nowhere to assist me when the world fell in on me. She has been with me ever since whenever I need her. And who has assisted me in writing this book? Whom I depend on and appreciate even with her faults. Her help in me writing this book has been enormous. Tyrese is also the creator of the book's front cover and is helpful to create the back cover as well.

To Georgia, I never got a chance to thank you for the bold but dangerous actions that you performed for me without ever asking for anything in return. I have not seen you since the days, weeks, and months, a long time ago that you made it possible that freedom once again knew me. I thank God for your bravery and your commitment to stand tall and strong in the hours, days, weeks, and months that I could not do for myself, what you so bravely did for me, and I thank you with all my heart and soul, and I will never forget you, or that I am indebted to you.

Introduction

God is most definitely in America and has been with America all the time while making it Possible for His Word to be witnessed, studied, and learned throughout America. As America grew from its adolescent stages to its present state of being a world leader, Satan continues to try blanketing the world with chaos, negativity, and sin. But God is more significant than great and better than the best, and His awesomeness is much greater than just being impressive and will endure forever.

Says so the belief of the author of this book.

God is in America and has been before the white man or any culture or creed of person, besides the original American Indian, ever set foot on the land of America. A land that does not worship idols, bronze or gold, but worships the creator of the wind, stars, moon, and humanity. The need for RIGHTEOUSNESS did find its roots here in America. RIGHTEOUSNESS is the way and order that GODLY people live, treat and respect one another while living a life that is pleasing to the creator of life and helpful to one another and the land. SO, BELIEVE MR. AND MRS. HERMAN PETTIFORD

CHAPTER 1

No Sin Comes To Earth and Evil Dare Not Complain

In evaluating man's purpose of the human race, the creator of life and authority sets a date for man to exit from his mother's womb and breathe the sinful air of the planet earth and a time for man to breathe the breath of life no more. Within that period, man's powerful will is to choose good and righteous, or evil.

That is the whole concept of *man on earth*. Man's fundamental idea, purpose, and reason to exist and survive on Earth is choosing good and righteous or evil. All that live by the ethics of goodness and righteousness after the A.D. period. Those who believe in the Son of the Creator also think that there is life after death. They believe in the Son of the Creator and live sound and righteous lives during their stay on earth {so they believe in the Christian religion}.

It is man's choice which choice he will live, but no evil man can be good and righteous unless he finds the Heavenly Father and the Son who will change his heart, mind, and soul, and at some point, in time, the Creator will judge all humankind.

Man, who does not live a good and righteous life and believes not in the Son of the Creator of heaven and earth, only believes what they see, feel, and can touch on the planet. And focuses on having power and authority while they choose to live sinful lives, and respect, not their brother humankind shall be strongly judged and punished by the Creator, {so believe the good and righteous}. Humanity who visions only eternal life, peace, and heavenly contentment after being judged by the Creator of heaven and earth on Judgment Day believes in life after death.

Man's survival upon the earth does not include man's survival in the womb of his mother before birth. Nor does man choose who his parents are or who his siblings are. Only Almighty {God} and righteousness can protect man while still in his mother's womb. While sometimes, the forces of evil are hostile towards the parent's pregnancy.

Each man that comes upon the face of the earth must face mental and physical pain at some time in his life. He must laugh, cry, discharge waste, and die unless the Creator of life and death sees fit to alter that pattern of life towards that individual.

A man comes to earth equipped with only love, trust, and dependence on family and loved ones. A man comes to the world sinless, without evil, and nonviolent. But anger *is* in man's nature. A man knows not sinful ways, things, or habits. Hatred, selfishness, violence, or no sin comes to earth with humans.

After coming to Earth, man acquires all sin, where a man learns to sin. Where {Satan} the devil or Lucifer, which is the original name he had in heaven. Many followed him and his sinful thoughts while in heaven when he was a top angel over all other angels.

There was no sin until {Lucifer} created sin because he is the originator of sin.

God is love, pure, and righteous.

Suppose Lucifer could convince many angels to follow him into sinful things. In that case, you must understand how easy it is for Lucifer to persuade humans to trust him, believe him, and follow him, especially when (Satan) entices man with worldly things that appeal to the wants and needs and desires of humankind.

As he the devil or {Lucifer}, or Satan, whichever name you choose to call him, continues to use more ways and avenues like drugs, guns, murder, selfishness, and thievery to convince a man to sin.

In all man's endeavors, goals, actions, and activities on earth during man's stay on earth, whether a man is a success or a failure. It makes no difference. Whether a man is a king or a peasant, rich or poor, in the eyes of God, it makes no difference, and whatever man sacrifices or what height or status man reaches in life. It only matters to God whether a man is good and righteous or bad and evil. Whether man believes in Jesus Christ, the Son of God, {so believe the good and honest or the Christians}

Christians believe in Jesus Christ as the Son of the only living God, except for Jesus Christ, who also is God.

In evaluating the difference of people, color, spiritual belief, and man's purpose on earth, man's inspirations, desires, wants, and achievements.

There is an organization that is well organized all over the earth wherever man visits, works, plays, lives, or ventures.

The one purpose of this anonymous organization is to rule the world of the planet earth through power, authority, and force. While being invisible to all and any who inquire of the origin of this so powerful organization, headed and led by Satan (the devil). Or his original name as an angel in heaven was Lucifer. This anonymous organization generates its power and authority through secretly ruling power structures and powerful forces of other lands, countries, and space that man occupies upon the face of the earth.

Many times, has this anonymous organization brought destruction or reconstruction to kings, queens, presidents, chiefs, lords, and many other power heads. That reason was to bring upon their growth of additional power—all to bring extra fuel and authority to their power structure.

{(123)} is an anonymous organization figure of high rank of this present day. He symbolizes one who can designate power, force, and authority in the name of the anonymous organization.

While as an unborn child in the womb of his mother. (123) was given a man-child still in his mother's womb also. That would be taught the art of self-defense. To protect the life of (123) for as long as both of them would live upon the earth.

{YaYa} was the name of the man-child that would be the bodyguard for (123), and Yaya's entire family was accountable for the actions that YaYa would perform towards his responsibilities as the bodyguard for (123). Even before either man-child came upon the earth, it was such a great honor for Yaya's family to be known and respected. The un-born man-child would protect the other young man-child, representing the anonymous organization. Offering its un-limited powers from all around the world to tear down, kill, and bring fear, death, and destruction to whomever, and whenever necessary. The anonymous organization has no heart or soul, no compassion, no love or trust. Power and the right to execute negativity are done through people just waiting to be chosen to be included in the anonymous organization's line of waiting participants. All have some-thing to offer the anonymous organization, whether power, authority, wealth, expertise, or their lives or souls.

They wait to be a part of those who believe they rule the world here on planet earth.

True, it is that destroying the Children of Journajesty is impossible. But true it is that the one most important goal in the lives and existence of the (123) Family is to create ways to stagnate, cripple, maim, hold back, confuse, misuse, and abuse the Children of Journajesty. The chil-dren of Journajesty being all that shares their blood, time, patience, honor, love, and jeopardize their freedom for the love of humanity, regardless of the color of one's skin, nor the choice of one's faith, religion, or the difference in one's language. They are spreading love, unity, equality, and free-dom to humanity.

Regardless of the situation, time, or place is the main objective of the children of Journajesty

All (123) family participants have the same goal. Which are to stagnate, cripple, main, hold back, confuse, misuse, and abuse the Children of Journajesty's incredible powers and ability to survive, excel, and teach the truth. Truth! Being in worship to God, creator of the mountains, rivers, seas, the sun, and the moon. The children of Journajesty, known for their brotherly love and belief that all men were created equal and deserved the right to freedom, equal opportunities, and the right to worship the creator. YaYa was the bodyguard's name for the (123) Family of this present-day time and generation. YaYa represented the (123) Family and was the present-day body guard under the authority of the present-day (123) rule here in America.

YaYa was dedicated primarily to and for the present (123) who created the decisions and strategies made in America concerning the children of Journajesty that his father had the same purpose as he, who came before him.

That purpose was to hold back, stagnate, abuse, and misuse the Children of Journajesty. There was nothing in existence that was more important than that. That is the purpose, meaning, and cornerstone for the very existence of the (123) Family. From the beginning to the end, it was created by (Satan).

The present-day leader of the (123) family whose name was (Live), and who headed the movement against the children of Journajesty in America, admired the performances of his fathers' and family in other countries, dedicating themselves against the same children of Journajesty types as in America. (Live's) father was named Evil, who was under the rule of Satan, (Evil) had been hand-picked by Satan himself. (Live) The present (123), he was referred to as (Live) by those in his absence. He knew those who were professionally and leisurely in the many years of acquaintances with him. For they were the only ones allowed to call him by the name (Live) without being threatened with death, for he wanted only to be known as a part of the (123) Family.

The (123) Family members were known to live long lives upon the earth according to the everyday life span of the average man. That fact was mainly because the (123) Family knew how to take care of themselves through food, exercise, sun, water, rest, silence, or meditation. Herbs, flowers, plants, and even dirt were included in the (123) family diet, along with a variety of fresh vegetables, fish, clams, and oyster eggs from the sea. The (123) family has never tasted the smell or taste of salt or sugar because they were taboo to the family of the (123clan.) It allowed the (123) Family usually a lifespan of about 100 to 150 years upon the earth.

The doctors on call twenty-four hours a day, for the (123) family children, always soon disappeared within 9 to 10 years later after each new (123) family child had been born to the (123) Family.

Each new family member of the (123) Family was never counted, mentioned, or talked about outside the (123) Family.

While the doctor of each new (123) family member always disappeared between 9 and 10 years later. Some believe that the doctor received some reward of total peace and happiness. The delivery doctor of each new (123) family child had to stay close to the child. Each doctor had to cater to and answer the child's every call and medical demand until at least nine or ten years of age.

At nine or ten years of age, a (123) child had the IQ equivalent to an average child of 18. He was well past the IQ of a middle child.

However, the absolute truth was that each new (123) child member of the (123) family had to kill his delivery doctor between nine and ten years old. They had to cut off the doctor's hands, feet, and head to pass the (123)-obligation test of being initiated into the (123) Family as a family member. New members of the (123) Family committed this deed after the ninth year but before the tenth year of life. It was endorsed by Satan, as a rule, to be followed with no exceptions, excuses, or failures in any way. Or serious consequences would be executed.

Evil was the father of the first (123) who came to the Americas. Evil saw that the natives of America loved and worshiped the Creator of life. The Natives of the Americas loved their fellow man. They loved the animals, the trees and the sky, the waters, and the earth while loving themselves because they were all creations of the Creator. The Native Americans worshiped no idols, buildings, or gods of stone, gold, or bronze in this era. They worshiped the Giver of life, the Creator of the seas, rivers, rain, the heavens, and the earth. When the men of white skin first came to the shores of America, they treated the Natives like savages and animals, but the Natives still showed the light-skinned men how to survive through their first winter. They taught them how to hunt, eat, live, and stay because there was no evilness in the Natives as a people. It is an actual fact that Our Lord and Savior Jesus Christ had not yet come to the shores of America, but the loyal native

American Indians did prove their loyalty and religion by worshipping the creator of life by standards they did to ensure thankfulness by using only what they needed of the supply of food, clothing, and worship and praise to the creator. Righteousness is what is called for the lifestyle that the American Indians did live in harmony with the land, the animals, their neighbors, and their worship and praise to the creator of life

It was then that it was brought to the attention of (Evil) from the Highest of the High of the anonymous organization {Satan}. That (Evil) was to send forces of destruction, chaos, and evil to the Americas, to misuse, abuse, stagnate and hold back the Children of Journajesty, who were considered anyone that loved the land of America, freedom for all, and equal opportunities for humankind in America. In hopes of someday making America a land of equal opportunity for all. Destroying the children of Journajesty strengths of love, honor, respect, and spiritual guidance was impossible to do. Still, chaos, unfairness, and evilness were on the turn for the children of Journajesty.

One hundred twenty-five years later, Evil still had not brought evilness, lies, and betrayal into the land of America in abundance as (Satan) had instructed him to do. Even though (Evil) had tried his best to accomplish that feat.

He was punished by (Satan) for failing to accomplish his mission. By stripping Evil of the right to have a birth name or any other kind of name. Also, by stripping Evil's family to be forever nameless for (Evil) failing to accomplish the mission that (Satan) had given him.

One hundred twenty-five years of still failing the task given to Evil by Satan, Evil sent his first son (Live), known as the first (123) (because he had no name), into the Americas. With the same goal of misusing, abusing, stagnating, and holding back the Children of Journajesty. Because their loving, forgiving, and honest ways would teach so much goodness, honesty, truth, and Godliness, followed by worshiping the Creator of life.

Truth and believing in the Creator of life. Who is also the Creator of the Americas, earth, and the heavens? First, learning is the beginning and introduction to the wisdom and the ability to relate and understand all that is understandable. The anonymous organization looked upon the Native Americans, the first of the Children of Journajesty. At least until the white settlers came to the land of America, bringing their religion of Christianity, Catholics, Muslims, and the Jewish. They also got the right to be free and worship as one pleases, giving the right of freedom to all that came to the land of America, and making them also children of Journajesty.

Freedom was the soul and backbone of the land of America, and America was taken away from the Native Americans.

The Native Americans were not perfect people, and there were many deficient or bad Native Americans, but there were no evil Native Americans.

The anonymous organization, headed by Satan, looked into the future of the Native Americans and the land. They saw that the Native Americans were good in their hearts and souls and carried no evil in their hearts and souls.

Nor was there acceptance for complete evilness or wrongdoing for the future of this land.

The Highest of the High, in charge of the anonymous organization (Satan), schooled and taught Evil to use one of the {highest of the high's} old standby tricks. The tricks of causing chaos between people with lies and misinterpretation of facts. Distortion of the truth and reality, which the highest of the anonymous organization (Satan) used for thousands of years. He used it on different civilizations and cultures to hold back, abuse, and misuse, other lands.

The Highest of the High of the anonymous organization (Satan) was once in charge of thousands of angels in heaven. The Highest of the High of the anonymous organization got many heavenly angels to follow him and believe in him and his lies through lies and deception.

The Creator of life, heaven, and the earth did throw them all out of heaven. And they are all to be punished at the right time.

So, the land of America did not fill with people of evil. Even though there were some, and (Evil) failed his mission. Lies and evilness did not serve the land of America.

Evil *did* fail his mission given to him by Satan of filling the land of America with hatred, evilness, jealousy and deceit, and liars.

Even though hatred, lies, and violence did erupt in America, the land of America was not yet filled with sinful and evil ways. But, it was at this present time that (Righteousness) had been seen as a way of life in the chapter of American life that the original American Indian was living.

Like a fresh coat of premium paint would cover the surface of the wooden panel. So did the (righteousness) of the similarity of the goodness of God that did cover the land of America. Even the Animals, the wind, rain and summer, fall and spring did also fit into the covering of (Righteousness) that was in the air. In coherence, the animals themselves sometimes seem to voluntarily give their lives for the (Righteousness) Of sacrifice for the right to be slaughtered and eaten for the sake of need and survival. All a part of the natural flow of the land and in God's ordinance.

Evil, accepting his punishment of losing his name and being nameless. Even for the offspring of his children and his children's names to become nameless.

For Evil dare not complain about his punishment or the highest authority of the anonymous organization (Satan) would surely devour Evil without a single afterthought. With all of the power and authority Evil controlled, Evil dared not buck, aggravate, or entice the Highest of the High (Satan), with a complaint or surely destruction would follow Evil wherever he went or tried to hide.

Evil's only comment was, "There is something about this land of America, something that kept evil from being accepted by all the occupants of the land in abundance."

"There was something about the land of America that was bad to the forces of evil which I have never seen happen before. But it was good to the people of the land. Something that made individuals of the land like kings, chiefs, and lords, people of influence were made not always by their birthrights. But by their accomplishments of honor and bravery. Their participation in activities for and about the people, tribe, or village. Or for the cause of the people of the land. Something about this land that brings honesty, loyalty, and honor before fortune, fame, and authority."

"There's something about this land of America that makes the people of this land choose their leaders from people or inhabitants of the land that was beyond a doubt, had given to the land pieces of their heart and soul, character, sweat, blood, tears, and ethics."

"But absent of a return for themselves of anything.

"Even a few of the white people who proved not to be liars, thieves, nor murders but showed loyalty were granted positions of honor and trust. Within the tribes first before themselves. That was the speech given by Evil. Not in defense of his actions but about what happened to him in the process of him trying his best to fulfill his orders given to him and entrusted to him by the sole commanding officer of the anonymous organization {Satan}.

Evil was trying to show he did not understand why America was so hard to endorse evil all over the land.

Man's purpose in America all over the planet earth continues to be good and righteous, or evil. That choice continues to develop Americans in their means to modernize America as the land of America grows in its later years while materializing into a stronger, more powerful, and religious country. From its adolescent and immature beginning of America as a vast, wild, dangerous, uncivilized land without the religion of Christianity, Catholics, Muslims, or Jews.

Worship was given to the Creator of life, death, rain, the trees, the seas, the moon, the stars, and the sky. The creator of heaven and earth. The only living God, by even the earliest of the inhabitants of America dating back to one thousand years A.D. of Christ our Lord and Savior, showing that God was in America, even then, and that is (Righteousness is in America)

While even then, Native Americans were in the Americas. Christianity, Catholics, Muslims, and Jews, which are the main religions practiced in America today, had not been brought to light because Jesus had not yet sent his disciples or teachers of the word of God to the so early land of America. The creator was worshiped through Almighty God's beautiful creations.

Jesus was and still is the originator, original, and Creator of the religion of Christianity, which will soon be the leader in faith in American society. {So, believe the author of this book}.

It is a fact that the (123) Family headed by the {highest of the high (Satan) of the anonymous organization continued its march forward in holding back, stagnating, abusing, misusing, and unfairly treating the Children of Jourmajesty.

No human is powerful enough, intelligent enough, or strong enough in any way, shape, or form to disrupt, dismantle, or even shake up the world of the Highest of the High in command, of the proprietor of the anonymous organization. (Satan)

Not without the help of Almighty God or the approval in some way, shape, or form of Almighty God. The structure or the evil kingdom of the Highest of the High of the Anonymous organization (Satan) is too robust for a mere man to penetrate.

Not without the help or say-so of Almighty God, the creator of the Highest of the High in charge of the anonymous organization (Satan)

He operates here on earth even after being kicked out of heaven many long thousands of areas of time ago by God Almighty for bringing sin into heaven. At the same time, he filled his heart, mind, and soul with thoughts and actions of evilness and deceit. He plans to try to be as Almighty as God Almighty himself.

With all its powers to tear down, destroy, eliminate or rebuild coming from the anonymous organization, it would be trembled, malfunctioned, and abused by a boy: a Christian boy, a black Christian boy on his way to manhood.

After the land of America was taken away from the original American Indians and put on reservations to live.

After (Evil) failed to make the land of America abundant with evil. After (Evil) was stripped of his name. And the name of his offspring by the Highest of the High of the anonymous organization. For not succeeding in making the land of America abundant with evil. After the first (123) was created or appointed by Evil

(Evil), the father of Live, who was now in charge of stagnating, abusing, holding back, and misusing the Children of Jourmajesty, who were those who gave their blood, sweat, tears, loyalty, and honor for the land of America, without looking for any benefits in return for their services. And those who believe in freedom for all in America.

After the buffalo disappeared, the iron horse came running over the tracks all over the land. After the great war of families fighting families concerning keeping the black man as a slave or giving him his freedom. Which divided the people of America into classes of good and righteous or evil. (so, believe the author of this book)

After the black man took the sir names of his slave masters, who took most of their first names from the characters of the Holy Bible. Which was the book of righteousness, holiness, truth, guidance, and the history of the biblical days of the Bible, on which the Christian religion was built

But excellent and righteous have always stood up for the American way. Even though sometimes it seems not so accurate but it is true, and it takes a while to put {Satan} in his place.

{Satan} is the creator and the originator of all wrong and evil. His strengths, army, and tactics are in full gallop, and he gains on the good and righteous.

In the next thirty to fifty years to come, (Satan) will have even more modern technology to assist him in contacting people in other cities and countries.

He will connect individual people who do not know one another. They will meet for the first time through this {so modern technology} that will allow people in other cities and countries to see one another and communicate verbally with one another.

This new technology will be so helpful, and {Satan} will use it negatively, sinfully, and for evil and perversion purposes. Cell phones, the internet, and a host of many other things that will come in the next generations of years {Satan} will use on people to turn their backs on God.

While true, it is that there are so many more lost souls in America presently because (Satan} has so much more ways and means to introduce sin to people.

Before realizing what is happening to them, they continue to have good times and use all the new technology for negative things more than good things.

The new generations are coming into the world not knowing our God, and they will be and are continuously tricked and deceived by Satan. Some older generations are also lost or just not teaching the truth.

And yes, America now has much more sin in it than ever before. This means that after hundreds of years, America is more sinful than ever.

There is plenty more work for the anonymous organization to perform in America. Americans still love teaching and helping one another regardless of whatever happens, Because God is in America. And inside the hearts and souls of those who believe. It always has been and seems to always will be. And that is *"Righteousness in America."*

That is why it is so hard for nonbelievers of our God to relate. The Children of Journajesty continues to teach the truth, love, and worship God. They enjoy the good living that life has to offer in America. The land of the free, brave, and the worshipers of the One and Only Living God besides His Son, Jesus Christ, who also is God.

All is never lost because one is for all. And all is for one, according to the Children of Journajesty here in the great land of America.

The battle goes on between good and righteous and destructive and evil as (Satan) tries to continue to turn America into a land of evilness.

After the Great War between the white people of America who were the ones to settle the land of America, and the blacks, Jews, people of Ireland, and many other cultures and countries all joined in to help make America great—making America ahead of so many other countries, while more and more technology and aviation were created in America.

So many new and powerful inventions have helped make America a leader.

The righteous white man stood up and fought his kin-folk about being good and righteous concerning Christianity and slavery.

Now! Even after blacks in America became free in one sense of the word free. But they were not yet treated equally. Nor were many other races, cultures, and colors of different people in America. They, too, were still mistreated.

The time passed on and the struggle between good and righteousness. The bad and evil grew while Americans also grew in bettering themselves, concerning living with one another and keeping the American dream of equality and freedom alive for all Americans.

Even though (Satan), through the (123) Family would keep evilness well and alive. Through shootings, hangings, fire bombings, house burnings, and of course through lies, murder, deceit. And many other tactics used by (Satan) to spread evil over America like a wildfire. With America still unwilling to yield or become caught entirely in that web of evilness, God is still in America.

It was presently one hundred years after the black man became a free man in America. The role of religion was of very high value and great importance within the new young and growing American people.

Christianity, Catholics, Jews, and Muslims were the main religious groups with lesser or additive beliefs of the dominant religions, of Christianity, Catholics, Jews, and Muslims.

All worship one God, the only living God besides His Son, Jesus Christ, who is also God. {So, believe the Christian religion}

God Jehovah, God Allah, God the Father, Heavenly Father, God of the universe, God the Creator of life, death, and all in between. God as in so many spoken languages, lands, countries, civilized places, and Creator of life, death, and all in between.

God of the human race, all life on land and in the sea, trees, and earth. While also the Creator of heaven and earth, the sun, moon, and the stars. The wind, rain, thunder and lightning, and all the planet's elements.

Time continued in America, and it had been one hundred years since the black man was free from chains around his ankles and could go about more freely. Blacks were still very unfairly treated and with no natural rights, and they did not have the rights of an American in America.

The anonymous organization was continuously moving forward in holding back, stagnating, misusing, and abusing the Children of Jourmajesty.

Though it was done through the (123) Family and in a more modern way other than iron chains, the black man has been free for one hundred years.

He came a long way from not knowing the language and not reading or writing. He knew no way to provide for his family, nor had the right to keep his family together with him or keep his wife or children from being taken from him or be beaten or sold.

The black man was not viewed as a man and did not relate to Christianity. It was now one hundred years later in America, and all Americans came a long way from not being treated fairly because of their culture, nationality, religion, or skin color.

Even though Americans have a long way to go in receiving equality consistently, Americans were moving on in the march toward equality and justice for all and had come a long way.

The struggle between good and righteous and evil also moved forward as the anonymous organization continued to try bringing evilness in abundance in America. Just like it was happening all over the planet earth through one that used the (123) Family in America to bring forth evilness.

While there was genuinely much love in America between Americans, it truly made evilness grow in abundance. As always, even from the beginning, a problem.

Evilness expanded in America, and so had goodness, righteousness, love, and fellowship towards and between Americans. Which just could not be understood by the anonymous organization.

Now! Equality, love, and justice were not equal for all in America, but those things came a long way in America and were steadily improving. But the anonymous organization was now functioning differently through the (123) Family to hold back, stagnate, abuse, and misuse the Children of Journajesty.

The (123) Family ventured into the world of illegal drugs to help hold back, misuse and abuse, and stagnate the Children of Journajesty. The (123) Family ventured into the world of drugs, both prescription and hard. The street drugs such as heroin, alcohol, cocaine, and others help hold back, abuse and misuse the Children of Journajesty.

The (123) Family made money with drugs. However, money was not the purpose for drugs in America, and it was the ruining of American minds, character, morals, and principles. It was more the reason for bringing drugs into American neighborhoods as a strategy for the (123) Family against the Children of Journajesty.

Like selling strong alcohol drinks to the Native Americans, it was to dismantle their minds, souls, and hearts. Drugs brought into America were viewed as *drug money going to other countries*. And to other organizations such as Cartels and the Mafia are tied in with (Satan).

They are organizations under the roof or order or command of (Satan) who is in charge of all evil. And is the creator of all sin and evilness on the planet earth. (Satan) disguises anything and everything to blame for the reason for drugs being in the land of America.

The white man was the first slave of (Satan) in America. The white man was convicted of everything Satan has done since he entered his foot on American soil, and the white man has been blamed for all Satan's sins. He also took the responsibility of being the originator of bringing drugs into America when it was Satan.

It was (Satan) as always, who just turned the situation around to disclose himself from the concept of being the sole proprietor of the whole situation.

Nothing could be more accurate and to the point concerning the real reason for drugs into America, which was to ruin the souls, minds, futures, morals, and principles of the good and righteous. And for no other reason than being a part of holding back, misusing, and abusing the Children of Jourmajesty.

Other reasons were to degrade the education system and separate the elders from the young. Through separate housing, the old Americans could not teach the young Americans. Also, being separated, the young lost the touch of love, respect, and the need to contribute to the elders.

Integrating American Music with violence and disrespect towards one another, especially females, was a new type of slavery introduced to America.

The disrespect from Americans was once again on the rise. The evil was indeed at a tug of war with the sound and righteous.

The Highest of the High in charge of the anonymous organization aimed to interfere and mingle directly with the religious institutions' members to bring corruption, envy, selfishness, lies, and lust into their midst.

The church institutions were places of the old and wise, and it was where the young teachers belonged. They were full of strength, guidance and were the very soul of the good and righteous.

(Satan) hoped to appear during the church to distract the attention from God to being on worldly wrongs of the worst caliber within the religious institutions.

As soon as one man was ejected from their mother's womb, The onward battle of good and righteousness and evil began.

The (123) Family was one of the ongoing carriers for bad and evil instead of the good and righteous here in America.

Now the present (123) in America was continuously not at peace with himself and could not understand why even though he created an abundance of bad and evil in America in the last hundred years.

The evilness brought murders, hangings, thievery, fire bombings, lots and lots of misery, pain, and deceit. Compounded with tons and tons of lies, fear, sorrow, and the thought of wishing one was not even born.

He couldn't understand why there had been just as much or more righteousness in America at the same time. Why was it still so many people willing to help other people?

Why did the haves in America still care about the have nots? And not just the haves of having money, but the haves in positions to help fight for freedom, justice, and equality. To put their lives on the line and endanger their family's safety. At the same time, sacrifice their careers, if need be, to help those who have not. Why were so much love and concern for others still all over America?

Who was this God that was so great, so dependable? With so much to believe and have faith in, so righteous, so forgiving, so tremendous, so Almighty and awesome? Why was this God in America?

Where did this God come from, and how did this God get in America? And oh, how sweet life would be in America without this God, thought (123).

God in America is my real problem and has been my problem from the beginning. Ever since I started to bring evil to America. Imagine an America without God. I don't understand why some men can't be paid any money to mistreat people, even when they have had nothing from the start.

Only because their hearts had to be good and righteous, and only because God was inside them.

So, that is what (123) himself was beginning to wonder about then (123) thought back to when he first brought so many different cultures and languages. So many other people came to America. Was this also when this God came to America?

Had this God of righteousness played such a reversing solution on (123), to bring all this righteousness to America? The evil plans that (123) thought to be created by bringing all of these people of different races, cultures, and nationalities together to create chaos.

Had God just jumped out of the sky or sprang up out of the earth like a tree or flower?

These are some things that (123) wondered about, as (123) realized why the Highest of the High, in charge of the anonymous organization, focused so much on church institutions and righteous family homes. God was a word never to be mentioned on earth within Satan's followers, as long as Satan was in charge of worldly happenings, or one's head would be removed from their body without the chance to explain why that word was used. Once inside the church institutions and the righteous families, Satan got a chance to strut his stuff about evilness, bad habits, bad thoughts, bad ventures, wrong goals to reach, activities to participate in. So, to sort of stealing their religion as they focused on him for a while. Or at least make these righteous people disobedient in serving their God. And being short on righteousness to their God, themselves, their families, and the world. By being curious and paying attention to and involving themselves in devilish creations of the Highest of the High in charge of the anonymous organization.

It was 1963 in America, 100 years after the black man became free men in America. In the State of Maryland, in Baltimore, and on the East Side of town lived a teenager named Pharaoh.

Only by a miracle would he soon meet the acquaintance of the present (123) of that era and time. (EVIL), the father of the first and present (123). Through the Highest of the High of the anonymous organization and the original creator of the (123) Family.

At eighteen, Pharaoh was considered one of the top-notch young professional hustlers of his day and was respected by all in his immediate hustling world. He sometimes mingled in other cities.

In this day and era of time, a hustler was not a drug dealer but could control the ability to make a fast and valuable amount of money by being a good gambler of cards, dice, horses, pool, etc. any gambling game.

Sometimes, having the upper hand or advantage in odds professionally while having the ability to hustle in any way provided him with a fast but pretty dollar.

Using his God-given wits and ability to produce the commodity needed for the hustling world was required, however, without cheating or lying.

Even though he knew how to cheat, but used his cheating ability to keep the heat off him. And to have the knowledge to know who was cheating and bet in favor of those that *were* cheating. He would only use this ability and understanding only in the cases of extreme emergencies while being known to speak words of trustworthiness, for his word was his bond.

Now Pharaoh was married when he was fifteen to a girl named Jazzy, who was also fifteen. They produced a daughter named Linda while Jazzy was again pregnant with another child.

True, the parents of Pharaoh and Jazzy signed papers for them to be married because they were both underages when their marriage vows were performed.

Pharaoh had been raised in a Christian family that loved and worshiped God and Jesus Christ, the Son of God. Pharaoh was religious, so Pharaoh went to God in prayer and told God that he did not want to marry.

He thought or knew it was his responsibility to get married. He told God that he was not marrying Jazzy for love even though he loved Jazzy, and he was marrying her so that he wouldn't disgrace her. And because {Mama Grace} told Pharaoh that marrying Jazzy was the right thing to do because he and Jazzy had one child *and* another on the way. So that Pharaoh would not disgrace Jazzy, Pharaoh married her.

Now Jazzy loved Pharaoh and wanted very much to be married to him, and true it was that Jazzy was Pharaoh's first real girlfriend. Pharaoh did not want to be married, and Pharaoh expressed that to Jazzy. He told her that he would try marriage for her, in hopes to to keep her name respectful and show Mama Grace he was a man and loved God.

When Pharaoh was still fifteen, his first child was born. She was a beautiful baby girl named {Lady Linda Lee Gold} whom Pharaoh loved with all his heart then, now, and forever and another always.

Pharaoh's foster mother, Mrs. Grace, was a very religious woman, and so was her husband, Mr. Grace. Pharaoh's love, respect, and devotion toward them had no end. Home and church, Christian teachings formed Pharaoh's wisdom, knowledge, heart, and mind towards Christianity as a young child.

His beliefs, prayers, dreams, goals, and expectations fell on the open heart and spirit of the only living God who indeed heard all of Pharaoh's prayers even as a child.

God showed favor towards Pharaoh, so say the words of humankind. Even though Pharaoh had been conceived from a sinful married woman to a lustful father, God found favor in Pharaoh.

God protected Pharaoh through a pregnancy of harmful activities as Pharaoh's mother tried to get rid of Pharaoh early in her pregnancy. In shame for getting pregnant. And, in contrast, being married to a husband who was away fighting the war for his country. Pharaoh's birth mother {Lolita} was a gorgeous woman with long, pretty black hair and pretty brown pimple-less skin.

Her heart, body, mind, and soul, was not yet dedicated to God as Mrs. Grace's was as of yet. So it was that God heard the prayers of the little Pharaoh. When he was but a little boy whose feet could not touch the floor of the church bench in which he sat and prayed, so meaningfully and sincere.

He asked God to come and go with him as he grew up and became an adult. Even though Pharaoh was still a little boy, Pharaoh understood the Word of God and accepted Jesus Christ in his heart as the Son of the only living God.

He not only understood the Word of God but understood the meanings of so many Bible stories that would, as an adult, create an understanding of his situations. Pharaoh knew his God as the Creator of life and death and the Creator of the moon and stars, the mountains and rivers, seas, oceans, and the heavens and earth. He asked God never to leave him alone.

To always be with him and teach him, bless him and guide him so that he would never drift far away from God.

These were the prayers of Pharaoh that reached the ears of God. Pharaoh knew that God led Mr. and Mrs. Grace to come and teach Pharaoh of the only living God. To see His Son Jesus as God also like God the Father and raise Pharaoh as a Christian and give Pharaoh family identity. Pharaoh knew that his teachings were indebted to Mr. and Mrs. Grace. Not just of God and Christianity, but all Pharaoh's morals and principles, and his manners.

Pharaoh's beliefs in what was right and what was wrong, His understanding of humanity, and the reason that Jesus came to the earth. To give his life by dying on the cross and forgive humanity their sins.

Jesus allowed humanity to be forgiven for their sins, be born again, and live life after death. Along with all those who believe in the Son of God forever in peace. Happiness and harmony without sin, pain, trouble, or death ever again.

Pharaoh was sixteen when he realized that no employer or company would hire him because he was under eighteen, which was the legal working age for employment in that era of time. While Pharaoh steadily filled out applications for jobs and was hired, he was also later fired. Because of Pharaoh's places of employment, they always found out within thirty days that Pharaoh was under the legal working age of eighteen. Pharaoh always had to be terminated from the job.

Pharaoh was sixteen when he started brushing down the pool tables, sweeping the floor, and racking pool balls in the pool room.

The pool room owner trusted pharaoh, and the owner found loyalty in Pharaoh.

Pharaoh had mad skills with cards, dice, and pool, which allowed Pharaoh to be in charge of backroom crap games control gambling without letting people cheat while outsiders engaged in the games.

Also, at sixteen, Pharaoh would go to New York to buy wholesale clothing. Soon Pharaoh would be going to New York to purchase drugs to sell. One of Pharaoh's lifetime friends {Jelly} would befriend Pharaoh a lifetime. He would later on in life be the one who gave the cookouts on his property and invited his old friends.

In real life, one could see many of the hustlers of the old that were somebody back in the day and survived yet another generation. To laugh and talk about the trials and tribulations it took to get there in this present generation. And how God has smiled upon their lives and stayed by their sides.

Pharaoh was known to have a variety of beautiful men and women suits, coats, and men's sports jackets. In that era, black men, young men especially, were known to dress very nice, neat, and expensive.

They were not aware that soon an era of time would come that it would be the style for young black men to dress shamefully. By wearing their pants hanging off their ass, and letting their underwear be showing, and a part of their naked ass be showing also.

Now unknowing to Pharaoh and (123), there would come a time when the paths of both Pharaoh and (123) would cross.

Pharaoh and (123) would meet, become acquaintances and associates. (123) would hate Pharaoh like (123) hated and despised all nationalities of people, including the white man. The (123) Family vowed to make slaves of the (white man) and remove all doubt of the ruling class.

For (123) felt that he, his family, and associates were the only people on the planet earth that were a ruling class, That the rest of the entire world was just slaves under their feet to rule. But (123) would come to respect and admire Pharaoh as a trustworthy, responsible, reliable, religious man who loves and worships his GOD, the only living God.

Pharaoh spent a lot of time daily in the pool room cutting crap games and card games, both day and night. Most of Pharaoh's time was spent in the pool room.

This particular pool room that Pharaoh worked in, trained in, and almost lived in, was located in East Baltimore on Harford Road.

Now, most of the hustlers in East Baltimore traveled through that pool room, flashing their skills and competing against one another. To win money in the dice, pool, and card games held there all day and night continuously with Pharaoh in control of the action.

While Pharaoh had his daughter with him, Pharaoh would always make time for his daughter.

He even brought her into the pool room many times before Pharaoh even brushed down the tables or opened the pool room. When the pool room was open, Pharaoh would sit and tie his daughter Lady in a very tall pool room chair with one of her old-time cloth diapers tied around her with the chair in a little corner to protect her. Pharaoh would begin to play pool with Lady sitting there always to remind him that he had to win so they could treat themselves to hamburgers and milkshakes.

Now it was late in the evening in November of 1961 that Pharaoh was riding with Gypsy, one of Pharaoh's best friends. Gypsy was a prizefighter who had never been knocked out in all his fights, nor had he ever been on the canvas.

Now Gypsy was positively an East Baltimore Great who could be a champion in that era. But Gypsy loved the street life and was a celebrity in the nightlife in Baltimore and other cities.

Gypsy knew essential people in each city he traveled to, both legit and illegitimate, especially in Baltimore, where Gypsy was born and raised.

Pharaoh rode with Gypsy to Gino's, a similar franchise, before the Baltimore McDonald's franchise. They both bought chicken and ate while Gypsy took them across town to Pennsylvania Avenue. Gypsy wanted to show Pharaoh some friends of Gypsy's who were of the utmost importance.

Now Pharaoh and Gypsy were coming from East Baltimore, where it was dark because most of the stores closed early or around 6 pm.

It was pretty dead and slow and boring, but the minute the car turned onto Pennsylvania Avenue in West Baltimore, it was like a different world.

It seemed to be in another world, With bright lights, pretty brand-new cars, and all sorts of stores and businesses vibrantly awake. With the most beautiful women Pharaoh had ever seen.

But more than anything, and more valuable than everything, was that the business owners were all black people, which Pharaoh had not seen too much of in his life. And the women were so black and beautiful, with their shiny, new, and expensive automobiles.

This was a new scene for Pharaoh. Gypsy introduced Pharaoh to some of Gypsy's friends, great bank robbers, stick-up men, nightclub owners. Big-time drug dealers, con-artists, pickpockets, assassins, lawyers, city officials, mayors, and other boxers like Gypsy.

Some were the finest black women Pharaoh had ever seen. Both whores and businesswomen of countless varieties and professions. Black women-owned residential and commercial properties and other businesses.

Pharaoh was hypnotized, Supremely emotionally and spiritually impressed with the people he had just met.

He fell deeply in love with the things and situations Pharaoh had seen and been a part of. Pharaoh knew immediately; this was the world he was born to be.

"Some of the bests of the best are not yet here, Pharaoh," Gypsy explained to Pharaoh. For most of the nightlife, people are just waking up from their endeavors from last night and early this morning. So, they won't come back on the scene until late tonight.

While Gypsy and Pharaoh talked, a man motioned to Gypsy to come over. When Gypsy went over, the man whispered something in Gypsy's ear. Gypsy, in return, told Pharaoh that {Little Caesar} wanted to meet with him that night.

Everyone knew Little Caesar. Especially every hustler in Baltimore knew Little Caesar's name. Even for those who never saw him, they had heard of Little Caesar's name. A name tacked onto a Baltimore Boy that entitled him to have national acquaintances in the hustling world. Those of the best of the young upcoming hustlers, locally and nationally.

Pharaoh then asked Gypsy where Gypsy would meet Little Caesar that night, and he explained to Pharaoh that there was only one place that the best hustlers in the city all met. Hustlers from other cities that we're visiting, or were in Baltimore for any reason, wanted to join in with the people in the know.

They all only met at L&N; it was a known hang out. After the bars closed and the people were ready for some of the best food in Baltimore, L&N was indeed the place to be, To sit amongst Baltimore's best of the best. Both professional legit and the illegitimate people of all reputations. They met, rubbed shoulders, ate, discussed, and made deals. They bargained, made friends and acquaintances while enjoying themselves in an atmosphere of social greatness. It involved a variety of races and cultures of different people, all functioning as one body.

Now Pharaoh was well acquainted with Little Caesar, who often came through the pool room in East Baltimore where Pharaoh was in charge of the crap games.

Little Caesar came to play crap or pool and was a champion player who participated in pool tournaments on national levels. He also drew spectators when Little Caesar played other ethnic groups on his home turf of Pennsylvania Avenue.

When Little Caesar came to East Baltimore to play crap or dice, Little Caesar always gambled to the highest level of the betting activities by betting three and four times the regular bets.

Little Caesar's activities were talked about for days and days on the gambling level scene.

Now Pharaoh admired Little Caesar and watched his every movement whenever Pharaoh got the chance. For Little, Caesar was only four years older than Pharaoh, and they both paid attention to one another when in each other's presence.

Now Pharaoh knew that Little Caesar was a drug man and the biggest and the best drug man of that era and time in the City of Baltimore in the early 1960s. Beyond a doubt, heroin was in the cities of America on account of (123). About him destroying the cities by having drug addict activities. At that time, heroin was only in use by a small number of participants. Mainly Musicians, some professional people, entertainers, and a small number of street people.

Heroin costs money that poor people had not. It was destroying the lives of many people of races and cultures. But, it was in the plans for the future for heroin to become a significant problem. Heroin would become dirt cheap, and poor people would soon afford it.

In the early 1960s, there were not a lot of drug addicts in the cities of America, and black people were a few percentages of drug addicts except New York.

New York was a haven for drug use and sale from the looks of some places in New York by the activities there. Now top-notch hustling for the use and sale of heroin went on in New York City. But in Baltimore, heroin had not yet reached 5% of its fullest destructive potential to the community even though heroin *was* being bought and sold in Baltimore.

Now an East Baltimorean named {Shark Skin} was a looked upon drug dealer with respect and hustling abilities, qualifications, and goals equal to Little Caesar, who was in West Baltimore but on a smaller scale. Both Little Caesar and Shark Skin were associates and competitors, but they were also friends.

Shark Skin was one of the few people from Baltimore selling drugs that did not get his drugs from Little Caesar wholesale. Instead, Shark Skin had his drug connection. Probably in New York, which put him in the major independent drug dealer class in the City of Baltimore. And Shark Skin dealt only with a few white people.

There were not but a few black regular junkies in East Baltimore or Baltimore period at that time and date. And they all had to go to West Baltimore on Pennsylvania Avenue to buy drugs, or the drugs in Baltimore usually always had to come from Pennsylvania Avenue in Baltimore City.

Shark Skin received his name Shark Skin because he wore many Shark Skin suits of many different colors and many Sharks Skin overcoats, which were the stylish clothes to wear then. Shark Skin was a constant participant in the pool room in East Baltimore on Harford Road.

Pharaoh loved and respected Shark Skin, and even though Shark Skin was two years older than Pharaoh, they were like neighborhood buddies, friends, and hustlers of the same excellent quality.

Pharaoh watched and learned from Shark Skin because Shark Skin was a master of selling drugs to white people. Shark Skin kept a pocket full of crooked dice even though Shark Skin rarely cheated a person, but it was already for those that did cheat. All the white people who bought drugs from Shark Skin came to the pool room on Harford Road in East Baltimore.

As soon as anyone saw white people coming into the pool room, everyone knew they looked for Shark Skin. The white people were always treated with the utmost respect and never robbed or talked to. A lot of the time, Shark Skin's associate, Shortie Black, was not there. So, the white people were told they had to come back to catch Shark Skin.

The surrounding East Baltimore neighborhoods had no heroin addicts as of that time in 1960. And if so, they were very few, and they were very discreet and low-key.

But it was the continued plan of the (123) Family. The (123) Family was always decades ahead of their projects, schemes, and proposals. To maximize the use of heroin or anything to a capacity far above expected.

Then afterward, the drug use would take the shape of a community monster through onwards usages into other drug addiction forms. That introduced other old drugs in a devastating negative new way, destroying the neighborhoods and the Children of Jourmajesty.

It was three in the morning when Gypsy picked up Pharaoh, and they walked through the door of {L&N} restaurant on West North Ave. Pharaoh was alarmed by the place's occupants, who were all dressed in expensive clothes and jewelry. Whom all seemed not only to belong, but all seemed to be a part of one another while they mingled from booth to booth, talking, laughing, and enjoying their meals.

Little Caesar was always a great attraction where ever he went. He was seen as a great local attraction, a celebrity, and a super one in Baltimore.

At the L&N restaurant, there were other city celebrities other than Little Caesar, professional people, rich people. Many people owned businesses and professions throughout Baltimore and in other cities.

People who were seen as nightlife people all met at the L&N restaurant. They were also visualized and seen as Baltimore Greats, Baltimore celebrities, and people in the know. Usually, after the bars closed, the nightlife began at the L&N restaurant.

Gypsy met with Little Caesar, and Little Caesar asked Gypsy to join in the two booths reserved for Little Caesar. Gypsy came over to the booths dedicated for them, and Gypsy introduced Pharaoh.

Even though Pharaoh and Little Caesar knew each other by sight, Gypsy introduced Pharaoh to Little Caesar as one upcoming young hustler, already bona fide and certified.

Little Caesar shook Pharaoh's hand, hugged Pharaoh, and told Pharaoh that it was a great pleasure to make his acquaintance even though he had seen Pharaoh a few times before. From one hustler with honor to another hustler with integrity, it was his honor to accept Pharaoh with honor to his acquaintance. Little Caesar's speech seemed slangish to Pharaoh. With Pharaoh not knowing that it was just a cool way of Little Caesar saying his words. To be cool or sort of slick to create his way of talking to go along with Little Caesar's style, becoming an original himself to be distinguished from all others.

It was 4 pm when Little Caesar knocked on Pharaoh's front door in East Baltimore. To complete the deal that Little Caesar had made the night before. Without the knowledge of anyone other than Little Caesar and Pharaoh knowing.

Little Caesar had brought Pharaoh five bundles of heroin with twenty-five paper glassine bags to a bundle. The bags sold for ten dollars a bag, which merited $250 per bundle, added up to be a total of $1250 for the whole five bundle package.

Little Caesar told Pharaoh that Pharaoh could keep all the money if Pharaoh found a clientele for the heroin. Or Pharaoh could decide to continue to keep making more money by continuing to sell the heroin. Pharaoh could buy some more bundles of heroin from Little Caesar for $100 per bundle.

Little Caesar explained to Pharaoh that his main objective was to give Pharaoh a chance to make money. Nothing wrong could happen to their new relationship, and neither of them could get angry with the other regardless of the outcome of this deal. That Little Caesar would watch Pharaoh's back in times of trouble until Pharaoh could watch his own back in the drug business.

Little Caesar then left Pharaoh with one piece of essential advice to remember always and forever. That heroin use was for two types of people: fools and losers.

To always remember that one crucial law and unchangeable rule. The use of heroin was for fools and losers regardless of who the user was and how close you are to a heroin user or whether they were your friend or blood relative. The same rule applied, heroin use is for fools and losers, and its use is simply taboo to all.

Now Pharaoh had never before sold drugs of any nature, nor had Pharaoh ever been interested in selling drugs. The pool room supplied Pharaoh with enough money to take care of his wife and daughter and give money to Mrs. Grace to help her with the house.

Pharaoh knew nothing of selling drugs besides what Pharaoh had seen Sharkskin do with the white people in the pool room. Pharaoh did know that the heroin sold for ten dollars a bag, and he decided to wait until Shark Skin was not available to sell some heroin to one of Shark Skin's customers to try to establish himself in the drug business.

Now Shark Skin had plenty of white people coming to the pool room to buy drugs and other corners that Shark Skin used for drug selling purposes.

Now Pharaoh had watched Shark Skin many times, ducking and dodging the police. There were only about six people on the whole narcotics squad in 1961.

And that squad patrolled the City of Baltimore, meaning east, west, north, and south Baltimore and the narcotics shift at midnight.

Now, these narcotics squads were not well trained in the field of narcotics. They knew very little concerning heroin or drugs as a whole. Pharaoh had watched the narcotic squad search Shark Skin's person looking for drugs.

Pharaoh had learned that as long as you didn't have drugs in your possession that you couldn't be arrested unless you had another charge. Learning so many things from Pharaoh just watching Shark Skin made Pharaoh also see Shark Skin's terrible mistakes. Mistakes of being so flashy and disrespectful to the authorities, especially narcotics agents. Because of sharkskin's nasty attitude towards them, they started to harass Shark Skin continuously. By searching his car randomly, searching his person, and following him constantly in hopes of catching Shark Skin doing anything wrong.

Two days after Little Caesar had given Pharaoh ten bundles of heroin, Pharaoh was sitting in the pool room when a white woman appeared before Pharaoh, asking if Shark Skin was available. Pharaoh replied that Shark Skin was not available but that he could get her what she was looking for, but it wasn't Shark Skin's material, meaning drugs.

The white lady agreed so; Pharaoh sold 30 dollars' worth of heroin to the white lady. She told Pharaoh her name was {Tony}, and in return, Pharaoh also gave Tony his home number. That was so Pharaoh's little brother's {John and Reuben} could walk around the pool room and tell Pharaoh if and when Tony called.

Only three hours later, Pharaoh's brother Reuben came to the pool room to let Pharaoh know that Tony had called and left a number for him to call her back.

Pharaoh immediately called Tony back, and she purchased ten more bags of heroin for her and her associates. Tony told Pharaoh that she liked the setup he was using with the telephone instead of coming to the pool room or street corners.

She loved the quality of the drugs, and she would tell a few of her friends about it to use Pharaoh's set up, which put so much protection on them.

So began the introduction to years of personal relationships with clients who would become friends and family of trust, honor, and joy, even though the drugs were the root of their relationships.

Pharaoh had no idea how much and for how long Satan would try to completely turn Pharaoh from God Almighty. Satan tried first introducing Pharaoh to worldly things and worldly people. To entice him and try to turn him away from God, day by day, year by year, through worldly excitement and the worldly pleasures of money and possessions.

It was 1960 when Pharaoh was married at age 15. It was also 1960 when Pharaoh gave up trying to get a job at 15. And it was 1960, at the age of 15, when Pharaoh started working in the pool room. Pharaoh worked in the pool room three years when Little Caesar brought Pharaoh ten bundles of heroin in 1963. One hundred years after, blacks became free from chains around their ankles.

It was seventeen years later, in 1980 when Pharaoh woke up and heard the rain softly splattering on the window. When Pharaoh woke up and rolled over, he rolled into a big plate glass window. He opened his eyes and gazed out the window. Being the type of person who traveled into and out of many other cities and is forever sleeping on trains, planes, highways, and byways, Pharaoh slowly thought to himself, *what city am I in? What hotel suite am I in?*

It was then that Pharaoh's eye opened, and he saw that he was gazing at his hometown of Baltimore. Looking directly at the harbor that Governor Shadows was responsible for building, he was mayor when the harbor was built. Shadows was a good man after becoming mayor of the city.

After becoming mayor, he became the governor of Maryland. He did such a good job that he repeated the governor's term three consecutive times of office. He had done so much for the City of Baltimore as mayor too.

It was raining outside, and Pharaoh realized that he was up high. On around the eighth or ninth floor, Pharaoh could see almost the whole City of Baltimore.

He loved to watch the rain, and everyone that knew Pharaoh knew that he loved the rain. He loved to watch God work, for only God can make it rain regardless of how bad the rain is needed, wanted, or not wanted.

Then still, only God could make it rain or make it stop raining. On that thought, Pharaoh realized that he never went to hotels in his hometown because he had a couple of homes of his own to go to in his hometown, not counting a few females that he was always welcome to come to who also had homes.

A key was turning in the door as Pharaoh thought it was a hotel maid. Then a lady in a black uniform opened the door and said, *"Feed up Mr. Pharaoh and welcome to the diagnostic penthouse."*

Pharaoh then realized what he refused to accept. He made himself believe it was a nightmare; he thought it was a dream. It was reality. Pharaoh was in jail and had been sentenced to six years in prison.

Pharaoh was in the diagnostic center. It was for inmates who were ready to be sent to one of the many institutions in Maryland to begin serving their sentence. It depended upon how much time they had, what their age was, how many times locked up before, and the nature of their crime.

The lady guard then left, but the door cracked and told Pharaoh he had two minutes to get up and come down to pick up his breakfast tray. Pharaoh came back to his cell after nibbling at the powdered eggs, toast, and cold cereal. He then laid back down to begin to get his thoughts together.

Once again, Pharaoh lay there gazing at the beautiful rain that only God could have sent. Pharaoh noticed the men working on another prison that they would be calling {Super Max} within a square radius all the way around. There was already a woman's jail, a city jail, a jail industry, a prison, a halfway house, a rehab center, and of course, the diagnostic center, which Pharaoh was.

A section of town in Baltimore was called East Baltimore. In which Pharaoh had spent the whole thirty-five years of his life. Even though he had traveled to many other cities and states, this City of Baltimore was his home. This city he was raised in and was the city that he loved.

East Baltimore was now being made into a community of jails, within a public gathering, Right in the center of town.

Pharaoh was on the 7th floor of the diagnostic center. It was a lucky number but an unlucky floor because most of the inmates on that floor were sentenced to large amounts of time. Time includes forty years, fifty years, life, double life, and other portions of time, while Pharaoh was sentenced to six years, and he had no idea why he was on that floor, except for thinking that God was showing him how lucky and blessed he was.

During the next few days, Pharaoh watched the young men with those extensive sentences. Most of the men who had those outrageous sentences were kids' rather very young adults growing into their manhood and ranging in ages from sixteen to their early twenties; ninety-five percent of them were black. Some were small, some were large for their ages, some were fat, and some were skinny, but few showed fear or regret. They laughed, played cards, ate sweets, and watched TV. Very few of them seemed as if they were fighting their case. So many of them seemed unconcerned, probably because the reality of their sentences had not yet registered in their minds as they played games and acted as though a verdict of 60,70,80 years or more was not heavy on their hearts and minds.

A few days later, Pharaoh lay in his bed watching the Super Max building continuing to be completed. Pharaoh was sentenced to six years; why he was on that floor was a mystery. He then remembered when only the prison and the city jail was in the community and how people went out of their houses, left their doors open and were not afraid of anyone breaking into their homes or being robbed themselves. Each neighborhood looked out for the others within the neighborhood, and there was minor crime in the community. Pharaoh was thinking to himself about how long ago that had been.

It was February of 1988, but he was only thirteen years of age thirty years ago. There was hardly any crime in the neighborhood of East Baltimore where he lived, about ten blocks from where he was now locked up, Pharaoh then thought to himself. "What was it that happened in the last thirty years to the community?"

A few factors came to his mind, but one factor stood out large in front of everything else. In the last twenty-five years, drugs have come along and caused the ruins of people's lives, dreams, goals, and even minds. The communities had boarded-up houses in record-breaking numbers. The people ran from the communities to avoid neighborhoods turning violent, run-down, and unsafe to raise their families. Drugs had always existed, but drugs were kept between Musicians, the pimps, the whores, and the few drug users that were then in existence in the communities.

Drug use in the community was irregular, and not even 5% of what drug use in Baltimore would soon become. The hustlers that hustle drugs weren't hustlers because they indulged in selling drugs.

They were hustlers because they hustled to make a dollar without stealing, lying, or cheating without doing backbreaking hard labor. Hustlers were people playing pool and being a pool champion. Being a card player who was extremely good and lucky at playing cards, people went to out-of-town warehouses to buy legitimate garments or any other commodity wholesale and then sold the commodity in the streets for a profit. Hustlers were people that sometimes bent or broke the law to those who were already lawbreakers. But they did it with some sort of code of ethics or honor to guide their way.

A hustler never stole a deal or gave a bad deal. A hustler gave deals that he profited from, but never a deal where he outright beat someone. He never led a kid astray or taught a kid the wrong way, and it was a no-no to introduce a kid to the selling or using of drugs. Most of all, a hustler's word was his bond, his trading right, and his identification card in the hustling world.

The young men that Pharaoh was presently meeting usually all said that they were hustlers, and they said that because they were or had been selling drugs. Today's young men were now calling themselves hustlers because they were drug dealers or thieves, robbers, stick-up men, and people that sold sugar or other make-believe substances in the place of drugs to beat people out of their money. They had changed the whole concept of the word hustler into being a crook or one of dishonest intent, even to each other or anyone.

Pharaoh was then gazing out the window and noticed that the very building he was in had a parking lot attached to it. Pharaoh realized that the parking lot used to be a building where Pharaoh sat outside when he was only seventeen. A building that used to be a whorehouse, and blacks were not allowed inside. At that particular time, Pharaoh sat outside the whorehouse after the bars had closed at 2 am. He would provide some of the girls with drug affiliations for a profit.

Now that was a part of Pharaoh's life that had passed, and it would be soon that he would be introduced to 123.

Evil was always creating services, laws, rules, regulations, understandings, teachings, and many other schemes and outlets to hold back, abuse, misuse, and stagnate the Children of Journajesty.

Evil has always been hard to successfully bring long-term or everlasting manifestation to the Children of Journajesty, who was anyone that believed that freedom was for everyone that was an American, or who gave their sweat, blood, And was willing to share their lives for justice in America, for all people, regardless of race, skin color, or religion?

One of Evil's earliest plans of leading to evilness was through the abuse to the land and animals that devilish white men brought into reality because the natives slaughtered, or butchered, nothing but what was needed. They did not harm or misuse the land and wasted or abused anything.

The white man was (Satan)'s first slave sent to America to bring evil to the land and to disrupt unity, peace, love, and worship to God. The white men whose hearts were full of evil intent did believe that they would be among the ruling class of the planet earth if they followed the commands of (Satan) in holding back, misusing, and abusing the Children of Jourmajesty.

While the white man slaughtered the animals by killing them for money and recreation, he Also cut down the trees for selling purposes also so that the Indians would have no meat or hide from the animals to make clothing.

Now in the entire existence of Evil's stay on the planet earth. Each knew Evil and every passing generation as a living legendary legend for his schemes, plans, and coordination of continually inventing ways of holding back, abusing, stagnating, and misusing the Children of Jourmajesty.

Evil was also known, credited, charged, and feared for carrying out and masterminding the assassination of the assassinator in charge of the well-being and security of Evil's son. He was known as (Live).

Not only did Evil set out to assassinate YaYa, the most trusted and valued person in one of the present (123)'s life, and personal bodyguard to the present (123), who was the son of (Evil)

Then Evil assassinated the entire family of YaYa, including all Yaya's aunts, uncles, brothers and sisters, mother and father, and even the pet goats of the family, and the two guard dogs. Evil burned down all Yaya's family's homes. He replaced the buildings with barns of hay after arranging a date scheduled for a celebration gathering for the entire family of YaYa, Which was an undercover massacre of fire and an individual bullet to the head of any of Yaya's family. That might not have attended the undercover massacre. It was supposed to be a once-in-a-lifetime celebration for the many years of so many different trusted services provided to the (123) Family by YaYa.

Then we move all events up to around one hundred and twenty-five years after Evil failed to make much progress in making the land of America evil. Even though Evil's plan of mixing the land of America with all types of different cultures and colors of people to bring strife and problems to the population of the new America. Other cultures came from all over and wanted a chance for a new life, freedom, and the right to worship as they please. Speak as they please, and be treated equally. They did stick to small groups of their kind, but there was not as much trouble, and problems as Evil had expected.

So, the land of America did not become filled with chaos. The new Americans did learn to become one people and deal with all of their differences, problems, and adversities so that the land of America did grow, blossom, and became a united territory and became states of the United States of America.

Now, after Evil accepts his punishment of losing his name. He is then handed over the authority of holding back, misusing, and abusing the Children of Journajesty to his son (Live). Because of the lack of trouble and evil that did *not* accrue in the land of America. Then Evil's son Live, also known as the first (123), authorized all events and procedures in abusing, misusing, stagnating, and holding back the Children of Journajesty into the future of the land of America.

Evil's life span is ending, and Live instead of Evil did the holding back, abusing, misusing, stagnating evil and sinful ways towards the Children of Journajesty. Evil, the teacher and the father of Live, is the present (123) of the present era of time. Live was by far the most advanced (123) of all time. Who knew and proclaimed knowledge of the very first (123) and who was, and is, the very first (123). He was chosen by his father (Evil), who first sent him to America after Live's father (Evil) had failed his mission given to him by Satan, who is the Highest of the anonymous organization.

America was still not fully populated with evil people even though there were bad and wrong thoughts in some of the population of the people. Many people were not evil and undid a lot of the evilness done to people by the corrupt and wrongdoers of the land. Sometimes it took many years to undo the harm and evilness done to people by the evil and wrongdoers of the land of America.

America was still mainly a land of people who loved the Creator and believed in loving and helping one another. For every setback of evil and wrongdoings towards each other came righteousness, and best done by the righteous people, that came just in a matter of time.

Though sometimes it took years to rectify itself, it always did correct itself and brought the fault to the surface to be viewed by all Americans.

It may bring the hopes of showing remorse and the pain and shame, but tell the truth regardless of the consequences. Hopes that lessons and deeds of righteousness may be accomplished. America stays a land of together people, irrespective of their difficulties and their social and economic, racial, and political problems.

It was 1962 when Pharaoh was only seventeen when he received the package of heroin from Little Caesar. Only two months later, Pharaoh had purchased a house in this new adventure of selling heroin. He created a small but sizeable clientele of business associates. He accumulated several personalized customers, and in return, they brought other friends and family to be a part of the clientele that Pharaoh had put together.

They all operated like families who had jobs to bring in income to support their families. Whether the job would be prostitution or a company job, steelworker, electrician, plumber, or etc. these drug users were responsible family-oriented people, even though they were drug users, instead of drug addicts, looking for a place to cop their drugs on the street for the sole purpose of being able to function correctly.

Pharaoh's drug business was run by Shorty Oscar, Pharaoh's lieutenant and lifetime friend. Also, the one overseer to run Pharaoh's drug business from telephone calls to a place that would come out and meet the clientele all day and night twenty-four-seven, in an area that was close to the house that the phone call was accepted. And then there was another number to call if you were treated wrongly or unfairly in any way. That other number would solve your problem immediately, but fairly, one way or the other.

In the 1960s, there was no narcotics shift in Baltimore after twelve o'clock at night at midnight.

Pharaoh was attending affairs with some of his drug clientele and their families. The invitations had nothing to do with drugs, but Pharaoh had accepted the invitations on the grounds of pure fun and friendship without the distraction of drugs in any way.

Pharaoh was always a smart student in school who was always at the head of his class, but he had quit school after getting married to support his family when he was only in the ninth grade. After getting married, he had returned to night school and entered a private business school through a female dean of the private business school located in West Baltimore. She saw great potential in Pharaoh as an above-normal business student who would be extra phenomenal in business ventures. Pharaoh had no credentials or diplomas to enter the private business school. Even though she could lose her position in the school and her job if caught, she gave Pharaoh the right to attend and learn business skills and how to operate a business.

Pharaoh's heroin business was operated with care, concern, emotions, feelings, honesty, and fairness. Which made the dirty business of drugs bearable, tolerable, profitable, and unimaginable to people on the street. Pharaoh's close-knit heroin clientele happened to be all white people because there were few black heroin users at that time, or probably just a few because blacks had no money to buy drugs (only a few)

It was just a standard procedure of business, habitual negative pleasure engulfed in trust, fairness, and friendship for people who used drugs, but was still responsible, worked, and took care of their families or themselves legitimately.

{Tommy Hank} was an East Baltimore great hustler who was well known in Baltimore. He was like a ghost because people knew not of his hustling expertise until it was too late. And they had been devoured by his versatility in so many games, strategies, and knowledge and his looks.

Because he was a big fat sort of sloppy man, with a plain baby face with the look of sloppiness in his hustling performances, Which was a hoax to hide his professional and expert performances in the hustling arena.

Even though Tommy Hank chooses only to be active in parts of New York City and all over his hometown of Baltimore, Tommy Hank was a hustler that could compete with the likes of the greatest of hustlers anywhere, any place or time.

Tommy Hank had known Pharaoh since Pharaoh was a little boy of seven, known in the adult Christian neighborhood circle. And primarily, the church is known as {Grace Memorial Baptist Church} and as {Sister Grace's boy} which was a very proud and neighborhood community strong title. Pharaoh had obtained that title by participating in church activities and regularly attending Sunday school and church services throughout the few years of his short life so far that God had blessed him with.

Now Tommy Hank was ten years Pharaoh's senior. He admired Pharaoh's coming up as Pharaoh progressed to some of the bigger boys in the community who also wanted to be hustlers but were all older by at least two or three years than Pharaoh.

Pharaoh, who outshined them all in the know, was urged to learn more than any other neighborhood or community young men, who had chosen the way of a hustler.

Now Tommy Hank was indeed a hustler, but he was also, at that time, a drug dealer of sufficient magnitude as he operated unknown, invisible, and unseen. Now it had come through the ears of Tommy Hank that Pharaoh had ventured into the world of selling drugs.

Tommy Hank's personal vow to enlighten Pharaoh on the heart and soul of the drug dealer's expertise was having the ability and knowledge to cut or dilute the drug to make the drug available for wholesale or retail sale and use. While also having a drug connection which divided the drug dealer from the individual who was just selling the drugs.

This knowledge or given information was called *pulling one's coat tail*. It was a way that one hustler enlightened another young hustler of some knowledge, information, or expertise to help and guide him along the way in some new field or area that the young hustler was getting involved in.

Tommy Hank was indeed a certified hustler, but he was also an authorized drug dealer. Tommy Hank and Little Caesar were both hustlers and drug dealers, but no one had the fame in Baltimore at that present time like Little Caesar. Both Little Caesar and Tommy Hank were hustlers first, gamblers and drug dealers second, and while Tommy Hank was from East Baltimore, Little Caesar was from West Baltimore; they were both friends. They were often at the same places simultaneously for the same purpose.

In the autumn of the year, in the evening around 7 pm in 1962. After shaking hands and giving formal acquaintances and greetings for that day to each other, because there were some days that Pharaoh and Tommy Hank had stayed up for days just gambling and helping one another win. Tommy Hank had heard through the hustler's world of communication and information for the top-notch hustlers' ears to be informed that Pharaoh was selling heroin. That Pharaoh needed the guidance and assistance of Tommy Hank.

Then Tommy Hank got right to the point of asking Pharaoh to get some flour, corn meal, and cake mix out of the house, which they took upstairs to Pharaoh's room. Tommy Hank took all the ingredients and brought them upstairs to his room. Tommy Hank did show Pharaoh, using those ingredients, to cut or dilute heroin, package heroin, distribute heroin, and maneuver all about concerning heroin. To sell heroin both wholesale and retail and to increase the heroin to twenty and thirty times its original amount. To make twenty to thirty times the amount of money that would have been made without the knowledge that Tommy Hank showed to Pharaoh.

Tommy Hank then handed Pharaoh an address in New York with Stokes on it. He said: *To Pharaoh, you now have the credentials of a real drug dealer, use them wisely, for you now qualify to do the same as Little Caesar only without the popularity and knowledge that he has, but time will lead you to expertise and popularity will come from the deeds you do for others in need, while favor you might not want in the drug world, but it has been my pleasure to pull your coattail since I've genuinely watched you grow up. Now Stokes is a personal friend of mine. He has handled more money than the president while he was in drugs. But who has now settled to be a drug addict, a wino, and a nothing? He and his wife live with his mother, a full-blooded Christian woman, who is just glad that God did not take her son's life, for he has been a real devil when he was in power. I have given you the credentials of a real drug dealer, and never again let yourself sell drugs for anyone except yourself. Do not forget to help others while realizing that there is no situation in drugs that could qualify you to take the life of no one involved in drugs for no reason. Whether it be drugs, money, love or hate, but for there is no reason under the sun to give you cause to take a life over or concerning drugs."*

CHAPTER 2

The Birth of the Lottery

It was confirmed that Pharaoh's life had changed drastically concerning the lifestyle that Pharaoh was interested in. While there had been many changes in his life to accommodate him into the hustling life that had brought Pharaoh money, power, new cars, and even blew up his reputation as a hustler, gambler, and a very low-key drug dealer.

More interesting to Pharaoh than anything was *Mr. Robinson's Crap House*! Mr. Robinson's crap house was a professional crap house that cut 5% of all bets laid on the table. It was an honest, no cheating, and no robbing but a respectful crap house on Pennsylvania Ave in Baltimore.

Mr. Robinson's crap house allowed anyone that came across that door to be entitled to a fair crap game where one could bet from a dollar to three thousand dollars, and the bet made would be covered by the house rules and would pay off if something could go wrong.

In Mr. Robinson's crap house, there was no fighting, or the bouncers would break up the confusion, and the starter of the trouble or whoever passed the first lick would surely pay the price and would be barred out.

And nobody that was a player in Mr. Robinson's crap house wanted to be barred out, for there was no place in the city to gamble and win and lose the kind of money that was won and lost but protected at Mr. Robinson's crap house.

Pharaoh was a teenager when he was first introduced to Mr. Robinson's crap house through Tommy Hank and Gypsy. Pharaoh was amazed to see the winnings of twenty and thirty thousand dollars by different players at different times as they summed up the winnings for that night as they packed up their cash in garbage bags, shopping bags, paper bags.

He watched as he saw men take off their coats and fill their coats with money. Pharaoh did not know then that he too would follow all those images, patterns, and traits as he too would walk out that door with those types of winnings and losses while he soon would gamble every night in Robinson's crap house for the next fifteen years.

Mr. Robinson himself was a number backer, a good man, an honest man, and not to think weak, timid, or afraid.

He was a prominent or rather significant number backer in West Baltimore, for there were no lottery games for the different states of the United States of America. All the lottery money that would soon come and go to the various forms was then money in the neighborhood distributed by hundreds or thousands of number writers that the lottery machines presently take the place of as the different states take the location of the prominent number backers like Mr. Robinson.

New hustlers coming through Baltimore to visit or live had to stop and play at Robinson's crap house. They were known to give any real gambler an honest and exciting crap game. That was rated only at Mr. Robinson's crap house in Baltimore on Pennsylvania Avenue.

After being escorted to the door, one could win from a dollar to twenty or thirty thousand dollars. He could leave safely, but only a selected few were eligible to participate in the circle of limited membership after someone in the know, trusted, and qualified had vouched for them to become part of the selected few that gamble there in Robinson's crap house.

The numbers game was a part of survival in most of the cities in America. Many people made their living by writing numbers or being a number writer for prominent backers who paid the hits off when people hit the numbers. There were as many number writers as there are lottery machines today that took the place of the number writers. It was one of the first cases of machines taking jobs from people. The legal system had declared that numbers writing was illegal. And had taken over the numbers game, they distributed the lottery machines throughout different states to take the numbers that people would play in place of the number's writers, which provided one of the first incidences where machines took over people's jobs.

The numbers game provided more money than one could imagine. All that money was distributed in different cities throughout different states, which provided money for the neighborhoods of large amounts even though it was said to be a *misdemeanor* charge to play the numbers game.

The numbers game was like a giant sea of cash that started with the little fish's money. An even larger fish backed the money that the bigger fish had too much of, and a backer that backed all the cash that was too much money piled up for bigger fish to back after accumulating so much money.

Mr. Robinson was a numbers backer that backed all the cash that was too much money for the number's writer, the numbers backer, and the large number backer to back, or stand behind, or be responsible for paying off after accumulating too much money on one number.

The neighborhoods, communities, and different parts of each city in almost every United States of America state. Would soon miss and long for the millions and even billions of dollars taken out of their possession. And given to the lottery game. Of the different states of the United States of America.

Pharaoh's gambling procedures at Robinson's crap house started at midnight or 2,3,4,5 in the a.m. Usually, it ran to about 7,8, or 9 am, even though sometimes an extra good game might last for two or three days and nights.

It was about a year before Pharaoh earned the right to be able to go upstairs in Robinson's crap house, even though while gambling, Pharaoh could not eat, drink, or do anything but have a bowel movement while gambling, and even to have a bowel movement, Pharaoh was listening to the dice being called after each roll of the dice which he could hear while being upstairs in the VIP lounge, and trying desperately to hurry up and finish his business in order to return to the crap game.

All players that were usual members and everyday players were allowed to borrow money from the house according to the limit of cash they could borrow by their status in the club and their individual relationship with Mr. Robinson.

Only a few members had unlimited amounts to borrow, like Little Caesar, who was a super VIP even in Robinson's crap house. Everyone at the crap table loved or respected him, even amongst the best of hustlers. He was respected, appreciated, and liked {Little Bill} who was also a giant of a person on Pennsylvania Avenue. After Little Caesar went to prison, he would become the successor, but Little Bill was a Robinson's crap house celebrity.

All the players in the crap house love to see him enter because Little Bill's money was long. His favorite pet number on the dice was ten which was one of the most complex numbers to make. Sometimes Little Bill made ten, and sometimes he didn't, but when Bill made ten for his dice point, he usually put a dent in the crap game! But Little Bill always would bet he made ten, and the players in the crap house would put their money together to total a larger amount of money to bet against Little Bill.

When Pharaoh was coming into the crap game, it was already the ending of a number's day. Which meant that day had already been paid off for numbers betting. And a new day of number betting was in progress. The players in a circle around the pool table all bunched up together. Sometimes just their arm in to represent their space so they could call their bets to different people who in return would call a bet back to that particular person. And all bets would have to be laid on the table, or either one person could call "bet" to another person. At the same time, the house would be responsible for all bets.

The circle of participants in the game would always involve at least five to ten different number writers. Usually representing other parts of town or writing numbers for various backers, but always three or four writers for Mr. Robinson.

It was the code mark of a hustler to throw money across the table to the number of your choice to have your number played for that coming number that would materialize for that new day.

Pharaoh played his number every night at the crap table for that following new day, usually with three or four writers. Because every hustler had a number that he could play called his pet number, and that pet number would be played daily each day, and when a hustler had a good night, he would pile up money on his pet number.

There was never a night that Pharaoh didn't put at least fifty dollars on his pet number. Even though Pharaoh had at least 100 dollars on his number most of the time, he hit some times over the next fifteen years.

Pharaoh was not a good husband to his wife Jazzy because Pharaoh was not ready for marriage. He still acted like a child when it came to being married.

Even though he never neglected his daughter Lady Linda Gold who was his first child, his heart and soul, until he had other children who Pharaoh loved just as much. He had no favorites among his children but loved them all equally. Pharaoh's wife Jazzy spent most of her time at her mother's house and usually kept Pharaoh's daughter Lady with her. She would regularly come home without Lady because Pharaoh's mother-in-law wanted their daughter to stay with them.

Pharaoh and his wife Jazzy stayed in continuous arguments and confusion concerning that matter. Even though Pharaoh had no problem going to his wife's mother's house to pick up his daughter anytime he wanted, his wife seemed never to bring their daughter home at night when she came.

Two weeks after Tommy Hank, he had given Pharaoh the lessons and equipped him with the necessary knowledge and expertise to become a drug dealer instead of a drug seller.

Pharaoh was preparing to take a trip to New York. Pharaoh had taken time out for him and his daughter to enjoy time together, like at the park or eat. He did this quite frequently with his daughter Lady. But this day before, he was to venture to New York to meet the man named Stokes. Tommy Hank had sent him to see concerning introducing Pharaoh to a drug connection, early in the morning around 3 am.

Before Pharaoh left Baltimore to New York, he packed two decks of marked cards and a small cloth bag with crooked dice in it, his Bible to read, and his pistol and shoulder holster. While also practicing picking up, switching, and putting down different dice, he picked up one pair and put down the other, all in one stroke.

These were just practice routines Pharaoh would do in his spare time while accomplishing the mission Pharaoh had set out to do concerning getting in touch with Stokes and getting the drug connection. He also took along three suits, three pairs of shoes, socks, ties, and two pairs of regular comfortable slacks.

For he had no idea how long he might stay or what problems he might encounter while fulfilling his mission with Stokes in New York.

Now Pharaoh had first learned his way to New York from Baltimore by following the Greyhound bus route to New York from Baltimore and even though the speed limit was 65 miles per hour.

In that era of time in 1962, then there was really no traffic on the highway in the wee hours of the morning, and Pharaoh could travel between eighty-ninety miles an hour.

It made Pharaoh's trip from Baltimore and New York around two hours and 10 minutes for the entire distance of the trip without the interference of the highway police because there was hardly any traffic on the highway for the highway police to police.

It was 5:15 in the am when Pharaoh began to follow the instructions Tommy Hank had given him to reach Stokes' house on Eighth Ave, right before the newspaper stand on 135th Street.

Tommy Hank had instructed him to go through Central Park to reach the Eighth Ave entrance to follow up to 134th Street, which would be his destination. It was 5 am, and the streets of New York were crowded with all kinds of people, all colors and from all walks of life. Some were going to work, going in to go to bed, walking their dogs, in groups talking, standing, partying in couples. Just being there while so many different languages were being spoken in so many other groups of people like it was 5 pm. There were so many carts selling pretzels, hot dogs, peanuts, soda, hamburgers, and all sorts of other eats and drinks that Pharaoh had never seen before.

Now coming through Spanish Harlem to reach Harlem, Pharaoh saw some beautiful women of different shades of color and beautiful shapes.

Upon entering the apartment building where Stokes lived, Pharaoh proceeded to the second floor, where Stokes lived with his mother and wife. Encountering three little kids between ages 9-11 that immediately asked Pharaoh was he interested in buying some good heroin for ten dollars a bag.

Being surprised at the little boys selling heroin Pharaoh felt shame upon who would let these children sell heroin. At the same time, Pharaoh felt pity for these kids exposed to such a dangerous, unlawful, dirty, sinful, and bad habit-forming ordeal as selling drugs.

Also, not have the slightest idea that children in Baltimore will also be selling drugs to their blood relatives shortly. They would be disrespecting their parents and not knowing or understanding the respect for elders from a younger under generation person

Babies would be having babies who did not know, from those who did not know how to teach.

While the knowledgeable were unsuited, cut off, and ignored, lost from those who did not know, following the negative plans of self-destruction forty years into the future.

For the Children of Jourmajesty, one generation at a time forty years into the future by preparing hardship, problems, drastic situations, and chaos.

Someone eliminated the lord's prayer from the public school system. This was to not teach God to the under generation of each new generation of Children of Jourmajesty. {So, believe the author of this book}

Along with creating distance, disrespect, violence, and lack of communication between the old and the young. For the future of the Children of Jourmajesty. Without the help or guidance from the knowledgeable who were separated from those who knew not, as a pretense to protect the knowledgeable, whose hair was beginning to turn gray from aging. They knew not the real purpose of the separation from their young. Still, they did realize and experience disrespect, violence, cruelty, and hostile attitudes from their children, who were then their under generation. They were their grandchildren, showing the same towards their parents and grandparents as planned forty years ago, into the now present future. By the (123) family With an increase of disrespect to their parents. Ignorance to themselves, their people, their country, and most of all, a detour in the following of God almighty. Because of The separation of the old from the young, then the wisdom of the old could not be taught to the young. Which was the plan of the (123) family forty years before.

Chapter 3

Children of Jourmajesty

It was 6 a.m. when Pharaoh knocked on the sturdy-looking apartment door where Stokes lived with his wife in his mother's apartment. Before Pharaoh could knock on the door again, a little old gray-headed woman's voice came squeaking through the cracked door as she spoke through the crack in the door, but then with a burst of energy, the old lady cried out!

"A HOLY MAN, no, I mean a man of God within." Pharaoh was stunned by the outcry of the old lady, which tilted Pharaoh from his gangster frame of mind to his humble frame of mind. As Pharaoh asked the old lady her name and did Stokes live there, but before she could answer, a hand opened the door completely, and the man behind the door said, "I'm Stokes! What can I do for you?" "I'm Pharaoh from Baltimore. Tommy Hank sent me to see you in hopes that you would pull my coat to a connection worthwhile."

The old lady walked away when Stokes opened the door, and she did not hear the conversation between Pharaoh and Stokes.

"Come in," Stokes said to Pharaoh. Have a seat, try and get comfortable."

Looking around, Pharaoh saw three rooms that Stokes, his wife, and mother had to share living quarters, eating, and sleeping quarters.

Stokes explained to Pharaoh that he couldn't get him a connection that day or at that time for buying drugs. But he could get Pharaoh something for himself that would make up for a link. The next time Pharaoh came to see him, Stokes would be able to introduce him to a dependable and top-of-the-line connection.

Now Stokes was smart and greasy in his deal-making, but he was not a thief or crook. Stokes had charged Pharaoh 1,500 hundred dollars, and he went out to purchase the heroin for that money. Pharaoh pulled him to the side and told Stokes in his ear that Pharaoh would kill every living thing in that apartment if Stokes did not come back with the merchandise Stokes had gone to get for Pharaoh.

It was then that Stokes stopped and looked at Pharaoh for a moment.

He smiled and walked away as Stokes mumbled to himself, "Damn! You just might do that to prove yourself in the hustling world you are entering. I'll be back as soon as I can to fulfill your request."

Stokes' wife was not a beautiful female outside but had a shabby don't care flaw about herself. She had a habit of eating the frost off the old-time refrigerator for whatever purpose or reason, besides being a heroin addict and a wino.

"My name is Ester," Stoke's mother said in a low and passive voice, breaking Pharaoh's thoughts about Stokes' wife.

I am a servant of Almighty God, a Christian, a mother, and the sole provider for my only child and one who communicates daily with Almighty God through prayer. I know you, rather I know of you. You are the one sent to give my son back to God through my son's spirit, the blood, and the humiliation of my son, and the significant loss my son has to suffer before he can see.

Many people come here looking for my son, but I see that you are different because God comes with you."

Handing Pharaoh a cup of tea in an old-time tin cup, the old lady smiled and said to Pharaoh. "I was only twelve when I gave birth to my son Stokes after I was raped when I was only 11 by a mad man with a twisted mind and a viral disease called syphilis.

The doctors wanted to keep my son and experiment on his mind and {supposed to be} deformed body, but they did not know that I had already talked to my God and asked for my son's life, physical and mental conditions to be put in my hands. And that I would be held accounted for my son's sins and would pay whatever the price if he would give my son to me whole.

There is no slump, crookedness, or any part of my son's body missing or deformed in any way. But my son has been a menace to his people through selling drugs to his people and being cruel, sinful, and perverted. But my son knows God, but he has set God down to do the work of the devil, and I live only to see my son reunited with our God after I, too, with my son, pay for the sins of my son. Then I will be free to go home with my Heavenly Father after fulfilling my responsibility of helping to guide my son back to God."

"I know that God walks with you, I know you are a man sent by God, and I know you are of Christian faith. For we Christians are similar to the angels that God has protecting us at all times, for we Christians are everywhere and anywhere we need to be to help one another, and we live, function, and perform on faith alone.

But faith believes in the unseen, believing in what you cannot touch. Believing in Almighty God and His Son Jesus Christ, and the reason Jesus came to the earth is to die for humanity and give life to all believers after death.

What is your name, young man? Do you know who sent you here?

Pharaoh had accepted the cup of tea out of complete sympathy, respect, and loyalty for the gray hair upon her head. And the Godliness in her heart and soul. He hoped that he would not get sick from drinking out the old tin cup. Thinking to himself, Pharaoh did not want the old lady to know that Tommy Hank had sent Pharaoh.

Even though Tommy Hank was not the old lady's sender, Tommy Hank was the only sender that Pharaoh knew of that had sent him to see Stokes.

There was hardly any difference in the old lady in Stokes' residence {Stokes' mother's residence} to Pharaoh's own adopted mother, "Mrs. Grace's" residence.

For they both were Christian sisters by faith, And their beliefs were identical because they both believed in God, the Creator of heaven and earth. The one and only living God, except Jesus Christ the Son of God, also being God.

Even though it was hours before Stokes returned, the time went past quickly because Stokes' mother was so into telling Pharaoh about private parts of her and her son's personal life that no one else knew.

Unbeknownst to Pharaoh, Pharaoh would enter into a relationship with Stokes' mother to bring Stokes' mother deep into the depths of Pharaoh's heart and soul. While Stokes' mother continuously taught Pharaoh things of spirituality that he knew not.

Stokes returned looking very energetic at times but then going into a nod, looking as if he was sleeping.

Stokes informed Pharaoh that he had to try the heroin to ensure it was good before giving it to Pharaoh. But then Stokes explained to Pharaoh that the heroin was extra good and that Pharaoh should try some along with Stokes and his wife. Stokes said that Pharaoh could make six times the money he had invested.

Immediately Stokes and his wife began to shoot the heroin into their veins. At the same time, the expression on their faces changed. The tone of their voices also changed from the results of the heroin entering their systems. They both desperately tried to entice Pharaoh to try the high from the heroin, which Pharaoh continuously refused.

For Pharaoh had already been taught that the use of heroin was foolish to even try. Pharaoh also noted in his brain that Stokes was one to introduce chaos to people's lives by introducing them to the use of heroin. It was a natural fact that one would enjoy the high, that the drug would give the body, but for the price of that feeling, then for eternity, you would lose yourself, pride, respect, and dignity to the drug.

Pharaoh said, "If you were to put the heroin in my arm, then we would need another person here at the table.

Because I soon would be like you, and we would then both need someone here to be able to offer us *both* a shirt. For we both would have a long time ago sold the shirts off our backs!"

Pharaoh did not smile or show any other expression on his face but waited for the response from Stokes. "Surely you are a young age, my friend, but your wisdom is sharp, as the words in which you speak are true, and I truly apologize for trying to tempt you into using heroin."

Stokes injected the heroin into his arm but told Pharaoh to pay attention to the expression on his face and the change in his voice that would be evidence that the heroin was good along with the scratching and nodding as is sleep.

Stokes explained to Pharaoh that the next time Pharaoh came to New York, Stokes would introduce Pharaoh to a lovely lady who could probably get Pharaoh the package he wanted. But before Stokes could say any anymore, Pharaoh told Stokes he was not interested in meeting a beautiful woman. He was only interested in getting a heroin connection.

Stokes sat down, took his hand, and patted on the chair closer to him to sit down. "Sit down for a minute, please, and listen to what I have to say. Just sit down for a second."

Pharaoh pulled the chair closer to him and sat down.

"Pharaoh! When you first came in here, I tried to get you to put some heroin in your arm. It's something that I do to all the Baltimore boys who come to me. I can only go around town and see who has the best heroin and buy the same ten-dollar bags of heroin just like you have in

Baltimore. But only the New York bags of heroin will be much more potent. And you can make three times the money you spend.

Everyone else that Tommy Hank sent to me was satisfied. And they did use heroin with me most of the time. But you are different. I like your style, and you remind me of myself, how I used to be all about the business before I got hooked on this heroin. And for the first time in my life, I'm ashamed of myself for trying to hurt the lives of young hustlers who came to me for help.

Especially you, but I swear to Allah that I will take you to one who can do what you want when you return. Even though I have never tried, I believe that favor is due to me from this connection from my past loyalty. But what you want costs money, so be prepared to pay when you return.

Stokes had already given Pharaoh a price of $3,500 for an eighth of a key, which could take a 20, meaning that Pharaoh could dilute the heroin 20 times more than what he had at first, and the heroin would still be good.

The Vietnam War that America was in during the 1960s caused many American soldiers to become drug addicts. The cities were filling up with the use of heroin, which was illustrated, demonstrated, and originated by no other than the (123) Family. Backed by the highest caliber individual being in charge of the anonymous organization to hold back, cripple, stagnate, misuse, and abuse the Children of Journajesty who were the American people that believed in fighting for, and would die for the good of America, and the interest of American people.

In all the cities of America, people of all nationalities paid no attention to the real reason why heroin was flooding the American cities.

They blamed many other reasons for the constant growth of heroin use and the rise in crime in America. While the real reason still is to hold back, misuse, and abuse the children of Jourmajesty on a large scale.

It was only ten days before Pharaoh returned to New York to buy an eighth of a key from the connection Stokes was supposed to take him to. Buying an eighth of a key would allow Pharaoh to sell heroin on a larger scale to people that were dealers like himself.

Stokes and Pharaoh left Stokes' apartment enrooted to an exclusive gambling nightspot half-owned by a gorgeous and intelligent woman named Maria.

Maria was a numbers backer and half owner of the bar and restaurant and the gambling casino in the back of the restaurant. Maria was once the wife of a very feared but respected Columbian man who had been gunned down eight years ago.

Since then, Maria, his wife, backed the numbers and ran the restaurant, bar, backroom casino, and gambling. It was what she was known for, but she had a partner.

The restaurant and bar were very exclusive and were worth a fortune within themselves. It was an establishment that her husband had started from scratch. Her husband had built the name of the bar and restaurant through the types of food, vintage wine, And champagne that came from worldwide. The backroom casino gambling was for those restaurant guests of the highest caliber and was run on a 5-percentage basis. A lot of money was being made, and the responsibility was all on the house.

The drug dealings that Maria oversaw were the dealings that she did through her father-in-law, a Columbian drug lord born in another country.

Stokes was giving Pharaoh the better and wiser half of himself, and Pharaoh saw that if Stokes wasn't a drug user, he could be positively dangerous.

Stokes had one time worked for Maria's husband before drugs overtook him. Stokes was a trusted soldier in Maria's husband's private army regime. Stokes still had respect from Maria even though he had fallen to become almost nothing. Stokes' only dealings with Maria were those of honor, respect, bravery, and big-time business, even though it was in the past, ten years ago.

It was just beginning to get dark when Stokes and Pharaoh reached Maria's club of fine dining and worldwide drinks of choice.

Now Pharaoh had, from the beginning of leaving Stokes' apartment, wondered why Stokes had washed under his arms and his face and even put on a clean but wrinkled shirt and trousers with a pair of old black runover shoes. Now Pharaoh understood. Stokes had even combed his hair.

After being ushered to a table, the waiter then asked, "Are you sure you are in the right restaurant?" but he said it in Spanish.

Spanish was a subject that Pharaoh had taken in school before leaving school.

Stokes had already explained to Pharaoh before they left that they would see the wife of his past employer, boss, and friend, Maria. So, Pharaoh had answered back in Spanish to the waiter, "We are here to see Senorita Maria."

"I didn't know that you could speak Spanish," Stokes said to Pharaoh.

"But be quiet and say no more, do no more, and just be quiet, I'll take it from here. For we need something that will make us super important."

The waiter disappeared for about five minutes, and when he returned, he brought the menu, water, and a smile.

"What is your name, senior? And why are you here?" the waiter said in Spanish.

"I am the loyal runner of Mr. Fernando. My name is of no value or importance, but I have blessings for Senorita Maria."

Looking surprised, the waiter left immediately, and Stokes said to Pharaoh, "This place brings back memories of when I was a tall statue of a man, instead of the shell of the nothing I have become."

Stokes explained to Pharaoh that knowing and speaking Spanish was indeed a good thing. But keep it a secret that you can speak the Spanish language when you're an outsider of Spanish descent, especially when involved in some business.

It was then that two men came out from the kitchen and sat down at the table across from Stokes and Pharaoh. One man was telling the other man in Spanish that his job was to make sure no one was standing directly behind {The Tigresses} cards. Immediately Stokes caught on to what was happening, being that Stokes understood and spoke Spanish fluently, and Stokes knew that The Tigress was the business name for Maria that her husband had given her. Some people still called her by that name, who was once involved with her husband.

Pharaoh was a young hustler. After talking to Stokes, Pharaoh figured out that Maria was being cheated in a card game.

Pharaoh also knew that if someone was looking at Maria's cards with scopes. That they also must in some way be relaying the findings to the opponent or opponents that were playing against Maria, so her opponent or opponents would know when Maria had a sound card hand or a bad card hand. Pharaoh knew beyond a doubt that to put together a good plan and stop the cheat on Maria, he must see the order and procedure of the cheat with his own eyes and expertise.

Pharaoh felt that these were not professional cheaters but amateur cheaters. Pharaoh then explained to Stokes that if Stokes wanted to, they might help Maria, but it might be dangerous. Pharaoh then said to Stokes that if they were going to help Maria. They must do three things. One, get up to the table for Pharaoh to exercise his expertise in the cheating. To figure out the order of the cheat. Two, get a note to Maria after getting to the table that would in some way make Maria trusting of the words on the note enough to stop the game, if only for just twenty minutes. To pretend that she was going to eat but instead sit down at the table with Pharaoh.

All that would be in order so that Pharaoh could have worked out a scheme when Maria reached the table where Pharaoh would meet her. And three, to execute the plan strategy, Pharaoh would have worked out from what he learned, assumed, and guessed at the card game. Pharaoh also knew that to relate any steps of a plan would have to come from some time {even if briefly} in which he would have with Maria and himself.

To Pharaoh, the thought of the whole encounter was breathtaking because most of Pharaoh's life had been competing with small-time hustlers. When Pharaoh had graduated to big-time hustlers and then professional hustlers, but not one time did Pharaoh demote himself or fail any test while competing with the best in his city and other cities also. Pharaoh felt that the action in which he was getting ready to engross was not that of the hard hustler's strategy but simply a way of knowing what was in the opponents' hands.

Pharaoh felt confident in himself and knew that the most challenging part would be simply getting Maria to come away from the table for a minute and follow the instructions of a mere stranger. Pharaoh's advantage was that from the conversation across at the other table, where the two men had been talking, then Pharaoh knew that someone behind Maria was looking at the cards in her hand by way of binoculars. Pharaoh figured that whoever was doing this deed was somewhere up high above the level ground, but not high enough, and that's why one man was conducting the other man to keep clear the path behind Maria.

Even though it seemed to be for her protection, it was really to her disadvantage. They were making it impossible for Maria to win.

"It is so odd how all my words and senses of direction seem to be returning to me as if I had just gone on nights drunk and I am sober again the next day in time to start my daily routine," was the thoughts in Stokes mind. Stokes was getting ready to pass that thought onto Pharaoh when the waiter returned and asked Stokes and Pharaoh to follow him.

Stokes entered the kitchen through the back door that led into a large hallway. Pharaoh smelled cigar smoke and knew he and Stokes were about to contact casino action.

The waiter pushed a button on the wall, and the wall turned around, and they were standing in the corner of the casino entrance.

Both Stokes and Pharaoh were looking at many card-playing tables and dice playing, but Pharaoh noticed a large crowd around one of the tables.

It was then that Stokes asked the bartender for a pen and paper.

Stokes wrote on the paper, "It is imperative that I see you, considered to be a life-or-death situation, Fernando's Stokes."

Stokes then asked the bartender to take the note to Maria in which he did, but he returned in less than three minutes, and when the bartender returned, he looked weary, beat, defeated, and betrayed.

The bartender passed by Pharaoh and Stokes as he mumbled words to himself, "She will lose everything soon," was the words that the bartender was mumbling to himself as he motioned a sign of coming on to Stokes with his hands. Stokes explained to Pharaoh that the old bartender was Maria's late husband's chauffeur and that he was now Maria's personal chauffeur and the one person she trusted.

Pharaoh then explained to Stokes that when Stokes reached the table where Maria was to then whisper in her ear that if she would just take a brief recess from the game, to go into the restaurant to have a bite to eat, then find the table that Stokes would be sitting at with another young black male. To then sit at that table and listen to the advice presented, Stokes would show Maria how to get her money back from those who were wrongly doing her by cheating her.

Pharaoh then told Stokes to purposely stand directly behind Maria so that Pharaoh might see the streak of light coming from the binoculars that would be looking for Maria's cards.

It was then that Stokes was getting ready to ask Pharaoh a question, but a short Columbian man came up to Stokes and Pharaoh and hand motioned for them to follow him.

The short Columbian man guided them to the table where Maria was gambling, and when they reached the table, it was a heated conversation between Maria and a man called {Mr. Morcetez} was the business partner that Maria had inherited when she inherited partnership in her late husband's restaurant.

It had been known before that Maria had inherited the club's partnership that she could have accepted one million dollars cash and had no affiliation in her late husband's restaurant, gambling, and worldwide alcohol business. Unknowingly and surprisingly to all, but because Maria said that her husband built the business himself and was known by all to be her late husband's baby project built from scratch to completion, and internationally known. Then Maria turned down the money but had to accept a partnership in business with Mr. Morcetez, a silent partner with her late husband in the restaurant. Now Maria had run the restaurant business for years with her husband before his death. She qualified more than anyone to run the company profitable, unique, smoothly, effective, beneficially, and professionally.

Now Mr. Morcetez had come up with an I.O.U. Debt signed by Maria's late husband for one million dollars and accepting Mr. Morcetez as a full partner in the restaurant until Maria's husband paid the debt. Now, everyone knew that Mr. Morcetez loved Maria and wanted to be her husband. Still, everyone also knew that Maria had not dated or been involved with any man since her late husband's death, whom she not only loved but respected and enjoyed being with. Her late husband had molded her into the brilliant, intelligent businesswoman she had become. Everyone thought that Maria would take the one-million-dollar cash that Mr. Morcetez was offering her in exchange for Mr. Morcetez having a partnership with the restaurant, which he did not want. Nor did he know what to do with a partnership in the restaurant. But he wanted more than anything for Maria to be indebted to him somehow. And giving her one million dollars, instead of him being a silent partner, was how Mr. Morcetez could indebt Maria to him, so he thought. Maria refused the money but honored the debt that her late husband had left with Mr. Morcetez. And Maria did stay the restaurant owner, but with Mr. Morcetez as her silent partner. Even though Maria's thoughts were to pay

Mr. Morcetez his money as soon as she could, and become
the single proprietor of the restaurant without Mr. Morcetez
as a silent partner or Mr. Morcetez having any affiliation,,
at all with the restaurant or Maria. Mr. Morcetez was an
older man than Maria but seemed to hold his age well, for
he looked younger than the age he was, and his cunningness
was said to have learned from Maria's late husband, whom
he idolized and tried to imitate. It was also said, believed,
and understood that Maria had taught her husband to be
the man he was, as her late husband also taught Maria to
be the woman she was, and that was why they were so close
like the both of them being one. They were both a part of
each other's teachings, they both were one, Maria and her
late husband, and they both were one. Even though people in the circle that Maria knew traveled in, did business
in, lived in, and survived in, did know that Mr. Morcetez
loved and wanted Maria to be his wife, but no one knew
the dark side of Mr. Morcetez. Or the dirty, scheming low
life plan that Mr. Morcetez had thought of to embezzle Maria out of a very sentimental piece of jewelry that was Maria's husband's necklace that had been stolen out of Maria's
apartment after the death of Maria's husband. The chain
was stolen out of a robbery set up on Maria's apartment by
Mr. Morcetez to lure Maria into investing the other half of
the restaurant in a card game that Mr. Morcetez was in the
process of setting up. If Maria would take the bait at the
right time to have control of the whole restaurant. To be
more into Maria's investments and control the restaurant's
ownership, he baited Maria to put up her half of the restaurant while Mr. Morcetez's put up his half ownership of the

restaurant, plus one million dollars to a winner take all type of gamble. Mr. Morcetez knew that Maria would do almost anything to have back in her possession her late husband's necklace. Which was worth only twenty-five thousand dollars and was one of the first pieces of jewelry that Maria helped her husband save up to buy at the very beginning of their relationship. But it was of absolute value and the most sentimental thing in Maria's life.

Mr. Morcetez had been able to track down the last buyer of the necklace, whose name was {Mr. Sweeney}, who was simply a successful card dealer that enjoyed playing big-time poker and was the third person sitting at the card table. But who was also a part of Mr. Morcetez's scheme to have control of the restaurant and to also have control of the things in Maria's life that she treasured more than anything. In hopes that Mr. Morcetez could have some type of control over Maria's mind, in order to be able to get Maria, after losing, to make a loan because she was the [house] or controller of the game. Mr. Sweeney, because he was also losing, had asked to borrow twenty-five thousand dollars on Maria's husband's necklace, which Mr. Sweeney owned. Mr. Sweeney was granted the twenty-five-thousand-dollar loan on the necklace after Mr. Morcetez had vouched for Mr. Sweeney to get the loan. Maria then also asked the house to borrow ten thousand to stay in the game, but Mr. Sweeney protested Maria's ten-thousand-dollar loan when he had to borrow and accept a debt of twenty-five thousand dollars. So, Mr. Sweeney felt that Maria should not be entitled to stay in the poker game for ten thousand dollars when he had to borrow twenty-five thousand to continue in the game but should have to borrow the new table stakes, which was twenty-five thousand dollars.

Mr. Morcetez, who was winning big time, had smiled at Mr. Sweeney and Maria for their disagreement, but who had sided and agreed with Mr. Sweeney while Maria's point was that she was the house.

And it was all her money, or at least she was supposed to be in charge of the capital. Maria had the authority over the funds, which included loaning, borrowing, cuts, and anything related to the money. {That was Maria's argument} She should have no set price to enter the game, and that was the argument that was in progress when Pharaoh and Stokes reached the table where Maria was gambling. Maria shouted that none of her rules, regulation, or wishes were being carried out. And her name was being disrespected.

During the process of the argument, Pharaoh had stood directly in front of Maria. At the same time, Stokes was inching his way to get behind her and then beside her. Standing in front of Maria, Pharaoh looked straight into the eyes of Maria and saw that her eyes were bright as stars and large as saucers. Still, they were tarnished with the criteria of tears, mental stress, and fatigue.

Her hair was black as the night, lengthy and thickly rooted, while her skin was light but tinted tan with full but not too large breasts. Her mouth was oval-shaped with teeth white as pearls, and Pharaoh couldn't help but wonder about the size of her body below her breast.

But being that she was sitting down, he could only imagine what his brain and manly features would like to have known them to be. By the time Pharaoh had proportionally looked Maria over, then Stokes had gotten exactly beside her. Stokes bent down to whisper in Maria's ear, and Maria graciously bent her head down to collect the info that was ready to come into her ear from Stokes.

Stokes had been instructed by Pharaoh that Stokes' time in whispering in Maria's ear would be limited, and all Stokes wanted to say, that Stokes wouldn't be able to. With all those things in thought, then Stokes simply whispered these words.

Let my past services be looked upon as you saw me in your heart and then trusted me with the life of your husband; trust me now to stop this poker game for twenty minutes while you have a bite to eat with me and an associate of mine.

I want to express to you what danger awaits you, and a way that you can deter your troubles, but gain vengeance by outwitting your competition, who are cheating and robbing you in this poker game."

Stokes straightened back up after bending down with Maria and was hoping that he had said something to Maria. She would prolong the poker game by taking a break to hear the negative information concerning Maria being cheated and a plan to bring Maria out on top.

Maria was intelligent, but she was wise, unpredictable, and a maneuver. When Maria had sat up straight from bending over to hear what Stokes had to say, she never let her eyes contact Mr. Morcetez, but Maria looked at Mr. Sweeney and smiled gently.

Then, she looked at Mr. Morcetez and winked her eye, which was the first movement of her body given to Mr. Morcetez as a friendly or passionate type of gesture.

Maria's relationship with Mr. Morcetez had been that of business, no more, no less, but always cold and to the point. In return, Mr. Morcetez considered Maria's winking of her eye to him at the poker table as a good sign that Maria finally felt trapped and ready to give in to Mr. Morcetez if the worst for her had to come.

"Gentlemen!" Maria said in a soft but feminine voice.

"After taking into consideration that you two men are whipping my ass in this poker game, and I understand that I must borrow twenty-five thousand dollars to stay in the game, which is not fair."

"Especially this being my poker game. Even though my partner Mr. Morcetez sways his vote along with Mr. Sweeney, saying we have new table stakes for this one pot of over $150,000 and my late husband's necklace that Mr. Sweeney has put up in the pot also to be won with the incoming card hand, so he too can participate."

"I will accept the twenty-five-thousand-dollar table stake for this hand, but only in hopes to try to win Mr. Sweeney's necklace that once belonged to my late husband. First, I would like to eat a bit of an early dinner and discuss business concerning a friend of my late husband. That has come across my path, which I'm sure I can do in forty-five minutes, so in all due respect to this poker game and the people in it, I ask for forty-five minutes recess."

"So, I can eat dinner in what is still my restaurant; maybe for the last time being, this restaurant can be foreclosed on by my partner if I lose this incoming poker hand. I have decided to give into you two gentlemen. And go on with this gamble, for winning my husband's necklace back in my possession means the same to me as winning my partnership in the restaurant means to Mr. Morcetez, and winning all the money in the pot means to Mr. Sweeney. Still, this last poker hand will be played under my rules, so in case I lose, I'll always know that the game was fair to all the players and of my way."

Maria was pushing back her chair from the card table to stand when the small audience of mainly sympathetic fans and customers began to clap their hands for Maria.

Some whistled and cheered as she smiled and nodded to the audience; she said, "There will be a forty-five-minute recess, and then the game will begin again."

Stokes guided Pharaoh back through the exit in which they first came and went back to the table in the restaurant in which they had been seated, and two seconds later, Maria approached their table, while Stokes stood up and pulled out a chair so Maria could be seated.

"Talk to me," Maria said as she sat down.

Now Pharaoh had watched Maria's every movement and had seen Maria's whole body for the first time. Pharaoh was terrified with delight from Maria's looks like a beautiful and astonishing, breathtaking woman. A woman of class, beauty, elegance, charm, and intellectual intelligence. Now Pharaoh was a leg and thigh man, meaning that Pharaoh's favorite parts of a woman's body to look at and admire were her legs and thighs and especially her thighs.

Maria was sitting in a chair beside Pharaoh, and Pharaoh's view of Maria was close up, direct, straightforward, and unbelievable. Pharaoh could not help but gaze across the chair at Maria's beautiful legs and thighs as she sat there beside him with her skirt worn up much above her knees. And her beautifulness and sexiness display also the perfect size, and lengthy but full and sturdy black hair, manicures, and diamond jewelry wearing self.

Pharaoh now began to quietly, secretly, and silently pray. Pharaoh prayed to his God and asked God to lead him to victory in helping Pharaoh find a way to help this beautiful creature God had created. Pharaoh prayed that this beautiful woman's heart and insides were as beautiful as her outside looks. Stokes then introduced Pharaoh to Maria and Maria to Pharaoh. Stokes then asked Maria to listen to Pharaoh and what Pharaoh had discovered concerning Mr. Sweeney and Mr. Morcetez had to be both working in partnership against Maria. And that they had a third person that could see Maria's cards, probably by using binoculars to see Maria's cards and then some type of relay system to communicate with each other. Then some type of hand signal in giving information concerning what kind of poker hands Mr. Sweeney and Mr. Morcetez also had. Pharaoh was just assuming and not knowing factually about Mr. Sweeney and Mr. Morcetez.

Pharaoh was perfectly correct in his analysis concerning Mr. Sweeney and Mr. Morcetez cheating Maria in the poker game. Stokes was then asking Maria to trust Pharaoh. Because there was a lot of truth in what Pharaoh was telling Maria even though Pharaoh had not put all the pieces together in Mr. Sweeney's and Mr. Morcetez's s schemes and cheating methods.

"OK!" Maria said bluntly, "I believe you, and it all makes sense, and you warned me just in time before I lost my restaurant. I'm glad you told me all this, but I have already put the money I borrowed in the poker pot, and I'm officially in the game, and I can't quit, so what am I supposed to do now?"

Thinking that Maria was a Muslim, and thinking that Maria was from Pakistan, or somewhere near or in that region, because of Maria's look and features. Pharaoh used the name of Allah instead of calling out the Christian name God to draw a parable that Pharaoh had the expertise and would trust in Allah to be with him as he used his expertise of dealing cards.

"Trust in Allah to get me to that poker game table, and let me be the dealer of the cards, and I will ask Allah to guide my fingers as I put my fingers in the deck of cards to give you any card hand I choose."

Maria looked at Pharaoh very strangely for a second, and then Maria told Pharaoh that it was her choice to get any dealer of the cards; that was her choice.

She did not know what Allah meant or who Allah was, or what Allah did, nor did she believe in God. At that moment, Pharaoh knew or thought that Maria was an atheist who did not believe in God.

He could not relate or understand how beautiful, intelligent, wise, and classy Maria was; she did not believe in God, Allah, Jehovah, or any name reference to God Almighty.

God is known in many, many different names and many other countries. But all the one Supreme Being.

The only living God, but the Christians of different countries, and who also believe in Jesus Christ, the begotten

Son of God. Who is also recognized by the Christian faith as also being God?

God the Father sent Jesus Christ, God's begotten Son, to die for humanity. To give humanity eternal life after death, peace, and happiness for all that believe in Jesus Christ as the Son of the only living God. Jesus Christ also being God, the Son of God the Father.

"Are you an expert card dealer?" Maria asked Pharaoh. "For you are much too young to be anything much more than a baby, but I will get you to be the dealer at the card table, for that is my privilege, to pick the dealer of my choice and pay the dealer's salary. Sit back, relax, and blend in with the audience, and I will choose you to be the dealer of the cards."

Pharaoh was at that present moment immediately after Maria finished talking; Pharaoh was then talking silently to his God. "Merciful Heavenly Father in heaven, awesome, and Almighty God and Creator of the heavens and the earth, guide my fingers through these cards that I deal so that I might help Maria keep her restaurant from being taken possession of by these thieves and their schemes."

"In return, I will introduce this beautiful female that you created to you and personally give her interest, understanding, and meaning related to you, Your Son Jesus, and Your Word, which is the Holy Bible. And I will take nothing in return for the services that you allow me to be successful with."

"Excuse me, young man," a voice was saying. {Maria talking to Pharaoh} "Do you know how to play poker?"

Pharaoh looked around and then pointed to himself in a gesture that meant, "Are you talking to me?"

"Yes," Maria said, surprised that Pharaoh said he did not know how to play poker.

" But I do know how to run the cards" Maria then looked at Pharaoh strangely for using the term "Run the cards" instead of saying "deal the cards."

Pharaoh was still standing up when Maria stated that it was her choice to choose the dealer of the cards and that she wanted to select someone she thought could bring her luck and a good card hand.

She said she had decided to choose the young man standing up, meaning Pharaoh. Maria then said, "Mrs. Maria is my name, young man, and I am called The Tigress, and I want you to deal these poker hands for me. But if any way that I find you unlawful to me, I will introduce you to what I'm called, as in action" looking into the eyes of Mr. Sweeney, and then Mr. Morcetez.

Maria said, "To all that offer any unfair play to me, this day they will bite the dust."

Asking Pharaoh to come up to the card table, but when Pharaoh started to walk up to the table, he began to sort of hop as he walked and when Maria, Mr. Sweeney, Mr. Morcetez, and people in the audience looked down at Pharaoh's feet, and his shirt hanging out his pants which was not the style of that era of time.

Maria was astonished, negatively amazed, and very much in doubt of this crazy stupid-looking young boy who brought all attention to his shoes being on the wrong feet. And his shirt hanging out his pants, then Maria started to doubt her decision of choosing Pharaoh to deal the cards.

"Why are your shoes on the wrong feet?" Mr. Morcetez said as Mr. Sweeney smiled and just shook his head, and giggles were heard from the audience.

As Maria was handing Pharaoh the cards, Pharaoh dropped the cards right there in front of everyone. But this was a scheme from Pharaoh to make people see Pharaoh not as a threat but as a joke while Pharaoh dropped the cards to pick them up and place all the cards he would need on the bottom of the deck in order to deal them when he needed them from the bottom of the deck.

Pharaoh had seen Tommy Hank put his shoes on the wrong feet and take his shirt out his pants to disguise his expertise, and while people laughed at Tommy Hank, he utterly robbed them by cheating them, by putting his fingers in the deck and dealing off the bottom of the deck. Now Pharaoh was indeed semiprofessional with cards and dice, but with his youthful look and sloppy appearance that he portrayed. No one saw coming to the performance that Pharaoh was about to perform at the poker table.

Pharaoh's performance at the poker table was magnificent. Maria won the first poker hand that Pharaoh dealt but two additional poker hands. That not only gave Maria back her restaurant but gave her winnings of Mr. Sweeney's and Mr. Morcetez's losses together of ninety thousand dollars.

Pharaoh had explained to Maria not to play more than three poker hands because Pharaoh knew his hands would become sweaty, sticky, and he would be unable to perform control of the cards after the third poker hand.

It was raining sort of complex when Maria, Pharaoh, and Stokes came outside to leave the restaurant. It was then that Maria's chauffeur rolled out a soft bear-looking rug for Maria to walk up to the limousine parked in front of the restaurant's door.

"Get in," Maria said to Stokes and Pharaoh. "So, I can take you to my place and share some of these winnings with you. And give you my thanks and appreciation."

Stokes was walking fast up to the limousine, but Pharaoh stopped and said he loved the rain. He wanted to walk in the rain while he thanked God for guiding his fingers through the deck and giving him victory over Mr. Morcetez, Mr. Sweeney, and the cards.

"It's raining out here!" Maria was shouting, "Get in the damn car so I can share some of these thousands with you."

"Keep your money!" Pharaoh was telling Maria.

"I have to walk and talk with God first because I'm thankful and appreciative of God's blessings and protection."

"You don't want any of these thousands? Are you crazy?"

"What good is money to those who do not keep their word to God, after God gives them what they ask for?"

"What are you saying?" Maria was asking Pharaoh.

He replied, "I promised God that if he guided my fingers through the cards, kept me calm, and successfully let me get you your restaurant, then I would not take any of the spoils from the success, and I would teach you of my God, His Son Jesus Christ, and The Word of God which is the Holy Bible."

"Don't be afraid of the rain Maria because your clothes will dry, and it is not cold enough outside to make you sick from getting wet."

Maria scolded, "If you think for one moment that I'm going to walk in the rain to talk to a God you can't even see, and that won't talk back to you, then you're crazy!"

Pharaoh responded to Maria, saying, "Just three hours ago, you were in jeopardy of losing your restaurant. You were mentally lost, confused, angry, and hurt, but most of all, you were afraid that you would lose your restaurant. Now all those fears are behind you, and you are no longer lost or confused. But what did you do to change such a drastic situation into a situation that you are in charge of like you are now. Who do you owe for your so negative situation into a positive situation? Tell me, who do you owe thanks to Mrs. Maria?"

Maria was stunned by the sharp and accurate reprimand that Pharaoh had laid on Maria's heart, and for the first time in their acquaintance, Pharaoh seemed grown, mature, and engaging. Not just the immature person that Maria first saw in Pharaoh. Pharaoh smiled at Maria very meaningful as he walked away from her.

"Wait, Pharaoh," Maria said as she was taking off her shoes. "My shoes cost a lot of money, and I don't want them to get wet."

"God has just allowed you to win much more than fifty thousand dollars, and you are afraid your shoes might get wet in the rain. Who is the crazy one, you or me?"

Skipping the question, Maria asks Pharaoh, "What's so important about the rain that you like it so much and want to walk in it?"

"To me, the rain is a cleaner from God to wash away some dirt and filth of the earth where people spit, shit, vomit, and do all sorts of the other filthy things," Pharaoh responded.

"While God cleans the earth and fertilizes the earth, grows the fruits of the earth, and brings rain to the farmers to grow the food and vegetables that you eat. The farmers sometimes wait for weeks, months, and what sometimes must seem forever for the rain to come, and the weather prediction people try to predict the times for the rain, wind, and snow. While their predictions are sometimes close and other times for the rain, wind, and other times accurate or way off, no one knows when it will rain snow or when the winds will blow for sure but God, and no one can make it rain but God. Man cannot function properly when it rains, and nothing man can do to prevent God's rain from interfering with man's plans or way of life because when it rains, everything that man does has to be done much more cautiously or differently. While rain brings caution and change, rain also brings sleep, tiredness, and comfort to both man and animal."

"What is the name of your God?" Maria asked Pharaoh. "God has many names and is called in every language in existence, by every person in existence." "What is the name that you call your God when you talk to him? And for what purpose do you talk to a God that does not talk back to you. Now, who is crazy?"

"Faith believes in God's timing, way, and order in which He does things. God is called many names, but God is known almost everywhere as The Creator or Allah. I talk to God and call God my Heavenly Father, God Almighty, Allah, Jehovah, the creator of heaven and earth. I use all those names and titles at different times when I talk to God. When I pray to God at many other times, I talk to God through my soul, heart, and spirit.

Then sometimes I talk with God as my companion or friend, the one that I know will always be there for me, and to deal with and cure my fears and problems regardless of what they may be."

"I am a Christian, and being of the Christian faith, we not only believe in God. But Christians believe in Jesus, the Son of God that came down upon earth in earthly form as man, who died for humanity, was buried and rose from the dead so man could have life after death. Also, we Christians believe that to believe in Jesus Christ, who is our Lord and Savior, and who is the begotten Son of God Almighty, is the only way that man can enter the afterlife of heaven, to be at peace and happiness forever, throughout eternity without death."

The rain had stopped, and Pharaoh and Maria had been walking and talking for over two hours, and they had not gone far because they were strolling. They occasionally stopped so that Pharaoh could explain the questions in detail. The limousine was still right there behind them even though it had to stop and pull over for the traffic a few times but caught up minutes later with Pharaoh and Maria. Stokes had gone to sleep in the limousine and was somewhat startled when Maria and Pharaoh returned.

Pharaoh was no longer remembering when he first met Maria when a guard came to Pharaoh's cell door. The guard informed Pharaoh that he had a visit. It was Pharaoh's first visit he had been allowed to have because all inmates had to be in this diagnostic center for ten days before being allowed to have visitation rights. Pharaoh smiled to himself, knowing that the visitor coming to see him was Goldie or {Brown Eyes} or one of Pharaoh's children because they were the only ones Pharaoh allowed to come to visit him.

After entering the visiting room, Pharaoh saw that it was Goldie who had come to visit him. She looked as good as a pitcher of water after crossing the desert on foot with one shoe on and a chain and ball around the other foot. He had not seen a woman in a dress which was one of his favorite sights. Goldie had brought Pharaoh's infant son Journajesty with her, and Goldie was two months pregnant with Pharaoh's second child. Goldie's hand palms were red as fire. That was another sign of Goldie's new pregnancy.

Just seeing Pharaoh's infant son and Goldie in a dress and knowing that Goldie was coming along alright with her new pregnancy made Pharaoh's Day for the next ten days, even in jail. Not knowing then that in years to come, Goldie would use Pharaoh's sons to try to fight Pharaoh.

The relationship between Goldie and Pharaoh would be no more because of a hex placed on them by other jealous females. Even though Pharaoh and Goldie would never forget in their hearts that God had been a part of their relationship and would not let them hate each other.

The visit lasted a half-hour and ended with a hug and kiss from Goldie and Pharaoh's infant son Journajesty. Upon returning to Pharaoh's cell, he was excellent from visiting Goldie and his infant son Journajesty.

After laying there on his bunk, still feeling the good effects and vibes of his visit, Pharaoh's door opened again.

The guard told him to sign for a package that he had received from Brown Eyes, another female friend of Pharaohs. She was an incredible, intelligent, and professional female who had been involved with Pharaoh for the last five years.

Brown Eyes was a professional career woman; however, she could get off her professional job. Pack a bag or whatever else necessary to be at Pharaoh's side in a flash. She would mean business for whatever she had to direct or be a part of or for or with Pharaoh. Brown Eyes was a very sexy, intelligent female whose concern was only about her daughter, Pharaoh, and her career. She was a good hustler because she had all types of legitimate contacts and connections. She could also be untrustworthy, a liar, and a cheat.

Jesus was what brown eyes talked about, believed in, and taught others. Brown Eyes said that Jesus is and would be there for her, to rescue her when she badly needed him.

Pharaoh had been in the diagnostic center long enough to receive a package, and Brown Eyes had sent it through the mail. It consisted of two sweatsuits, two pairs of silk underwear, two pairs of sweat socks, an am and FM cassette radio player. Which was a procedure that all inmates participated in if they had someone to send these items, and they had been there long enough.

Brown Eyes sent Pharaoh's package that day, but she also visited Pharaoh, which gave Pharaoh a good double day. After signing for the box that Brown Eyes had sent Pharaoh through the mail and visiting with Brown Eyes, which was also very pleasurable and exciting. Brown Eyes knew how to wear revealing clothes to make Pharaoh's visit even more delightful, exciting, and sexy.

Pharaoh then returned to his cell to find a cell buddy. The cells were made for two inmates to be in a cell, and Pharaoh had not yet received a cell buddy because the traffic in the cells was always moving to take one inmate out and immediately bring in another.

While Pharaoh had left the cell to pick up a package and visit Brown Eyes, a new inmate had been put in the cell to share the cell with Pharaoh.

His new cell buddy stood up and extended his hand for a friendly handshake upon entering the cell. He told Pharaoh his name was {Edward}. After some preliminary conversation, Edward admitted to Pharaoh {in a sort of guilty way} that he had twenty years because he ratted out his younger brother to the federal authorities for him to get twenty years with the eligibility for parole. In comparison, his younger brother got forty years without eligibility for parole, only because of Edward's testimony against him. Edward told Pharaoh that his younger brother was always getting glory from other people, and he received none.

Edward was a drug user while his younger brother was not. Edward finished his conversation by saying that he was the oldest and should have received all the glory that his younger brother had gotten, That he should have been making the money that his younger brother was making.

Pharaoh immediately thought of the story of {Joseph} in the Bible. When Joseph's brothers sold him into slavery, he was taken to another country, and Joseph's brother told their father that Joseph had been killed and eaten by a wild animal.

It was then that Edward confronted Pharaoh by reaching for the package that Pharaoh had just received from Brown Eyes. "I'm tired of watching everyone else receive money and gifts all my life while I get nothing!

CHAPTER 4

Edwards Threats to Pharaoh

Pharaoh very much so loved and worshiped God daily even though Pharaoh was now venturing out in the world of worldly things, ideas, and activities. Soon unbeknownst to Pharaoh, he would be stepping and then wallowing into sophisticated fun, still trying to hold on to most of his morals and principles that being a Christian demanded of him.

Pharaoh did not like Edward because Edward was a snitch, and the lowest of the low in the hustling world is to snitch on anyone, especially his brother. Pharaoh had no conversation for Edward, no words, no expression, and no contact of any kind.

Two hours passed in silence before Edward broke the silence by talking as he got up to pee in the toilet and told Pharaoh to give him the package that Pharaoh had just received from Brown Eyes.

"I'm tired of watching everyone receive money and gifts all my life while I receive nothing! So I'm going to take *your* package for myself!" Pharaoh very much so loved and worshipped God daily. Now Pharaoh was venturing out into the world of worldly things, ideas, and activities. And soon, unbeknownst to Pharaoh, he would be stepping and then wallowing into sophisticated fun while still trying to hold on to his morals and principles that being a Christian demanded of him.

Pharaoh was thanking God for the wellbeing of his infant son Journajesty, and the well-being of Pharaoh's unborn child, still in the womb of {Goldie}. And for the visit and package of Brown Eyes when the threatening words of Edward broke his prayer to God.

It changed Pharaoh's prayer to plead to God not to let Edward die from what Pharaoh was about to do to Edward. Edward bent over drinking water out of the old half-working water fountain in the cell with Edward and Pharaoh. When Edward threw his head back to swallow the water, Pharaoh quietly and slowly rose off the bunk and chopped Edward in his Adam's apple with the side of Pharaoh's open hand, causing Edward to choke and gasp for breath.

Pharaoh then hit Edward with his fist between Edward's chest and Edward's stomach, which doubled Edward over and brought Edward to his knees.

Pharaoh then took Edward by his head and bashed Edward's face in the steel toilet, knocking Edward unconscious.

Helping Edward up, Pharaoh then stuck Edward's whole head in the toilet and flushed the toilet so the cold water could run all over Edwards's head and face to bring Edward back to consciousness.

He then bashed his head back into the steel toilet, knocking him out again. Pharaoh then called the guard and told the guard that Edward was jumping off the top bunk headfirst, trying to commit suicide.

After wiping some of the blood up off the floor, Pharaoh then turned on the radio that was Pharaoh's private possession, that Pharaoh had just received in his package from Brown Eyes.

WWIN was a top-rated Baltimore radio station that had been around for a long time in Baltimore. And had just recently added on an FM station and kept its AM station.

Pharaoh used to listen to rock and roll Music on the WINN station many times; Pharaoh also listened to the 96.3 stations in Washington, a celebrity station.

It had excellent contemporary rhythm and blues Music for Baltimoreans, just like WWIN FM station in Baltimore was to Baltimoreans. The news on WWIN was referring to {Winston Clearance} a respected businessman and congressman whose wife was a judge. He had been found guilty of perjury on the grounds of accepting money from, or in a roundabout way, from a celebrity drug dealer. And for lying on the witness stand.

The fact that the media and daily newspaper had scandalized the event so intensely. It discredited Winston Clearance, his wife, and his family.

More than anything, authorities seemed to discredit the caliber of his family name. And the fact that his family had dedicated a lot of years getting to the prestigious title. And affiliation that his family has accomplished through a long road of intensive fighting for the rights of black people.

The news on the radio went into the fact that Governor Shadows would be going to Canada to increase the trade market between Canada and the United States, and looking into Medicare would be his next project.

Governor Shadows had been a hell of a mayor in the City of Baltimore. Before he became the governor, his tasks were many for the people of Baltimore. He had tremendously helped poor people in the process of tearing down old buildings and neighborhoods and building them back up to be excellently renovated and proud for anyone to live in. The senior communities that he rebuilt also helped the city's appearance. Combined with the Baltimore Harbor, Governor Shadows, as Mayor of the City of Baltimore then, was responsible for building the new image of the City of Baltimore, was of class and excellence.

Shadows, as mayor, had also played a part in introducing one of the top middleweight fighters from Maryland. He also helped to back, advertise, and forecast for the fighter's superiority in boxing. Way before the original happening of the boxer becoming a world champion and bringing thrills and excitement to the world of boxing.

Pharaoh's thoughts and listening patterns were then interrupted, and Pharaoh stopped thinking about the past when Pharaoh's cell door opened once again. Three large guards stood there to take Pharaoh to lock up until further investigation was done on Pharaoh's cell buddy Edward's brutal situation.

Pharaoh's lockup cell was high on a tier away from the general population where Pharaoh could hear the noises of the jail and the many conversations; all rolled into one. Even though he could not determine what was being said or who was saying it, it was just all mumbles and jumbles of noise.

The lockup cell was massive in size and reminded Pharaoh of a cave or place where a bear might hibernate for the winter, so Pharaoh did lay back on his bunk and began to remember where he left off concerning Maria.

He was closing his eyes to meditate and refusing to worry about his present situation concerning his cell buddy Edward. Pharaoh went back in his mind when he and Maria walked in the rain, and Pharaoh had been teaching Maria about his God.

Maria had given Stokes ten thousand dollars upon the request from Pharaoh after Pharaoh refused to accept the ten thousand dollars because Pharaoh promised God. What if God would guide Pharaoh's fingers through the deck and let Pharaoh be successful in bringing Maria out of debt with Mr. Morcetez and Mr. Sweeney. Pharaoh said that he would not take part in the booty and would teach Maria of his God. Instead, he asked Maria to give the money to Stokes for his role in being a part of the success that had come from the card game with Mr. Sweeney and Mr. Morcetez.

After Stokes received the money, he got down on his knees and folded his hands in prayer. He gave thanks to God with tears in his eyes. Stokes vowed to befriend Pharaoh forever. He would show Pharaoh a different Stokes. A Stokes with morals and principles that his Christian mother so diligently taught him as a boy.

And all these things Stokes swore on the human head of his mother whom he loved so dearly. Maria, not understanding why Stokes had sworn on the head of his mother and was Stokes a Christian like Pharaoh, did Stokes and Pharaoh Worship the same God.?

Looking at Maria with a smile, Pharaoh told Maria that there was only one God, the only true and living God.

"Yes," Pharaoh replied to Maria.

"Stokes and I both worship the only living God. One God, and we both are Christians. True believers in Jesus Christ the one begotten Son of God."

I thought all Christians were supposed to be good and righteous people who do not sin," Maria said to Pharaoh.

"No," Pharaoh answered to Maria.

"All Christians sin in some way because Christians are still humans. All humans sin except Jesus Christ, the Son of God, who is the only human in the world that has never sinned. Jesus Christ is the founder of Christianity and introduced Christianity to the world. And that which is named after Jesus's name, the religion of Christianity. Like his father in heaven, he never sins, and who *can't* sin. Because sinning is not a part of God's nature or protocol."

"All humans, whether Christians or whatever, all sin in some way. Lying and even being envious of others or wishing for something or someone that belongs to another is sinning. One can do so many things to sin without meaning to sin. God intended for all to be righteous and holy like Him until Satan brought sin into the world and gave humans the beginning of sin by getting humans to disobey God, which was a sin, the very first sin."

"Then why did Stokes ask this great God of the both of you to bring down punishment on his mother's head if he did wrong? Why would someone want someone else to pay for their wrongdoing if they were a Christian and especially their mother?"

"Stokes did not mean those words to mean what you think they mean," Pharaoh explained to Maria. "But instead,

Stokes was putting tragedy on his mother's head instead of his head because Stokes loves his mother more than he loves himself. And what he can't do for himself in lack of willpower, then he can do for his mother. Stokes' power of love for his mother is greater than Stokes' love for himself. Stokes believes that nothing can make him hurt his mother, so Stokes put all the weight of failure to his mother because he believes that he will never let his mother down to have to pay for his sins."

Maria asked, "What if Stokes, in some way, shape or form, refuses to keep his honor and word for the sake of being untrue to his word and vow to your God? What will happen to his mother? Will your God serve his mother for the broken debt, or will your God keep not the broken vow in debt?"

Pharaoh replied, "That is a question I cannot answer, Maria, for I am not God. Nor does man know how to think or function like God, and God's ways and meanings are foreign and incapable of humans before they see that God's way is always the right way and is best for them even when one has to suffer first sometimes. Before seeing the glory."

Pharaoh knew that he had been blessed to accomplish all he had for Maria and Stokes. Even though Pharaoh loved and worshipped God, he was a part of worldly living. And he reminded Maria of the original game plan and purpose of Pharaoh and Stokes coming to see Maria, which was to buy heroin in weight.

"I said that I don't want any of the booties that came with the card game. But I do want to fulfill my original purpose of meeting you, which was to have a heroin connection."

Pharaoh watched Maria as her lips began to part as she smiled. "You are so right, Pharaoh," she said as she motioned for the chauffeur to pull the limousine up to her as she asked Pharaoh to come with her.

It was still early when Maria and Pharaoh pulled up on 141st and 7th Ave in New York. Later Pharaoh would find that this place was one of Maria's heavyweight stash houses. Upon entering the building with a key, and then proceeded up two flights of stairs to an apartment in which Maria gave some sort of coded knock-on, which was opened by a man wearing a shoulder holster. He had a holstered gun around his leg near his ankle. And he stood there like he was on guard between what seemed to be the kitchen and the bedroom.

There was a middle-aged man in the bedroom with what seemed to be his wife, and three children, and two mattresses on the floor. Pharaoh later found out that one mattress was for the man, his wife, and three children, and the other mattress was for the soldier that stood like a guard.

Maria then took Pharaoh into the next room, a large empty room with a big table with glass covering its length. A measuring scale, many measuring spoons on the table, and decks of cards on the table also.

Maria introduced the man with the gun in his hand as {Tito}, then Maria introduced the other man as {Manwel}, and his wife {Cuchi}. Maria then told those people that Pharaoh was Champagne to her. Champagne is the name that Maria gave to Pharaoh that day. Pharaoh would keep the name Champagne for over fifty years with that sign and culture of people throughout the generations to come.

Maria thanked Pharaoh once again for all he had done for her and told Pharaoh that she would never be able to repay him. Still, she would do whatever was in her ability and reach to do whenever or whatever Pharaoh wanted that was reasonable and dignified.

Pharaoh told Maria that he only wanted what he and Stokes had initially set out to get from Maria, a heroin connection. Also, the expertise to cut, sell, manufacture, and distribute large-scale heroin ounces, and halves, quarters, and keys of heroin, So that he would have the ability to give his clientele the best deals and quality as possible, for as little as he could. Not to rob people or take advantage of them, but to still be making plenty of money while providing a safe, convenient, and comfortable way.

Taking Pharaoh back to the room with the glass top table, Maria showed Pharaoh the measuring and explained that the largest spoon on the ring of measuring spoons was called the jumbo spoon. Four jumbo spoons evened off was an ounce of heroin, and every four spoons afterward was another ounce of heroin. Four ounces plus an extra half jumbo spoon was a large eight of heroin or an eight of a key, and eight-eighths of a key was a key. That would be moving into big-time heroin selling and distributing. Maria explained to Pharaoh that a particular caliber or grade of heroin could take a twenty cut. That meant that one could be twenty times their original amount of what they start off with. And that the more cut one could allow on the heroin is the more money one could make. Good heroin usually starts around a twelve cut, meaning that one could be twelve times the original amount. The higher the cut one could do was the better the quality of heroin. The better the quality, the more money one would have to pay for the product. The more money one had to pay, the more money one would make when finally putting the product on the market to sell.

A big eighth of heroin taking a twelve to fifteen cut usually sell for thirty-five hundred dollars. From that price and ratio, you will learn how to add on cuttings agents to make your heroin product take a lesser cut. By diluting the product with a cutting agent like quinine and Bonita mixed,—lowering its caliber so that you can still make plenty of money and still have a good heroin product to sell.

"Pharaoh!" Looking straight into Maria's face realized he was fascinated, hypnotized, and in love with Maria, which is what he told Maria as he looked into Maria's eyes.

"I'm truly in love with you, Maria," Pharaoh said as he reached down and took Maria's hand inside his hand. "I believe that you are ALL that! And much more. You are like a mythical super character who lives only in a make-believe world but has become real. I truly love you."

Maria smiled at Pharaoh; she took Pharaoh to a corner of the room where no one could hear their conversation and told Pharaoh that she was thankful for all Pharaoh's contributions. She was overwhelmed concerning all his outstanding qualifications and expertise in being a fine young hustler, professional gambling tactics, and abilities. But she avoided a love affair forced on her and tried to buy her concern.

Without looking into Maria's face, Pharaoh replied, telling Maria that he wasn't trying to force himself on Maria, and neither was he trying to buy her. Maria ended the conversation by saying, "Let's finish taking care of business first, and then there is a small matter that I would like you to do for me."

Now Maria also saw Pharaoh as a talented young soldier like her late husband was, and Pharaoh was the first interest Maria had seen in a man since the death of her husband. But more than anything, Maria saw the youth in Pharaoh and the will to learn to be the best.

Maria offered Pharaoh a key of heroin that could take a twenty cut. Still, Pharaoh had refused to accept a large amount of heroin and had explained to Maria that that was entirely too much heroin for his small heroin business. And until he ventured out to other territories and acquired more and better ways in which to dispose of the heroin, then he would only need something more minor like three or four ounces of the same caliber of heroin that could take a twenty cut.

Now the (123) Family was well aware that heroin was cheap to use, especially for soldiers in the Vietnam War with America. That would also bring the heroin drug back to their country of America from Vietnam, and the heroin boom would start in America.

But it would not last forever because the younger generations afterward would see the harm caused by the heroin addicts destroying themselves, their neighborhoods and families, their principles, morals, and without having the control to stop using heroin. Even if they so desired to, were once addicted, and that the after generation would not follow the trend of their mother's and father's trend of heroin use. Cocaine was already set up to be the next trap for the Children of Jourmajesty that would cost the lives and family's heartache ten thousand times the negative impact of heroin use.

Cocaine would cause wars between countries and destroy ten thousand times the deaths, loss of souls, morals, principles, and corruption amongst power structures of countries, families, husbands, and wives, sisters, and brothers. While the righteous would be pursued by the commander and chief of the (123) Family himself, cocaine use, unlike heroin use, cocaine could be disguised as having fun, partying, and use without addiction also could be used as a disguise.

Two days and nights had passed while Pharaoh had been involved in the situation with Maria, Mr. Morcetez, Mr. Sweeney, and the introduction to Maria's stash house employees.

It was late in the evening; Maria pushed the button in the limousine for the window to go down, which broke the silence between Maria and Pharaoh, as Maria told the chauffeur to stop past the fruit store. A large variety of fruits, flowers, and vegetables were displayed outside. Maria had stopped the limousine and uttered in a Spanish accent as she was leaving the limousine.

"Come, Champagne. "Pharaoh turned, looking in the other direction. "Who me?" Not knowing who Maria was referring to.

"Yes, Pharaoh. Champagne is the name to you because you have brought happiness and excitement into my life which I have not had for a long time" and then Maria brought a dozen oranges.

Pharaoh noticed that there seemed to be a fruit stall combined with a delicatessen on every corner of the city part of New York, now upon leaving the fruit stand, it had begun to rain, and once again, Pharaoh started walking in the rain.

"Is walking in the rain something that you do every time it rains?"

"No," replied Pharaoh, "not every time it rains but when God is all over my soul, spirit, and body like he is now. And my bones cry out for me to acknowledge His greatness, His superiority, His wonderfulness, and his creativity."

What man could have been so powerful and intelligent as to create the rain? And give the rain the many jobs and purposes in which the rain has? Walking in the rain is one of the things I like to do and show God his appreciation for the rain and its many purposes.

Now Pharaoh had begun to feel the curiosity of Maria concerning his God. Pharaoh went on to tell Maria some of the things that he told Maria the first time they had walked in the rain. After Pharaoh had first beaten Mr. Sweeney and Mr. Morcetez, they left Maria's club, which is once again owned only by Maria. Maria was showing interest in Pharaoh's God, and Pharaoh saw it. Pharaoh reinforced his conversation with Maria. Concerning God and the beautifulness and meaningfulness of the rain. But Maria struck back by shouting, "Who is your God Champagne? Is your God a Catholic, Baptist, Muslim, Protestant, or what? Being that Americans have so many Gods? Pharaoh turned to Maria smiling."

"There is but one God, except the begotten Son of God, so believe all Christians. All the different religions that you named all worship the same God. Even though they may call his name differently, they might worship him differently. They all worship the same God. Not just here in America but all around the world, people who worshiped God worship the same God unless he worships idols or images that they have created with their own hands to worship."

"I like hearing about your God," Maria said. "I just wonder if He can do things that you have said He has done like create the rain, but I would like to know how long did it take your God to teach you how to deal cards like that, and would he teach me?"

"My God does not participate in tribunal things such as the cards, but God was there to protect me; God is in my heart at all times."

"Pharaoh! You are lying because there is no way a person gets small enough to get into another person's heart. That cannot be so!" Maria said, "Can you close your eyes and see your husband, Maria?"

Maria stopped immediately. "Why would you disrespect my husband asking me a question like that?"

"I meant no harm or disrespect to you or your husband, but I was trying to show you a situation that would make you understand God being in my heart."

"I sort of understand the parable that shows me your thought of someone being in your heart, but my husband is not your God, Maria said."

"No, Maria, your husband is not my God, but just like you can communicate with your husband in your heart, then so can I spiritually identify, relate, speak to and be with my God as my God is with me in my heart, and I am under his protection at all times from the world because my God is awesome."

"What do you mean, Pharaoh? What do you mean your God is awesome?"

"Well! How can I explain how my God is awesome?" Pharaoh said to Maria.

"My God took a cloud from the sky and wrapped it around the new birth of the sea that had just exited the womb of its mother; God used the cloud as a swaddling blanket to cradle the new young sea. My God knows the place with thunder, lightning, snow, and rain is stored, and only God can tell the ocean where to stop and go no further because it is the seashore. My God created the sun, the moon, and stars, but my God takes time to feed the birds. But He forgets not the bugs in the dirt or under rocks. And he mingles with the creatures of the sea that have been there for billions of years. My God created all wisdom and knowledge in the universe, on land, and in the ocean. My God knows the exact count of hairs that your mother, father, sister, and brother have upon their head.

While he is a forgiving God to all, who ask for forgiveness and mean it from their hearts and souls."

Maria stopped Pharaoh from talking anymore by putting her finger over her lips and chin, saying, "Yes! Your God is awesome."

Now Pharaoh was very tired but had been able to stay up because of the excitement, the learning experience of the scale, cocaine, heroin, and of course, the company of Maria. But Pharaoh began to wonder himself, does this superhuman woman ever get tired because Maria had shown no signs of tiring.

Maria told Pharaoh that there was just one more little favor that she needed from him, and she would see to it that Pharaoh got some rest.

After driving from the city in about thirty minutes in very little traffic, the chauffeur brought the limousine a stop in a secluded rural section of the city.

For some reason, Pharaoh knew that this was the home of Maria. It seemed to be an apartment building of five stories high, and the doorman immediately ran out to greet Maria with a greeting that seemed warm, friendly, and protective, but loyal and worthy to be of any service necessary like even dying for, as the doorman escorted Maria to the elevator.

The doorman pushed the button to the second floor after the chauffeur had first stopped the limousine and opened the car door for Maria as Pharaoh watched all this royal service being awarded to Maria constantly. Maria seemed taken by Pharaoh's worship to his God. Maria was quite astonished and fond of Pharaoh's noninterest in money when it came to Pharaoh's commitment to his God, while Maria saw that same matter as honesty, loyalty, trustworthiness, and dependability in Pharaoh.

This was the first lavish apartment Pharaoh had ever seen in New York or anywhere else. And from what Pharaoh was allowed to know, he was amazed.

Maria's apartment was large, spacious, very creative, and moderately decorated, situated and laid out the parts that Pharaoh was about to witness. The apartment belonged to Maria even though she paid monthly upkeep on the condo.

The first floor of the apartment had a living room, dining room, kitchen, and two double large spacious baths. The second floor had three spacious bedrooms with full bathrooms and sauna rooms in each bathroom, while these had made as a master bedroom with patio included in each one. The third floor had ping pong tables, pool tables, massage facilities with showers, a swimming pool, and a tennis court. Now the first floor had a drop in the bottom. A reduction in the floor had a genuine leather sofa with cushions all around the wall to create a private, comfortable room, surrounded by soft pillows and pure soft leather.

Now Maria dares not show Pharaoh too much of the apartment building because it was where (123), director and CEO in charge of holding back, mistreating, abusing, stagnating, and misusing the Children of Jourmajesty, would stay whenever (123) was in New York.

This is where he resided. The apartment building was made to travel all over the apartment building from floor to floor, from room to room. It was not just Maria's private living quarters, but also Maria's husband and (123)'s, which they all had combinations to open up the walls and closet ways.

While the building had four secret ways out of the building leading to the streets and back doors of New York, but there were only two entrances into the building. Maria and her late husband shared the building with (123), who was the Godfather to Maria's late husband, and even though Maria knew nothing about the (123) Organization or the goals, purpose or definition or description of the (123) Organization. Maria still existed there but was naive to all that the (123) Family did or was a part of. Maria did know that anytime she was in need or needed anything, all Maria had to do was ask for it, and it would be done. Maria also knew that anything that she received from the (123) Family would from that moment make Maria subject to have to give or do any that would be asked of her from the (123) Family.

Now that den in Maria's apartment was surrounded by soundproof glass, and even though it was glass, one could not look in even though one could look out. It was a safe house for the privacy of Maria and her husband, and the only thing in the apartment that Maria installed herself was a private telephone line in her bath and her bedroom for the privacy of her and her late husband.

While it was true that no one had ever been inside of this den except Maria, it was also most definitely true beyond a doubt Pharaoh had fallen in love with Maria. Because Pharaoh related most things to the Bible, Pharaoh related his feelings for Maria to King Solomon's feelings for most of King Solomon's thousand wives, mainly foreign women who worshiped idols. God had told King Solomon not to mingle with foreign women, and Pharaoh had always wondered why King Solomon had continually disobeyed God by continuing to indulge with foreign women that worshiped idols and believed not in the true living God.

Pharaoh tried to turn his feelings for Maria off, but Pharaoh could not, so Pharaoh gave in and gave his heart to Maria. While knowing it was wrong to do because Maria did not believe in the only true living God besides God's Son, who is also God, so believe the Christian religion.

Pharaoh was amazed by the beauty and shape of Maria's body, but Maria's outfit had a crucial and devastating effect on Pharaoh. After peeling the oranges, like Maria had asked Pharaoh to do.

Pharaoh heard Maria as she whispered in a low voice, "Hit me, Pharaoh hit me with the oranges she cried out to Pharaoh in a whisper of a voice that became louder and louder as Pharaoh did hit Maria with the oranges. Pharaoh threw the oranges like a pitcher in a major league baseball game, pitching a no-hitter.

"Harder!" Maria cried as Pharaoh added more power to his accuracy as he hit Maria with the oranges. Upon receiving the double direct hit from the oranges with the power and accuracy of the impact, Maria showed explosive signs of climaxing every time the oranges hit her body. The juice from the orange was sticky wet juice upon her body. Maria gave Pharaoh many back shots because Maria had already explained to Pharaoh not to hit her in the face, breast, or stomach.

"One more time Pharaoh! Act as if the bases are loaded, and the count is complete on the batter that you are throwing two for three and two outs in a baseball game. Pharaoh was impressed at the stance Maria was portraying as Maria stood tall as her knee rested upon the sofa and her butt sticking out, but as the oranges came to her at full speed and power, then Maria was knocked off the couch, on the floor, and out of her senses as Pharaoh ran over to see if she was all right. Picking Maria up off the floor.

Pharaoh asked Maria if she was all right, and after coming back to her senses, Maria replied, "I will be just fine if only you could repeat that last throw one more time!" Pharaoh was bending over Maria with a wet cloth that Pharaoh had got from the bathroom. As Pharaoh tried to kiss Maria, she turned her head and faced away, so Pharaoh tried to wipe the sticky juice for Maria when Maria protested, saying, "Don't wipe it off my body. Let the sticky juice stay on me!"

One more time, Pharaoh bent down to kiss Maria again, but again, Maria turned her face away from Pharaoh. Pharaoh had got up and left Maria, still calling for Pharaoh to throw more oranges at her. But, Maria realized Pharaoh was leaving her apartment even though Pharaoh knew not the right entrance into Maria's apartment, nor the way out of Maria's apartment. Catching Pharaoh by the arm just before Pharaoh opened Maria's kitchen door that led to the den in the floor, Maria, with tears in her eyes, asked Pharaoh to stay as she apologized for her strange behavior.

Pharaoh then turned to Maria face to face, and it was then at that second that Maria realized that for the first time since the death of her husband. Maria wanted to be intimate with a man, but not any man, because Maria wanted to be intimate with Pharaoh, and only Pharaoh.

Maria then realized that she wanted Pharaoh to hold her, caress her, and feel Pharaoh's body against her body as Maria longed for the human touch of a man from Pharaoh.

Pharaoh left the den and went through the kitchen door, even though Pharaoh had no idea how to get entirely out of the building with its secret entrances, exits, connecting rooms, and secret closets. That turned into hallways that led to other rooms. Most of all, how to get past the door-man, who seemed to be the protector of Maria with his life.

Maria finally realized Pharaoh had left the den, went through the kitchen, and was just about to get lost in the secrets of the apartment before Maria caught Pharaoh by begging Pharaoh not to leave. Please forgive me, Pharaoh. I apologize for my unforgivable ways, my insults toward your manhood, and my lack of explaining why my so crooked ways of pleasing myself; please forgive me, Pharaoh Maria cried out behind a streak of tears. This is no way to repay you for the miracles in my life.

"Please, please, Maria! Show me the way out and let me be alone for a while is what I ask of you because I have done for you what you have asked me, even though I don't understand, but I'll leave now and maybe another time you might want me, as I want you, for my companion."

One year passed since Pharaoh left Maria's apartment, and even though Pharaoh had not seen Maria since then, Maria had asked Pharaoh more than once to come to New York to visit. She had even requested Pharaoh just to call her when he was in New York. But Pharaoh never let himself be in the Company of Maria again.

Now Pharaoh and Stokes were the best of friends, and while Stokes did do business with Maria, Pharaoh only did business with Stokes concerning heroin.

Stokes had moved his mother and wife to a better neighborhood. He bought his mother and wife both cars even though his wife nor his mother would drive, but would leave all three vehicles for Stokes to drive.

Pharaoh was getting topnotch heroin from Maria through Stokes, which Maria gave Pharaoh an eight of heroin every month, while Stokes brought a key every month, and Stokes gave Maria Pharaoh's phone number, while Pharaoh did occasionally talk to Maria over the phone when she called.

Now Pharaoh was getting top-grade heroin from Maria through Stokes, but the big heroin dealers in Baltimore were mainly or rather all from the west side of town, and they had a club called {Flats}. They would not buy heroin from Pharaoh because Pharaoh was an East Baltimorean. So, Pharaoh kept his business with only the white professional people he started with, knew, believed in, and trusted.

In the sixties, East Baltimore had no authority or say in the drug world but was led by West Baltimoreans who chose the best hustlers out of East Baltimore to give heroin to. The West Baltimore circle of hustlers was very close-knitted, and they all had drug connections to big-time drug dealing. They needed not to venture out no further than their own West Baltimore circle of close-knit hustlers who provided the need and demand for buying and selling drugs of all amounts.

Even though it had been two years since Pharaoh had seen Maria, Pharaoh had been to New York many times to see his excellent friend Stokes, and occasionally, Pharaoh came to visit Stokes' mother. They went through the Bible, or you can say that they both studied the Bible together with much enjoyment from them both.

At that present time, Stokes' mother and Mama Grace were the only people Pharaoh studied the Bible with, even though Pharaoh did sit in on Mama Grace's Bible study sessions in Mama Grace's house and with the members of Mama Grace's church. Mama Grace's church friends and associates who together called themselves the {Christian

Church Mob}. They were somewhat like Mama Grace's {Prayer Mob}. They brought extreme prayer methods to God in favor of severe cases. Calling on God to answer their prayers for whom or whatever the case may be. It always ended up with some positive results for the situation brought to God by the Prayer Mob.

These positive results given to the Prayer Mob from God Almighty made Pharaoh feel invincible because Pharaoh knew that if and when an extreme case of trouble or disaster would ever fall on him, Pharaoh knew that through Mama Grace's guidance, and the Prayer Mob would bring his situation before Almighty God. In concern for help and deliverance, Almighty God would not turn His back on Pharaoh.

Especially if Pharaoh's case was never distrusting God, but staying within boundaries of asking for God's forgiveness and protection. Which Pharaoh had vowed to himself that whatever he did, he would find a way to do whatever in a way that he would stay in God's favor, in all the things that Pharaoh would do. Even though Pharaoh listened and learned, Pharaoh never intervened or took part in the discussion of The Christian Church Mob or Mama Grace's Prayer Mob. Pharaoh did listen diligently while he took notes of their teachings to better study by himself, which he loved to do when studying The Word of God.

Through Stokes, Pharaoh knew that Maria had left America for a year and returned to her own country but was back in America. She was asking Stokes of Pharaoh's wellbeing, of his present situation.

She told Stokes to relay to Pharaoh that she had never stopped thinking about Pharaoh and God. That she would like to see Pharaoh and learn more about Pharaoh's God, even though she had been studying Christianity in her spare time.

It had been two years since Pharaoh last saw Maria, the day in which Pharaoh had thrown the oranges at Maria in a sexual setting for Maria's pleasure.

In those two years, Pharaoh had received many packages of heroin. Good grade heroin, and even though it was a good grade of heroin, Pharaoh had much trouble trying to sell the heroin in or a wholesale market. The wholesale heroin market was locked tight by West Baltimoreans that knitted themselves and the wholesale heroin business in Baltimore. Pharaoh had stayed close to his original heroin clientele family of white people he had first contact with. The clientele that had been looking for {Silky} but had been interrupted by Pharaoh. Pharaoh built it from those individuals a close family of heroin users, which Pharaoh, by their heroin needs, supplied with a grade of heroin that was above the norm.

This bought Pharaoh close feelings, relationships, and trust to his clientele family of heroin users, which resulted in not just good honest, dependable business, but a close friendship that lasted a lifetime for some.

Now Pharaoh did do some wholesale heroin business with some East Baltimore hustlers who knew Pharaoh personally and gave him a chance to grow the wholesale heroin business. They were delighted with the product but became a nuisance to Pharaoh by always giving their heroin business problems to Pharaoh.

Never having the right amount of money to spend for the good product they were receiving, but always tried to hold back a few hundred dollars. Pharaoh started to decline to deal with anyone other than the white clientele he built from Silky's old clientele. Which Pharaoh had transferred over to a business of his own.

It was back in 1964; it had been two years since Pharaoh had seen Maria and hit her with the oranges. Pharaoh had been in the heroin business off and on for almost three years. He had done well supplying the white clientele that Pharaoh had become friends and associates with while providing the white clientele while fulfilling their need for heroin in an honest, understanding, and natural business way.

Pharaoh and Stokes were the best of friends, while Stokes, like Pharaoh, had greatly grown in his heroin business. Stokes' mother was glad to see Stokes walk away from the tragedy that the use of heroin was bringing upon their family and especially Stokes. She knew that Stokes had not found his way back to God, but Stokes had made an advancing move forward by discontinuing his use of heroin. Stokes' mother knew that her son would soon find his way back to God and would stop even selling heroin just like he stopped using heroin.

In 1964, the heroin addiction and the Vietnam War had been planned by the anonymous organization forty years ago. It was now in full blast to provide ways, avenues, reasons, and routes to make this Vietnam War play a key part in holding back, stagnating, abusing, and misusing the Children of Jourmajesty.

Because it was 1964, the Vietnam War had made heroin so cheap and easy to get and bring back into the United

States. The heroin problem had become a real problem to the American citizens because the heroin was so cheap but potent, then heroin became a major problem to the authorities in trying to stop the selling, buying, distribution, and sale of heroin.

CHAPTER 5

Tommy Hanks Brings Maria to Visit Pharaoh

Now more people were paying their bills on time and sending their kids to better schools. They were now wearing clothes with no holes in them, wearing new clothes, new shoes, and even giving their children Music lessons and even involving their kids in amateur sports clubs.

Heroin distribution, selling, and using provided money for nightlife and clothes to wear on the nightlife scene, but much attention was put on the betterment of their children and their children's affairs and activities.

Poor people, regardless of race, culture, and faith, and especially blacks, were into legit businesses that they never could afford or dream about being in before. All those luxuries were upon the shirt sleeves of the addicted, who were the backbone and the rug to wipe your feet upon—gaining all that was to be gained from the selling, buying, and distributing heroin home and afar, and on the street level. All the while, heroin never discriminated between the difference and the color of people, their culture, or their faith.

It treated all the same, which was heaven that turned into hell, but it made different people mingle together.

The Vietnam War brought much death, sorrow, and pain back to America. More than that, the Vietnam War produced heroin users on a scale that was phenomenal, outrageous, and almost unbelievable in America.

Many American Veterans who lost their limbs, minds, and themselves Used heroin to cope with the physical and mental pain. They, as veteran soldiers, were dealing with while in Vietnam and upon their arrival back home in America. It seemed as if overnight, America was flooded with quality heroin that was dirt cheap, and the users multiplied gigantically in number.

No one knew that one of the (123) Family plans was to destroy, maim, abuse, and misuse the Children of Jourmajesty through heroin here in America.

Since its birth in America, the purpose was in its adolescent years of building and shaping. At the same time, future America blamed many for the growing problem for the cause and destruction that came with the use, selling, and distributing of heroin. Americans knew not the real reason for heroin being in America.

Nor did America know who the original planners of the plan of heroin being brought to America were the (123) Family. Surely no one knew the drastic methods of the anonymous organization of the (123) Family's projects that originated forty years before its time and before the beginning of America's success.

It has always been to abuse, misuse, stagnate, and dismantle love, equality, and togetherness. They were trying to destroy the Children of Jourmajesty with alcohol, hatred between whites and Indians. Slavery of the black man, hangings, firebombs, murders, and many other terrible things were just some of the things that the anonymous organization of the (123) Family did in trying to destroy the Children of Jourmajesty Before bringing heroin into America.

It was early in the morning, around 4 or 5, when Pharaoh pulled up in front of his home after coming from Mr. Robinson's crap house and spotted the limousine parked across the street from his house. Before he could be startled, he saw Tommy Hank getting out of the limousine while Pharaoh was exiting his car.

"Good morning, Young'un," Tommy Hank said to Pharaoh, using a name that the older hustlers sometimes called Pharaoh because he was so young.

"Good morning to you, Tommy," Pharaoh said back to Tommy Hank, thinking that Tommy Hank had some out of towner in the car that was probably here in Baltimore to gamble. Pharaoh was surprised when Tommy Hank told Pharaoh that Maria had come down from New York to see him.

It was then that Maria stepped out of the limousine, and Pharaoh saw her beautiful face and notoriously beautiful body. Immediately Pharaoh's heart melted into butter. For the first time, Pharaoh then realized why he had refused to see Maria face to face, or Pharaoh's heart was weak as a fly, and his love for Maria showed from his head to his toe.

"It is so wonderful to see you, Pharaoh, because I have missed you terribly and wanted so badly to see you, so

I came to you, I have been studying about your God and the Christian religion, and there is much I want to ask you to explain to me."

As Maria finished her last sentence, she reached out her hand and took Pharaoh's hand. She put it over her heart as she told Pharaoh to feel her heartbeat because her heart was beating for him.

As Pharaoh touched Maria's breast while feeling her heart, He ultimately set aside the memory of the orange throwing incident between Pharaoh and Maria. Pharaoh watched the tears begin to flow down Maria's face, in shame for her performance given to Pharaoh in their last meeting after Pharaoh had done so much for Maria and asked for so little in return.

Now it was early in the am and Pharaoh knew that his home was a Christian home and that he could not bring females in his home unless he sneaked a girl up to his room now and then. Pharaoh knew that Maria was not the kind of woman that you sneaked into your room.

Maria was saying that she was hungry, so Pharaoh took Maria, her chauffeur, and Tommy Hank to eat, and of course, they went to eat at {L&N} where nightlife people of importance rubbed shoulders with the elite of the world of nightlife people.

It was first light outside, around 6:30 or 7 am, when the limousine dropped Tommy Hank off in front of his home, and Maria thanked Tommy for his part in bringing her to see Pharaoh.

"How did you know how to find Tommy Hank Maria?" Pharaoh asked. Maria explained to Pharaoh that she had

Tommy Hank's telephone number and three other individuals who could contact anyone she wanted to in Baltimore.

Then smiling, "I can find anyone I want on the west coast or the east coast that has ever lived there," Maria said with a look that had changed from a smile to a face of seriousness.

Pharaoh was rather glad when Maria had insisted on getting a hotel room to stay the night even though Pharaoh had suggested that Maria stay the night with him and his household, but only in hopes that Maria would refuse, which she did.

The Staten and Hill hotel was where Maria chose to stay, and unknowing to Pharaoh, Maria had a credit card that was good in any Staten and Hill hotel in America. Pharaoh had no idea that he would also possess the Staten and Hill hotel's prestigious, mad luxurious VIP, one-of-a-kind credit cards one day soon.

It was not long before Maria had comfortably settled in her suite in the hotel, and Pharaoh was bidding Maria good night with a kiss on the cheek and backwardness in his step as he stepped back towards the door to leave.

"Stay with me, Pharaoh, stay with me this night as I have longed so many nights to ask you to stay with me for just one night, stay with me tonight, please! Stay with me tonight."

There were no other words in the English language that Pharaoh would have instead heard than the words that Maria had just spoken, and by the expression on Maria's face, anyone could see that she meant every word that she had just said to Pharaoh.

"Do not let past events, fear, doubt, or any reason or occasion steal these precious moments that I have saved for you. Because I swear to your God, that you believe in so much, that my heart cries out to you, as you call out to your God for forgiveness, as you ask for another chance to right a wrong that can be exchanged for a right when the heart is willing and able. This thing I ask of you in the name of your God, for I have waited and prayed many nights to your God for this moment, and I have asked your God to guide your heart, mind, and soul, for I only mean you well-being, warmth, and unity."

It was 9 pm when Pharaoh awoke. It was like being in heaven as Pharaoh remembered entering the body of Maria after he had touched her all over, squeezed her, and smothered his face in the softness of her long soft silky hair that he loved so much. Maria's skin was soft as cotton, and all the parts of Maria's body that God had given her were perfectly in place and perfectly perfect.

Pharaoh had spilled into Maria's body before he had fully and completely entered Maria's body. Still, Pharaoh's body was humbly caressed, petted, and kissed until he seemed to have bounced back from the terrible explosion he had when relieving himself into Maria's body oddly enough, after the first entry.

Pharaoh awoke with Maria handing him a glass of orange juice and a hamburger with fries, and it was then on the second go-round that he heard Maria cry out in ecstasy, joy, and complete satisfaction as he too reached his second climax. The lights went out in his mind as he once again drifted off to sleep, feeling as though he was in heaven.

It was now 9 Am, and Pharaoh only awoke then because he had to pee so badly, and as Pharaoh got up to pee, once again, he looked over to view the beauty of Maria's body. He realized that he had never before been sexually, mentally, or morally content like that before. Nor had lovemaking ever been so enjoyable, beautiful, and fulfilling to a complete zone of satisfaction. Coming back from the bathroom, Maria joined Pharaoh as she too went into the bathroom to relieve herself. After she was done, Maria playfully pulled Pharaoh into the shower as they together showered.

Now Pharaoh was still young, and even though he had plenty of wisdom concerning his God, and was indeed a young expert in the field of gambling, marking and dealing cards, survival in the streets. Pharaoh was even a good drug dealer because his methods were responsible, caring, and not selfish. But Pharaoh had never been no further in the field of ladies than taking them out to dinner, dancing in clubs or discos, to the movies, and sneaking them into his mother's house. Taking showers in a hotel with a woman was a new phase to Pharaoh.

Pharaoh had lady friends like him, and they were young in heart and love. And even though females were all over Pharaoh at one time or another. They both were mainly only looking for sex. But Unbeknownst to Pharaoh, Maria would teach Pharaoh Things that most men knew not but needed to know.

Pharaoh was trying to get Maria's ok to travel with him to meet Mama Grace, whom Pharaoh loved and always told Maria about. Maria did call her chauffeur in the hotel and told him that she would be back shortly. Pharaoh was always telling Maria about Mama Grace, whom he loved so much, and who was the person that had brought God into his life before Pharaoh was even potty trained and that had introduced him to the church while still an infant in arms. All Mama Grace's church friends, associates, and friends knew Pharaoh as Sister Grace's boy.

Pharaoh had many times told Maria of Mama Grace's Prayer Mob, that met in Mama Grace's house to pray for the sick, lonely, diseased, and people confined to beds, hospitals, and institutions.

The prayer mob also prayed for lost souls who had become overpowered by (Satan). Many times had Pharaoh seen the positive results of the Prayer Mob's prayers answered. Many times, had Pharaoh seen the positive effects of the Prayer Mob's prayers that were responded to through the coming future that was redirected in beneficial ways that no one could have expected. Through the ever-knowing knowledge, supreme and superior wisdom of God, the results of the prayers came at a later date with a different meaning. But not a minute too soon or not a minute too late, and the Prayer Mob's prayers were answered in another way, other than expected, but always to God's awesome discretion, will, and decision.

It was getting late in the night, maybe around almost midnight, when Pharaoh came through the front door after he had already called Mama Grace to prepare her for the introduction to Maria, and it was a great meeting between Maria and Mama Grace. Still, it was already the central fact that sooner or later, Christianity would become the main topic of the whole three-way conversation of Pharaoh, Maria, and Mama Grace. Now Pharaoh's home with Mama Grace was immaculate in cleanliness, and her home was covered with the type of things that middle-class families prided themselves in having in their home. Even though cell phones, computers, and 20th century appliances, technology, and modern-day ways and means were not available.

Mama Grace's living room was furnished with marble tables, completely carpeted floors, and lovely furniture equipped with brass smoking stands and brass statues that Mama Grace polished every Saturday morning. As a little boy, Pharaoh always wondered the purpose of all that beauty in the living room because no one was ever allowed in there, except when Mama Grace's church friends held meetings or Mama Grace's Prayer Mob met and held prayer services. At the same time, even Pharaoh himself, as a little boy, had to sneak into the living room to shoot marbles on the beautifully decorated carpet in the living room. Mama Grace's dining room was equipped with a beautiful dining room table, a China closet filled with exquisite dishes only used on holidays when dinner was served on the dining room table instead of the kitchen table.

A dining room buffet table, which sat upon it, was more family photos, like in the living room. Then two fruit bowls that sat on crochet patterns all over the furniture in the living room and dining room that Mama Grace had herself personally made.

In Mama Grace's kitchen, all her appliances were up to date and modernized with a toaster, waffle iron, and even a clothes iron. A large mirror on the dining room wall covered one whole section of the dining room table. That had taken the place of the old iron and ironing board that sat in the corner of the kitchen, which was her all-day job every Tuesday, after her all-day wash day on Mondays. It was a miracle to see Mama Grace be able to sit down and iron her clothes after watching her having to stand up all day on Tuesdays to iron. Her ability to maneuver credit and loans with the different department stores, and loan companies, because her husband's job status allowed them to buy anything they wanted and then pay for it in reasonable small monthly payments.

Not only was Mama Grace a spectacular gifted woman that took in children and raised them like they were her own. But Mama Grace was also an educated woman from Atlanta, Georgia, with a college degree in business that decided to be a housewife. She granted her gift of raising children to children. Raising children was her first desire, and Pharaoh was Mama Grace's lifelong son forever, except Mama Grace was not Pharaoh's biological mother. Maria told Mama Grace how amazed she was at the beauty and love inside the hearts, minds, and souls of privileged children who lived, studied, and practiced Christianity in Mama Grace's home and attended church on Sundays. It was then that Maria mentioned to Mama Grace that Maria had heard so much about Mama Grace's beautiful living room. Which was the place that the Prayer Mob gave awesome worship to God Almighty as they prayed for the sick, needy, institutionalized, hospitalized, and the lost souls of the world. Especially to the church friends and anyone in need of prayer brought forth by one of the Prayer Mobs for any reason, especially if it was a church member or the family of a church member.

Mama Grace looked at Pharaoh with a look of surprise. Not surprised that Pharaoh would talk of actions done or taken in the Prayer Mob's prayers to God, but that Pharaoh shared such a great thing with the outside world in teaching what he had been taught by merely paying attention.

"This is a Christian home, and we all here are of the Christian religion and faith. What religion are you? "Mama Grace asked Maria.

"I have been studying the Christian faith since I met Pharaoh, and in the last year, I have studied Christianity hard but understand little. Christianity seems so confusing to me, yet so hard to believe, but I believe in your God and the many wonderful creations that Pharaoh has taught me that God has created. Like the rain, which Pharaoh loves so much, the trees, the mountains, snow, seas, stars, and many other of His creations that Pharaoh has just recently taught me. But in doing my studying, and investigating my curiosities and unanswered questions about Christianity, then I am so lost, confused, and so mixed up until I am just about to give up on learning about Christianity."

"What is it that is so confusing to you about Christianity, Maria? And what is so hard for you to believe? But most of all, what can't you seem to understand about Christianity?" "I can't seem to understand how a woman can have a baby without the act of having sex with a man, so how was Baby Jesus conceived, and what God of so many powers and strength would allow a mere man to crucify His Son." Mama Grace was smiling.

"The religion of Christianity is nourished, backed, and stern in faith. Faith believes in the unseen, faith believes in the wisdom of Almighty God, faith that everything will happen in the right timing for man, as a man will see it is the right timing for him, and cry out to joyous rewards, says so, the belief of the author of this book. The glory and wisdom of God who in the right timing provided the right thing in the right way at the exact right time for each man's situation, while still, a God that creates mountains, seas, oceans, trees. And who Himself is the Creator of man, cannot, He also bring forth the fertilizing of a woman without the help of a man?"

"Faith is believing in a God that you cannot see, feel, or touch even though God can make you feel His presence all over your body, and throughout your bones, and once you have a relationship with God. Then He will communicate with you through your mind, spirit, and soul. Then once reaching that plateau, sin is hard to do because your conscience belongs to God, who does not sin or do wrong. This makes you feel guilty if and when you do wrong."

"It is logical, even understandable for me to relate to all the things that you have presented to me, Mama Grace, concerning faith in the religion of Christianity and faith in all its meaning concerning Christianity," Marie said. "Faith is the backbone of Christianity, so to speak, but why did your God let this be done to His Son? That is beyond my understanding, and I can't understand that. Why? Mama Grace? Why? Why did your God let this happen to His Son being that He is such an Awesome, Almighty, and Righteous God?"

Still smiling, Mama Grace said, "For you Maria, for you and me, Pharaoh, your children, and mine, and for the whole wide world, even other countries, all land, and sea, and wherever people live, survive or come from or belong to. Almighty God sent his begotten Son Jesus to die on the cross to pay in full for the sins of the world.

So, when people die now, then they can live again forever in peace, harmony, love, and happiness in eternal peace in heaven."

"The reason for the Son of God to come to the planet earth was to bring Christianity and to die for the sins of the world, to pay the world's debt for sin. So, because God loved the world so much, and the world had sinned so much, then God sent His Son Jesus to be crucified on the cross, to pay for the sins of the world."

"Which Jesus took upon himself the obligation of shedding his blood, being crucified, dying, after being disrespected, and humiliated. So that the people in the world may be able to have everlasting life after death for all that believe that Jesus is the begotten Son of God and that Jesus is God. Just like His Father is God, and that Jesus did die on the cross so that humanity could be forgiven for their sins, and live eternally in heaven forever."

Not understanding a parable of such multitude, Maria accepted this theory for hearing it, not knowing or taking it for wisdom, knowledge, or facts. But instead, just taking it for truth because it was told to her by someone of great character, such as Mama Grace. Now reality was beginning to set in Pharaoh's mind, and the heart for Pharaoh realized that Maria had to leave, so she did, without knowing how long it would be before they would see each other again.

Pharaoh realized that he had not seen his kids for a while and that he had never put anyone before his kids, but he wanted to spend just a bit more time with Maria before they both departed. Maria was also hesitant about leaving Pharaoh even though Maria knew that she had exclusive and important business to take care of, concerning the arrival of her father-in-law in New York. The input she had to give concerning the past drug deliveries she had made and the new drug deliveries she was about to make.

Now Maria and Pharaoh both enjoyed greatly talking about the Creator of heaven and earth. It was indeed a pleasure, for Pharaoh to teach some of his teaching of the creator of heaven and earth to his one and only student, Maria.

It had gone well into the night, the conversation of how it was that Maria just couldn't understand how or why it was that the three religions of Judaism, Islam, and Christianity.

Three of the world's oldest religions were taught to Maria by Pharaoh and the only religions that believe in a living God. And who all believed in the same God but did not harmonize in their religions. They greatly but secretly mocked one another for their different beliefs of the same biblical characters. The difference in the roles in which the biblical characters are portrayed, and these religions even had wars.

"How can this be?" asked Maria.

"Godly people who have faith in their God, worship their God, but does not respect the worship, and belief in others who also worship the same God."

"Remember, (Satan) Lucifer, who is the mastermind of all negativity and the inventor of lies, selfishness, murder, evilness!"

"And while yes, Lucifer is the cause of strife, dishonor, confusion, and even wars between the three religions, Judaism, Christianity, and Islam. And even though the characters in the Christian Bible are the same as the characters in the Holy Quran, the Bible for Islam. Islam does not believe that Jesus is the Son of God. Islam believes that Jesus was just a prophet sent by God."

"Only the Christian religion believes that Jesus is the begotten Son of God and that Jesus is God because God the Father is God. Jesus being the Son of God the Father makes Jesus God also. {So, believe the author of this book}

Jesus tells you all through the Christian Bible that He was sent here to earth by His Father, which is God Almighty, the only living God except for Jesus, who is God also.

Now! In the days of biblical times, when those activities happened, they were written, and that is the Word of God, which is Jesus and the Holy Bible. It creates the ingredients for Christianity, which gives Christianity its birthplace and the coming of Jesus Christ himself to the earth. Judaism is the old religion that the Jews were the beginning of Christianity studying and was the first religion to have one God. Instead of having a variety of gods for different reasons and occasions. A living, breathing, everyday functioning God, God, the Creator of heaven and earth.

Christianity had not yet been born because Jesus had not yet come to the planet earth, and man knew nothing then of Jesus even though Jesus was there in the beginning when God formed the world and divided the land from waters and called the waters seas, oceans, rivers, and streams.

God also called the earth land, says the Christian Bible, which reads in 1st John, Chapter 1: "*In the beginning was the Word and the Word was with God, and the Word was God.*" Jesus is the Word, while Jesus is God, just like His Father, who is the only living God, worshiping God is done by Islam, Judaism, Christianity, and Catholics as God the Father.

Islam and Judaism believe that there is only one God and that Jesus is not the son of the only living God, but that Jesus is a prophet sent by God.

Also, Jesus is only a mere man and not the Son of God, so believe the religion of Islam and the religion of Judaism. This brings the account of the separation of Islam, Judaism, and Christianity into perspective.

"Now, true it was that God sent His wise men, His prophets, and His priests to advise, teach, and show humanity how to live by God's Ten Commandments, too live like righteous men.

Men chose to continue to live in sin, so God destroyed the sinful world with a great flood, and leaving behind only a man named {Noah}. Whom God had advised building an ark that would float on the water. To put inside the ark two of each type of animal upon the earth, along with Noah's family.

For forty days and forty nights, it rained. It destroyed every living thing that was upon the earth. The floodwaters finally stopped, and Noah did find land, and he released all the animals from the ark.

While Noah and his family also left the ark and began to live once again upon the earth. The people on the earth did multiply over hundreds and thousands of years. But the people were yet sinful again." {So, believe the Christian religion}

"I had told you before of one that God created who was above all others. God created out of all the precious jewels such as diamonds, pearls, emeralds, gold, and other precious gems unknown to man. One who God let rule over all other angels and who was nicknamed {The Morning Star}. Then, he or Lucifer became jealous of God and decided that, like God, the Creator of heaven and earth, then He, or Lucifer, wanted to be worshiped.

Which was the main thing that he had not to be like God, so *he* felt."

"For there was no sin in heaven before Lucifer's selfishness brought sin into heaven. Who, with all his might, power, and intelligence, loved himself so much that he began to think of himself as one who could be God too.

"Through his selfishness and the lies that he told to a great number of other angels caused thousands of angels to follow him into trying to make himself like God Almighty, Creator of heaven and earth."

God did kick Lucifer and all his followers out of heaven while throwing many of Lucifer's followers into pits of dark and endless depths.

"Before I continue, Maria, I must know if you have understood the things I just told you concerning Lucifer, his powers, his intellect, his position, and caliber in the heavenly ranked. Most of all, do you understand what

Lucifer's sin was and how he was able to get many angels to follow him?"

"The heavenly conversations that you teach me are of the deepest concerns and the most profound conversations that I have ever heard of.

But yes, Pharaoh, I do understand what Lucifer's sin was. He wanted to be worshiped like God was. And he loved himself too much

I understand that was also the first sin committed in heaven, and I know that all that was a part of the sin, which was thrown out of heaven, for there is no sin in heaven."

"Pharaoh! God himself placed Lucifer in charge of many angels, whom Lucifer told what to do," Maria said.

Pharaoh replied, "While his superiority was above them. They believed in him, trusted him, and doubted him not."

"Even though I can't relate to the angel's mistrust of God Almighty, Creator of heaven and earth, and everything in heaven and on the earth," Maria said.

Smiling to himself, Pharaoh wanted so much to tell Maria of the many powers of (Satan). Who at one time was even the brightness in the eye of even God himself. For the creation of Lucifer, so felt Pharaoh, had no right to even have a thought on the matter of such a Godly situation.

Even though Pharaoh's opinion was that God did at one-time smile upon how God had created Lucifer. And of what God had made Lucifer from. He had not meant any negativity or wrong, or judgment towards God in any way.

It was three a.m. when Pharaoh realized that he was watching Maria while she slept in the sleeping compartment on the train as they rode to New York City.

Pharaoh had not been in a sleeping compartment on a train before, Nor did he know how many times he would take his children to affiliate them with the trains and planes soon. The New York train sounded like a Baltimore City streetcar taken off the track and put into a tunnel roaring into the train station.

As the train slowed down to stop at the New York train station, Maria talked to Pharaoh for two hours straight nonstop. It was only the last twenty minutes just before the train pulled into the train station in New York that she had gone to sleep, and Pharaoh had just enjoyed admiring her beauty while she slept.

For whatever reason, most likely Maria's trust in Pharaoh had come because Maria was a worldly person. A person with characteristics, morals, and principles of the world instead of Biblical, Christian, or "righteous" ways would indicate being followers of God.

While Pharaoh's professionalism as a card player interested Maria enough to make her pay attention to him,

Pharaoh's relationship with God was like no other that she had ever seen or heard of before. His introduction to his God to Maria was above all she had ever known spiritually. And beyond all, she had ever heard of.

Yes! Pharaoh had won Maria over to not only salvation. Pharaoh had won Maria's heart, body, mind, and soul. And above all, categories, subjects of meaningful, positive, and exciting things of the greatest on Earth.

Maria mentioned to Pharaoh that she did beacon to her father-in-law's every request and demand, or whatever you would like to call his wishes. He never requested anything from Maria in a demanding nature, nor did he order anything unethical. When asking Maria who her father-in-law was and what his occupation was, Maria answered Pharaoh by saying, "Because of who my father-in-law obeys, he is on call twenty-four hours a day." "There is no formula that could conceive the mixture of your wonderful God and the likes of my father-in-law, nor the employer of my father-in-law, in the same breath stroke. "And so, you could say that my father-in-law is one of the most influential authorized humans on the planet earth. When it comes to getting negativity done through persuasive authority, Maria explained to Pharaoh that she had lied to Pharaoh about not having anything to do with her father-in-law's work or employment. She had filled in for what her husband used to do for his father before her husband was killed.

Maria's husband was the connection that met people from different cities, states, and countries to bring drugs into the various cities, states, and countries. Money was not the commodity used for gain. Instead, the payment was to cripple, maim, and destroy cities, states, and countries with poverty, murder, plague, mental instability, deceit, and lies. Many other negatives destroy love, unity, and righteousness. All while bringing death, sadness, and the lack of hope to those who would then turn to drugs for a crutch, and a way to survive the hell given by the drugs invented by (Satan).

For a short time of pleasure, the good in people was starting to turn sour. The true goal of the drugs was brought into the different cities, states, and countries.

While few knew that these were some of the plans of the anonymous organization even in its earliest stages of organizing, its schemes were structured to cripple, maim, confuse and destroy, if possible, the true Children of Jourmajesty.

Before the death of Maria's husband, Maria and her husband worked as partners bringing drugs to different cities, states, and countries.

To give souls to (Satan), By bringing drugs to the different cities, states, and countries worldwide. Maria and her husband knew not the impact of what they were doing wholeheartedly on the minds, souls, hearts, and cultures of masses of people and nations of people.

Maria had been tired of participating in the drugs for her father-in-law a long time ago. Now that her husband had been killed, Maria disliked drug participation even more even though her father-in-law had told Maria to get someone else to help her in the drug distribution to take Maria's husband's place.

Maria kept telling her father-in-law that no one could take the place of her husband. Something in Maria had changed drastically because Maria had done the truly impossible by bringing a companion, Pharaoh, with her on her latest assignment.

Now the hotel chain across America by the name of {S and H Hotels}. They were all made in the same way of having everything located in the same place in every hotel room.

Her husband taught Maria how to enter the hotel room—first opening the hotel room door and pushing the door back to the wall. That would show the two mirrors in the room, allowing you to see through to the other two mirrors on the wall. One mirror on each side of the room to visualize the entirety of the whole room, including the bathroom. Which always had an open door that would allow you to see the second mirror on the wall, which would visualize the whole floor of the room.

This one hotel always showed the provisions necessary to enlighten safety or foul play coming from anyone, Maria and her husband had to deal with within the hotel room before they entered.

Now precautions were being taught to Pharaoh as he went into his fifth mission with Maria while she sought to do her job as a drug deliverer. As Maria taught Pharaoh the expertise in delivering drugs throughout America, Pharaoh was only allowed to watch, look, listen and learn but not participate.

It truly amazed Pharaoh that money was never mentioned in any drug transactions concerning Maria and her drug clients. Pharaoh would soon find out that money meant nothing to Maria's father-in-law. Selling one's soul was the price, the return of profit to Maria's father-in-law.

It had become a thing with Pharaoh to keep the hotel room that he and Maria used to meet Maria's drug clients so that Pharaoh, unbeknownst to anyone, would come back to that same hotel room with his children the next day every so often. So that Pharaoh would give his children a chance to learn how to be on a plane, train, and travel by car. To indulge in different cultures, languages, and the fun of other cities, whenever he could. Especially when Maria rented the hotel room for more than one day. Sometimes made Pharaoh think Maria knew that Pharaoh had brought his children back to the hotel room, that Maria had used to meet her drug clients the day before.

Now! when Pharaoh was in New York. He never failed to say hello to Stokes and Stokes' mother, who, of course, would have a prayer and Bible reading session with Pharaoh.

Sometimes Maria would also come with Pharaoh to meet Stokes' mother, while the three enjoyed themselves with a dose of heavenly or scripture session together. Talking and teaching and learning the Word of God. Stokes' mother was indeed well-versed in the scriptures and worthy of teaching the Word of God.

Now! This particular day Pharaoh was in New York and stopped by to pay Stokes and his mother a visit. Afterward, he had planned to study the Bible with Stokes' mother but was disrupted by the news Stokes' mother related to Pharaoh. She let him know that, in her opinion, Stokes was interfering with ungodly people who were aliens from a war-torn country of long ago. Who was still fighting the same old biblical war that they were fighting back in Biblical times?

True, Pharaoh did not understand what Stokes' mother meant when she called the Brothers Three "aliens" Nor did Pharaoh understand what Stokes' mother meant when she said that the Brothers Three and their hired assailants were from a {war torn} country.

Pharaoh thought about Stokes' mother's statement concerning the Brothers Three and their companions being dangerously violent and from a war-torn country.

"Why were the Brothers Three and their assigned friends' aliens? Aliens, like from another planet other than earth?"

"No," replied Stokes' mother, "But aliens referring to men from a country that denied God to be their king and that instead asked for a man to become their king like other ungodly and sinful countries that worshiped many idols. Fake gods, different and unholy cultures, even after God told them that if they had a man-king, that the man-king would soon take all their young men to be inducted into war."

"God's chosen people still screamed and hollered for God to allow them to have a man-king." Turning his head towards Stokes' mother very slowly, Pharaoh then asked Stokes' mother if she said that Almighty God, Creator of heaven and earth, told his chosen people that he would be their king. And if God's chosen people refused to let Almighty God be their king.

Instead, asked to be like tribes and other cultures of people near and far who all had a man-king. Other tribes, cultures, nations, and villages worshiped a variety of gods instead of worshiping God Almighty, Creator of heaven and earth, and the Giver of life.

"Yes, Pharaoh," Stokes' mother said, as she shook her head in sorrow and pity for the decision that God's chosen people had made.

"That is the reason why today God's chosen people are still fighting the wars that their forefathers fought with the surrounding tribes, villages, and nations of people that they have had wars with for thousands of years."

"Which they would not have had negative outcomes of war if Almighty God had been their king, instead of the men kings that have ruled their country, and have made them have a war-torn country."

"Their country is always being torn up. Over and over again from fighting wars for thousands of years with the same nations. Millions of God's chosen people were hated and killed in other countries at later dates simply because they were God's chosen people."

"They would not have been slaughtered like they were if God had been His chosen people's king, (so believe the author of this book.) Almighty God, the Creator of heaven and earth, was asked by His chosen people to choose a man king for themselves. So Almighty God sent his trusted, sincere, and reliable servant {Samuel}. Who had been offered to God as an infant baby from his mother? As soon as he was weaned from his mother's breast, he served Almighty God for a lifetime.

"God directed Samuel to the family in which their first king would come. A father who had many sons. Samuel told the father that Almighty God had directed him to choose one of his sons to be the first king of God's chosen people. After going over all the sons of the father, Samuel had not found the son that Almighty God would be content with."

"So, Samuel asked the father any more sons, and the father replied that he did have one more son. Samuel told the father to go get him, and when Samuel laid eyes on him, he knew that this was the right son to become the first king of Almighty God's chosen people."

"But the second king, which would be King David, would be much mightier, more powerful and famous. He would be a king more loved by the people, and God would also love him.

Blinking his eyes and shaking his head, Pharaoh focused on the original conversation. Her son Stokes' involvement with the Brothers Three and their *Hit Squad*.

Stokes' mother knew without a doubt that violence, murder, evil, and ungodliness awaited anyone involved with the Brothers Three and their cheesy put-together Hit Squad. They showed no pity, mercy, or consideration for anyone's life. For all, they have ever known all their lives in their war-torn country is death and destruction, with no understanding for over a thousand years.

She was afraid for Stokes and wished that Pharaoh would talk to him. Pharaoh knew immediately who Stokes' mother was referring to as ungodly people. These brothers of death, violence, and destruction were indeed masterminds and brought Stokes along with them.

Now Pharaoh's acquaintance with the Brothers Three was not a new acquaintance.

The Brothers Three had warned Pharaoh of their dislike towards Pharaoh and their intent to bring bodily harm to him the next time that the Brothers Three saw Pharaoh again. {So said one of the Brothers Three}

It was concerning an incident where Pharaoh had spoken negatively concerning the Brothers Three's conduct towards disrespecting Stokes' mother and wife.

The Brothers Three had talked of dirty sexual things in the presence of Stokes' mother and wife.

Stokes had before promised to depart with the company of the Brothers Three and did not keep his promise. Instead, Stokes had contributed money towards bringing in three other low-life and ungodly men to join forces with the Brothers Three. To give the Brothers Three, they're *supposed to be* Hit Squad.

When Pharaoh returned to Maria's apartment, it was late, and Pharaoh was introduced to YaYa, a bodyguard to Maria's father-in-law. He was also a caretaker for the family, Maria, her husband, and Maria's father-in-law.

Pharaoh had made his acquaintance with YaYa years before; YaYa had never before talked to Pharaoh or even spoken to Pharaoh.

Ever since Maria's husband had been killed, YaYa had been at her side, constantly protecting her from all evil. With the promise of death to all who threatened Maria in any way, shape, or form. But he never interfered in Maria's business or life unless Maria asked him to. Maria told Pharaoh about YaYa being her father-in-law's bodyguard since they both entered the world from their mother's wombs. And how Yaya's entire family was responsible for the up-keep, protection, and safety of the life of Maria's father-in-law with their lives also.

Six months had passed since Pharaoh had last seen Stokes, or Stokes' mother or wife.

Pharaoh had communicated to Stokes through runners, transporters, or delivery guys, or people that had just kept the two of them in touch with each other.

Even if not visually or physically, just by word of mouth. Pharaoh could not stop thinking about Stokes' mother's last conversation concerning Stokes' safety regarding the Brothers Three. But more than anything, Pharaoh could not stop thinking about the words in Stokes' mother's prayer.

When Pharaoh returned to Stokes' apartment after realizing that he had not closed Stokes' mother's front door tight, he then heard Stokes' mother's words.

"Merciful and Almighty God in heaven. At the same time, supplying warmth, safety, love with ears, eyes, and love in the middle of the seafloor. And protection at the mountain top and all in between. To those of his choice and desire, King of all kings, and Creator of life, death, and forgiveness. And to the only One who has no known beginning or end. I spread my naked, cripple, and worthless body down. I stretch out on the cold floor, asking you Almighty God, to bring my son's pain to me instead of him, that he may see through my pain another chance to rehabilitate his life through the hurt of my pain so that once more, he will have a chance to give his life to you Almighty God in remembrance of me. For my son knows my love for You, and I have taught him of You and Your Son since he was a baby."

After hearing the prayer and closing Stokes' mother's door, Pharaoh started to Baltimore.

The narcotic business that Pharaoh had in Baltimore was operating fine. Baltimore's lawyers raised the bail price because many people were locked up for drugs. The bail bondsman and the prosecutors and judges sat down and realized the volume of money that these drug dealers were getting.

They realized that they could move their families to better neighborhoods. Send their children to better schools and dress their families in better clothing. They could also open up legitimate businesses.

Plus, the risk of giving people bail and them not coming back to court raised the bail situation to almost ten times the original price it had been before.

Bails for narcotic charges raised from one thousand to five thousand dollars, to five thousand, to twenty-five thousand dollars seemed like overnight.

In the sixties and seventies, money was so plentiful in the streets. Partying peaked, and people enjoyed getting high off heroin, reefer, and pills. Then the newly added drug of cocaine, which was then used for partying, and it was without the effect of getting strung out.

This drug did sneak into many American homes as a device to enjoy fun and experiment with sexuality through cocaine. Heroin use was at its highest because it was being used by Americans who got it into the United States due to the Vietnam War.

It was offered at a high grade of pureness while selling it at a low price, which allowed many Americans to get hooked on heroin.

So that was the strategy of the anonymous organization that was behind it all, as it would soon spread out to be the corruption, terror, blood-shedding, and useless killings that would plague the cities of America for decades.

The upcoming generations of Americans would realize the cruel and unjust murderous hand that heroin brought into lives.

So by the time the next generations of Americans realize these things, the anonymous organization will have yet another trap for the forthcoming generations of Americans.

Whether it be pills, powder, liquid, or whatever, it will be for sure some poisonous formula of some sort to continue to hold back, destroy and feed harmful poisons to the minds, hearts, and souls of the Children of Jourmajesty. Through their fathers, mothers, brothers, sisters, and themselves, they are those who have shed their blood, tears, dreams, and goals to the land of America.

So be it that America stays a free land for those born here or their relatives who have died here.

The newcomers to America, the foreigners, have to participate wholeheartedly in keeping America "The Home of the Brave and Honorable" and "The Land of the Free."

So, their children could be born as Americans. Americans that helped uphold, enforce and speak up loud for the American dream. For sure, that (God) is in America for sure.

From before, all our forefathers came here to America, and while only the forefathers of the red man were born here, so be it then, God was also here in America.

Even in all America's mightiness the differences of the color of people, the systematic religious and racial problems still find time to give worship to Almighty God.

While they praise God in their lives, even if not always everyone, every day, but enough to continuously show God is worshiped. That He is glorified, believed in, and loved every day.

Just as the forefathers of the red man, back then, believed in and worshiped the Creator of heaven and earth.

The afterlife, the Creator of the mountains, rivers, streams, animals, land, plants, and other things that the

Creator of life and death has done for the world in which we live today.

True, all who believe in God Almighty and Jesus as the begotten Son of Almighty God are usually of the Christian or Catholic religion. But lately, some of the other religions that believe in one God instead of a variety of gods for different reasons and seasons factually think that there is but one God, God Almighty, Creator of heaven and earth, life and death.

They also have changed their philosophy of Jesus. Instead of believing that Jesus was a prophet, they now consider the possibility of Jesus being the begotten Son of God.

Or they turn a death ear to understand what, who, and which belief is true. {So says the opinion of this author}

To what and which particular religion aims their thoughts to God Almighty, while they are letting each religion share in its own belief, as long as his first belief is in God Almighty, Creator of heaven and earth.

They turn not a silent ear to his cause, reason, and occasion. For being here on the scene at one particular time as it states in the scripture, *John Chapter 1: In the beginning was the Word}* meaning, *the origin of the world or planet earth in which we live, and the Word was with God, and the Word was God.*

Yes! Jesus is the Word, speaks the words of His Father, and is the Son of God. While Jesus tells you all through the Christian Bible, *My Father sent me, dividing the two to be separate, not one but two.*

Now all these biblical things of fact and scripture are embedded into the mind, heart, and soul of Pharaoh. But his present concern was on Stokes' mother and the prayer in which Pharaoh last heard her pray.

One night that was cool but not chilly or cold, Pharaoh returned from Robinson's crap house. He won sixty-seven hundred dollars. That was after giving out at least a thousand dollars in playing his number heavy and giving money to those who in turn gave to him when they won.

Pharaoh started on his way home as he was pretty tired. His nostrils were still filled with the smoke from cigarettes, cigars, reefer, and funky smells from those who were gambling with no go money. Which made their stomachs growl and their butts fart for fear of losing a bet that they couldn't afford to lose.

Pharaoh saw a long black limousine sitting in front of his front door as soon as he turned the corner onto his block.

Pharaoh knew immediately that something was super good or super bad in the relationship between Pharaoh and Maria.

Getting out of the car slowly, Pharaoh proceeded towards the long black limousine. Immediately the back door of the limousine opened up, and Maria jumped out with her arms wide open to hug Pharaoh as she greeted him with rivers of tears running down her face.

As she reached Pharaoh, throwing her arms around him, she whispered in his ear, Stokes' mother has left us and went to be with God. Her soul is at rest, and there is no more pain or misery in her life. Pharaoh's arms just instantly dropped down from around Maria's waist as the words of Stokes' mother's death registered in his mind, heart, and his soul as he just stood there in shock.

"What happened?" Pharaoh asked. After a minute of complete silence.

"Where is Stokes? I must get to Stokes. He is probably having a nervous breakdown right now."

"Stokes is presently in the hospital and has not uttered a word since his mother died two days ago," Maria said.

"And I don't know the particulars of what happened to Stokes' mother, but I do know that Stokes and his wife are alive."

"There was some argument or fight with some people, and Stokes' mental condition is a question. He is spending a brief stay in a mental institution at a state hospital. And his wife is in the hospital for being sexually assaulted and brutally beaten."

While Maria was telling Pharaoh these things, she purposely did not tell Pharaoh that Stokes' mother had been brutally sexually attacked. She was sodomized with a piece of a broom handle and with a human penis. Arriving at the hospital, it was a downhill walk, and like walking down a cement downward sloped hill with rails on each side and a big iron door at the bottom that seemed to open magically when approached by anyone.

Pharaoh had left immediately with Maria and her father-in-law's bodyguard, who had driven Maria to Baltimore to see Pharaoh.

The bodyguard had then driven them back to New York, To visit Stokes and his family. To find out about their well-being, what had happened to them, and why.

After coming down this long hallway that they had been directed. To reach their destination in the hospital to see

Stokes, and after coming down the long hall that led to the sloped hill with the iron doors that opened almost magically.

They came to a big iron grille with bars that separated this small portion of the hospital from everything else. Maria's father-in-law's bodyguard stayed in the car while Maria and Pharaoh had ventured into the hospital to visit Stokes.

Upon seeing Stokes, Maria nor Pharaoh recognized Stokes. At first, it was because Stokes was facing the wall with his back towards their front.

Stokes was never a big man in size, height, statue, or even weight. Stoke's shoulders were sunk in, his posture was the pits, and his shoulder bones were sticking out of his skin. His frail hands and fingers fitted like a pair of gloves that were emerging from beneath his skin.

At this time, Maria and Pharaoh were standing in front of Stokes, still not recognizing his identity. They were startled to see the tear-drawn face of the man sitting in the chair that was now facing them. The snout had dried up all over his face, with newly developing tears making way to travel over the dried-up snout. The tears had already demanded authority over certain areas of his face.

It was only a few minutes more before Pharaoh and Maria both realized that the snotty nose man in the chair with the tears running down his face was Stokes.

An hour later, Pharaoh and Maria had placed chairs close to Stokes and tried to talk. But Stokes had not said one word. Nor had he opened up his eyes not once during the entire hour that Pharaoh and Maria had been there.

The room in which Stokes was sitting was full of silence. The room was so quiet that when the beautiful young nurse's voice was heard, it immediately brought attention from both Maria and Pharaoh.

The nurse handed Pharaoh a small white envelope while stumbling over the pronunciation of Pharaoh's name that she had gotten from seeing Pharaoh sign-in on Stokes hospital chart.

Handing Pharaoh the letter then smiling, the nurse then walked away. Pharaoh and Maria both looked at each other, sort of dumbfounded. Pharaoh opened up the letter, a picture of three men sitting in a car.

When Pharaoh looked closely, the three men were sitting in the car was across the street from Pharaoh's house in Baltimore.

The picture was with a note that read, "I'm in the waiting area, come quickly." Immediately Pharaoh knew that the person in the waiting room was the Brothers Three!

Pharaoh's skin crawled while his blood pressure rose enormously, and fear dared not to approach Pharaoh. Because in the back of his mind, he believed that the Brothers Three did positively have something to do with this terrible situation that involved Stokes, Stokes' wife, and his mother.

"Be right back," Pharaoh said to Maria, bringing the letter with him.

He left Maria still in the hospital room with Stokes while Pharaoh quietly closed the door. He went to the waiting area to see the Brothers Three, whom Pharaoh knew the letter was from.

Smelling tobacco, whiskey, beer, and whatever else, Pharaoh flinched as one of the Brothers Three placed his arm around Pharaoh's shoulders while thanking Pharaoh for coming to the waiting room to see them.

The Brothers Three wanted Pharaoh to know the truth about what happened to Stokes, Stokes' wife, and his mother.

While the one brother of the Brothers Three that disliked Pharaoh, the one that had the previous argument or misunderstanding with Pharaoh, was now standing behind Pharaoh.

He had placed a gun in Pharaoh's back and pushed the gun in Pharaoh's back as he pushed Pharaoh into the car on the parking lot.

"Introduce me to the heroin connection that you and Stokes share, and your lives will continue as usual. Or, you can choose to take the same road that Stokes chose, and I will humiliate your family, fuck your mother, and stick a broomstick up *your* mother's asshole, and get my rocks off on watching your mother. In pain."

"Just like I did that skinny bitch of a piece of shit Stokes' mother. I laughed at her in pain because it was so funny. Oh yeah, the dumb bitch asked her God to forgive me for what I was doing to her, but she forgot to ask her God to make me stop."

Unknowing why, but for some reason or another, Pharaoh was not afraid. Pharaoh knew he had to be wise because either one of the Brothers Three would shoot at any given moment without thinking about the consequences.

Neither of the Brothers Three was smart enough or intelligent enough to think inside the fact of reality or future actions. So Pharaoh tried to act according to how he felt the Brothers Three wanted him to work. But Pharaoh was furious in his heart, and for the first time in his life, Pharaoh felt hate for the Brothers Three.

The cowardly insane perverted acts they had committed and the Brothers Three's threats they had threatened Pharaoh with. Pharaoh wanted the Brothers Three dead!

Pharaoh wanted to kill the Brothers Three, while not never before had Pharaoh felt this monstrous and dangerous feeling that grew larger and larger inside him as the moments went by.

Never before had Pharaoh ever felt the feeling of hate or considered taking the life of another human being. The Brothers Three had changed all that because Pharaoh was ready to draw the last blood, especially when the Brothers Three were taking turns telling what they had done to Stokes' mother and wife, how Stokes had cried like a baby.

Stalling for time, Pharaoh told the Brothers Three he would talk to his connection and put in a good word for them. Pharaoh would try to meet for the Brothers Three to meet up, talk with, and purchase heroin from Pharaoh's connection, Maria.

But in all actuality, Pharaoh would never put Maria in jeopardy of the cold perverted hearts, and sinful minds of the Brothers Three. Who knows only pain, death, and destruction for the answer to all and everything that came their way.

Pharaoh had to find justice for the crimes that the Brothers Three had committed to Stokes, Stokes' wife, and especially for the physical and mental pain, humiliation, and everlasting grief that would hang over the heads of that particular family forever.

Immediately the Brothers Three agreed to the meeting with Pharaoh's heroin connection. The Brothers Three were under the impression that Pharaoh was afraid of them and would gladly shift the weight pain and sorrow to someone else to save himself.

The Brothers Three were under an absolute falsehood because Pharaoh was looking for a way to kill all three brothers and punish them personally.

Pharaoh then began to witness the freight of fear, being caught or killing one or two of the Brothers Three and then being punished by the third, but most of all, Pharaoh was afraid that his God might not forgive him for taking the lives of three human beings.

Even if he could do it, Pharaoh knew how merciful his God was to all, not some, but all. Pharaoh knew how vital a soul was to his God, especially a soul being taken off the face of the earth without taking advantage of the opportunity to repent one's sins.

After carefully thinking about it, Pharaoh decided to go to the one person who could do the Brothers Three's triple hit murder job, and it would make him feel less guilty about the murders of the Brothers Three.

Pharaoh even wondered if he could get God to turn his head away while what was needed be done to the Brothers Three.

CHAPTER 6

Stokes' Mother Portrays
the Angel in White

It was not any more than maybe an hour after Pharaoh had left Maria in the hospital room with Strokes that he did return. Before Pharaoh went back into the hospital room with Stokes and Maria, Pharaoh went first to the limousine. YaYa, Maria's driver and family bodyguard, still sat, waiting for Maria to return from the hospital room.

Pharaoh made sure that he let YaYa see him. At the same time, Yaya acted as if he did not see Pharaoh approaching the car. It made Pharaoh wonder whether YaYa saw him as he approached the limousine.

When Pharaoh had thoroughly approached the limousine, Pharaoh stood directly outside the driver's window of the limousine. YaYa still acted as if Pharaoh was not there until Pharaoh knocked softly on the driver's window.

It was then that YaYa laid his eyes upon Pharaoh but did not cast so much as a smile as YaYa politely rolled down the window. YaYa asked if everything was alright and if Maria needed anything. Was there any harm or potential threat upon Maria

Hesitantly Pharaoh mumbled, "Maria is fine, but I would like to let you know that the Brothers Three has killed Stokes' mother and sexually assaulted Stokes' mother and wife. I would like to ask you to make them all three pay with their lives, even though I hope and pray not to offend you. I would pay you ten thousand for the death of each of them with hopes that I haven't offended you in any way, some type of torment before their death comes upon them, I will add."

After listening to Pharaoh, YaYa simply rolled up the window without saying a single word. Pharaoh! After not understanding Yaya's response to Pharaoh's question. Whether or not YaYa would kill the Brothers Three and bring suffering to them before their last breaths were taken. Because YaYa never said anything to Pharaoh whether or not he would do the murders, Pharaoh knew or rather felt that he had in some way spoken out of turn, unauthorized, or just simply wrong to YaYa.

Pharaoh felt disorganized because Pharaoh knew that he knew YaYa not and thought he was 100% out of character and out of place. Pharaoh could not take back what he had already said to YaYa even though Pharaoh wished that he could in some way take back the whole conversation that he had just had with YaYa.

It had been an hour and a half since Pharaoh had got up and left Maria in the hospital room to go and talk to the Brothers Three and then to YaYa.

Now Pharaoh was back at the hospital room with Maria, and Pharaoh explained to Maria what he had said to YaYa. In hopes that Maria could tell him some sort of advice to help heal or help in some way the position that Pharaoh had put himself in with YaYa.

Maria began to cry while Pharaoh looked on in complete concerned curiosity. Wondering if he would ever again gain Maria's concern, trust, and love, he wonders if he had lost Maria's love for him. Maria cried out to Pharaoh in a burst of tears as she fell on her knees, hugging Pharaoh around his legs.

"He is an authorized, unified, bona fide, qualified, super respected enforcer of the laws of his country. He has the status of the right hand of a king, who protects the king, and the family of the king, with the legal right to kill, injure, harm or destroy anything that shows any potential harm to the king."

"Denial of any of the king's wishes or the king's family's wishes, or anything that belongs to the king in any way, shape, or form will he protect. He will deny himself the glory, happiness, and contentment of being able to enjoy the simple things in life, like a wife, family, or children."

"The glory of even spending money because money isn't allowed to be spent by him, because anything he wants, needs, desires, or could think about having is given to him. While Yaya's wants only are, whatever my father-in-law needs, wants, or desires are. Yaya's mother, father, sisters, and brothers all are honored to be the highest in his country. This is with the understanding that the heads of Yaya's family lie on a chopping board. For any dishonorable deed, thought, or activity that might catch Yaya's attention and pull him away from his obligation to my father in law, or the family of my father-in-law."

"These things I tell you, Pharaoh, is for the one purpose that you may understand Yaya's situation. I sometimes feel so sorry for him because he is trapped inside a shell that has taken away his privilege in life to have a life of his own.'"

"Not even a hello or goodbye kiss has YaYa ever had so for him not ever to miss it. As a child, was he taught to honor, put first, above all others, and everything and anyone, the concern and well-being, and protection of my father-in-law, and my father in law's family."

Pharaoh had been listening to everything Maria had said but simultaneously. Maria's skirt had come halfway up her thigh, which exposed the most favorable part of Maria's body that Pharaoh most enjoyed looking at the most.

While Maria was hugging Pharaoh's thigh, his Johnson shot down his thigh like it wanted to greet Maria and just be touched. Pharaoh had felt this tremendous sexual desire approaching him as he first peeped at the exposed thigh of Maria as she hugged his leg. Pharaoh was ashamed of his sexual desire for Maria at a time of so much grief and despair.

It was like Pharaoh's Johnson was acting independently without the input of Pharaoh himself. As Pharaoh picked Maria up from the floor, he swiftly ran his hand over Maria's ass, slowly pulling Maria's body to his body. Sucking Maria's bottom lip Pharaoh secretly discharged with a sigh of relief. As Pharaoh released Maria from the tight grip he had on her, Pharaoh excused himself as he went into the bathroom to wipe the come from all down his leg and in his draws because he had secretly climaxed.

It was only five minutes before he was back out of Stokes hospital bathroom after cleaning himself off from the sexual incident Pharaoh had just had with Maria secretly. It wasn't until Pharaoh and Maria decided to see Stokes' wife that they found out that Stokes' mother was there, still alive in intensive care and on life support. In the very same hospital as Stokes and his wife.

Now, it was apparently for the good of the hospital Stokes' mother and the staff that the doctor that serviced Stokes' mother's wounds and medical concerns paying much attention to her mental and spiritual status suggested taking Stokes' mother home to die.

They decided it would be the best thing because the hospital could do nothing more for her. Stokes' mother was on the tenth floor of the hospital, and because Maria was dreadfully afraid of heights, she had a severe problem with the tenth floor.

Once while exiting the tenth floor, she was faced with walking down a complete glass hall and on the other side of the aisle, giving a stunning view of ten floors straight down. It also created a nightmare for Maria just looking down because Maria was terrified of heights.

Now YaYa had known Maria for quite a long time and had rescued Maria a few times before from places that were high or even semi hi.

So it then struck Yaya's remembrance that Maria and Pharaoh had to go to the tenth floor, and he remembered Maria's secret of being terrified of heights.

At the exact moment, YaYa was hurrying up out the limo, and to the elevator, in the hospital was the very moment that Maria had seen the glass side of the hall. The ten stories gave Maria a horrible panic attack like Maria had never had before.

It sent Maria into a state of panic. Her brain was unstable, and so were her body parts. So much that she could not walk or talk, it frightened Maria so bad that she lost control of her water and pee peed on herself then lost consciousness for a few seconds.

Maria cried out, "Oh God! My God in Heaven, Merciful and Almighty God, send down your angel to walk with me down this hall. So that I can be finally and fully magnified in your glory while having from this day and forever faith."

And it was at that moment that coming down the hall, on the other side of the aisle where the glass wall was, and where Maria's fright was, appeared wrapped in a white sheet from head to toe with all gray hair, upon her head, an image of God's sent help to Maria.

Who stretched out her hand to receive Maria's hand and walked her down the hall as she told Maria in a shallow and squeaky voice {like she was sick} to focus only on her,

As she opened wide, her garment wrapped around her whole body; it shielded Maria's vision entirely from the view of the street below. Maria could see nothing but the white of the robe-like material.

Now it was just about then that YaYa had reached the tenth floor, and as he opened the door of the hallway leading to exactly where Maria was, YaYa started towards Maria.

The God-sent messenger wrapped in a sheet stretched out her arm and hand in a halt position. YaYa did stop in his tracks as Maria proceeded to the tenth-floor hallway exit. Right in front of the elevator where Maria closed the door behind her.

After realizing that she was safely out of the tenth-floor hallway, Maria immediately fell on her knees with her hands folded in prayer, giving thanks to God for rescuing her from such a ghostly and frightening ordeal.

In all praises, "There is no praise higher than calling on the name of the Lord, the only living God, except His Son, Jesus Christ who is also God."

"Glory to the highest form of praise that can be offered to our God Almighty. Oh, thank you, Lord, for giving mercy to those of us who are not worthy of your mercy but obtain it because you are so understanding, forgiving, and so wonderfully wonderful!"

It was then that Maria looked up and saw that the God-sent messenger was Stokes' mother!

She had been wrapped in the white sheet because she was getting up to release herself from the hospital's intensive care unit.

She said she heard God calling her. {So, she said} Stokes' mother looking speechless, Maria and Pharaoh both stood there in amazement, not believing what had just happened.

Neither knowing how or why it happened because Maria and Pharaoh had just left Stokes' mother fifteen minutes ago on her dying bed, in the intensive care unit, and she was now saving Maria!

She was walking and talking like she had never been sick. Indeed this had to be the glorious and excellent work of Almighty God. No one was as puzzled, curious, or without understanding as YaYa, because YaYa knew God not, nor anything concerning God.

YaYa just knew that something supernatural had just happened, something unexplainable because YaYa came behind Maria and Pharaoh when they had visited Stokes' mother in the intensive care unit.

YaYa had remembered Maria's fear of heights and had come looking for Maria to shield her from her fear of heights. YaYa had peeped in intensive care hospital room where Stokes' mother was lying and had seen her unconscious hooked up to those machines and about to die.

YaYa had heard the doctors discussing that there was nothing else the hospital could do for Stokes' mother and that she needed to go home to die.

The doctors were discussing that Stokes' mother would never walk or talk again, nor would her insides ever again be useful or viable because of the broom handle.

It was those curious and unexplainable thoughts that were running through Yaya's head when Stokes' mother collapsed in front of the elevator inside the hallway of the tenth floor.

Running to her rescue and picking up her frail body in his arms, it seemed like a magical sight with the great strong muscular YaYa, picking up the petite, soft lady as though she was a rubber doll. YaYa did escort Stokes' mother in his arms back to her hospital bed with no one ever knowing that she had ever left her room besides Pharaoh, Maria, and YaYa.

"May my God bless you and keep you safe," was the words that Stokes' mother spoke as she held her head up and said after YaYa returned her to her bed.

With a smile, Stokes' mother closed her eyes to rest, not to die, and for the first time in his life, YaYa felt warmth and compassion for someone as he watched the smile appear on Stokes' mother's face.

YaYa knew the smile from Stokes' mother was for him, not for play or to receive recognition but to YaYa, from Stokes' mother with warmth, love, compassion, For worthiness that YaYa had well deserved was the worthiness he was now receiving from Stokes' mother.

Now Yaya paid a great price for this worthiness of compassion, love, warmth that he was receiving from Stokes' mother. For Yaya realized that for the first time in his life that YaYa wanted to kill.

Not for Maria's father-in-law, but he wanted to go out and kill the Brothers Three, who were the ones that had done this terrible thing to Stokes' mother.

At the same time, YaYa realized the threat that he was gambling with. Just the thought of harming someone because of a problem other than the threat or act of disrespect to Maria's father-in-law or the family of Maria's father-in-law's family was insane to think about.

YaYa remembered his blood oath to Maria's father-in-law to pay for any disloyalty towards Maria's father-in-law.

It would put the heads of his own family back in the old country on the chopping block. It would bring death to every member of his family, including the family pet, until Yaya's entire family was erased.

That was the penalty that YaYa would have to pay if and when YaYa gave his allegiance to anyone, anything or for any reason other than Maria's father-in-law. Or the family of

Maria's father-in-law, through bloodline only. But in the proceedings of life, the death of Maria's father-in-law would relieve YaYa from all duties and connections to Maria's father-in-law or the family of Maria's father-in-law. And to the old country in which they both were born, then and only then could YaYa be free to live his life in which way he would see fit.

One year and six months had passed since Stokes, his mother, and the Brothers Three had brutally attacked his wife. Also, while Stokes' mother had been sexually assaulted with a broom stick handle in her butt, it left her internally injured, but Stokes' mother had never uttered a single bad word towards the Brothers Three.

She had constantly asked God not to be too hard on the Brothers Three and if any way would allow them to walk free of their misbehavior towards her and her family.

That was the prayer that YaYa heard Stokes' mother praying to God one night after YaYa was taking Pharaoh and Maria home from Stokes' mother's house. One night, YaYa was taking them home from visiting the mental hospital after a visit with Stokes. Who still had not said one word since the day Stokes first came to the hospital.

That night, Maria had asked YaYa to drive her and Pharaoh to the hospital to bring Stokes' mother home to die, even though no one but the hospital staff believed that Stokes' mother was going to die. Now it was that night that Stokes' mother was coming home from the hospital one year and six months ago that she had asked Pharaoh to vow to her that he would not retaliate or bring harm in any way towards the Brothers Three for their past crimes toward her or her family.

Smiling at Pharaoh, Stokes' mother said,

"And I will live to see if you keep your promise."

Pharaoh replied saying "Your continued life on the planet is surely enough to respect your request until the day that God sends for you."

Now Maria, in regards and respect for Pharaoh's life, did make way for the Brothers Three to have a drug connection. With the understanding that this privilege for the drug connection for the Brothers Three would last for two years.

Until afterward, if the Brothers Three remained in good standing, they would then be allowed to buy straight from Africa. With a known address of their own and African residence to travel back and forth and throughout the country.

Now Pharaoh knew nothing of this arrangement concerning the Brothers Three and this drug connection that Maria had hooked up, being afraid for Pharaoh's life and Pharaoh's family's lives.

Unbeknownst to Pharaoh, Maria had made these arrangements with the Brothers Three, and in return, the Brothers Three had not bothered Pharaoh in any way.

But there had not been one single day in Pharaoh's life since the assault on Stokes and his family that Pharaoh didn't think about it, and Pharaoh had developed a natural solid and factual hate for the Brothers Three.

Pharaoh vowed to make the Brothers Three pay for Stokes and his family's dirty, rude, filthy, and sexual acts.

Pharaoh's vendetta towards the Brothers Three grew and grew with the ongoing torture of Pharaoh's soul.

Pharaoh had accepted the Brothers Three's threat towards him concerning causing harm to him and his family.

He had not yet retaliated on the Brothers Three for their cruel, vicious, and perverted acts upon Stokes and Stokes' family because Pharaoh loved Stokes' mother so much.

Pharaoh wore the harm from the Brothers Three on his mind and in his heart daily. Pharaoh continued to visit Stokes at Stokes' mother's house as he had been released from the mental section of the state hospital in New York.

Even though Stokes was beginning to talk somewhat, Pharaoh nor Stokes never talked about drugs or money or the ordeal between the Brothers Three and Stokes' family.

Usually, he only talked about God and Jesus Christ. Stokes began to speak by first telling Pharaoh that one's life does not start until that person willingly accepts who Jesus Christ and God Almighty are.

"That one must accept Jesus Christ in their hearts, and then their lives begin to be worthwhile. Then they will be like me, wanting only the things that God Almighty gives them or wants them to have, and for all that I have gained without the blessing from God, then I want no more, nor even to talk of those ungodly things that I purchased without the help or blessing from God Almighty."

Now Stokes was already familiar with God's Word, which he had learned from a child. Stokes had walked away from God's Word and picked up the use of drug-using and selling. But in the entire eighteen months that Stokes was in the mental part of the state hospital in New York, he studied the Bible every day.

While prayer was his daily reliever though Daniel in the Bible prayed four times a day, Stokes was now a spiritual advisor! An advisor of all types of different types of troublesome, complex, and unbelievable situations, in which people paid Stokes for his spiritual advice. Hundreds and thousands of dollars! But he would only take thirty dollars to pay the phone bill or whatever the rent was; the gas bill was; etc.

Stokes never took any money unless it was money to pay a bill or cash to buy food. God blessed Stokes with always having enough money to survive on and eat. Through the funds that Stokes was given for surrendering his spiritual services, and knowledge of the Word, through advice and conversation to those who sought his wisdom and confronted him.

He welcomed and counseled everyone who came to visit him but always with wisdom concerning God first. Then worldly advice and conversation concerning knowledge and understanding that God had allowed Stokes to accomplish concerning life, death, survival, and some of the many trials and tribulations that life encounters that Stokes had indeed experienced through in his lifetime on the planet earth.

Again, it had been eighteen months since Stokes had come home from the mental section of the state hospital in New York.

It had been just about the same amount of time that Stokes' mother had also been home from the hospital after the ordeal she had with the Brothers Three.

The time seemed to have passed by so quickly for Stokes to have established such a well worth business with the public on the teaching of God Almighty, worldly and life involving incidents.

Today was a day of difference, sorrow, and the bidding of farewell because today, Stokes' mother died.

Everything was in an uproar while everyone seemed relaxed and calm, but today God Almighty called Stokes' mother to come home.

Stokes' sorrow was understandable. Maria's sorrow was understandable. But YaYa was emotionally array, lost, and uncontrollable. Even though YaYa tried very hard not to show his true feelings and emotions. In the arrangement of this situation, something was very much out of place. Something did not make sense, or something did not belong in this equation.

Maria, Stokes mother, Stokes, YaYa, Pharaoh, and Stokes' mother's death and The emotional feelings brought on YaYa for Stokes' mother's death were unimaginable.

Stokes and Pharaoh never talked about drugs, money, or any of the deals that Pharaoh and Stokes had done in the past.

Pharaoh never tried to go back behind Stokes' back to meddle in the unfinished business that Stokes had just walked away from. Concerning Stokes drug business or Stokes' part in the hitman company, Stokes had been a part of on the down-low.

Pharaoh's drug business back in Baltimore was a hit, a winner. It was really on even though Pharaoh ran the business like a help group center because he communicated with the clients. At the same time, he attended their parties, get-togethers, and even some of their children's school activities.

Pharaoh's drug business was set up to protect the clients from robbers, cheaters, and the police. It gave the clients some order of having some say-so over cases where they were mistreated, cheated, or even had a dispute over anything concerning their drug transactions. Or negative discussions concerning anything or anyone.

All Pharaoh's drug customers were white. In the early sixties, blacks were rarely into drugs, nor did they have money to buy drugs.

The Vietnam War had come along and provided plenty of drugs for plenty of people. That's when blacks got into drugs heavy.

And, of course, the drugs were potent and very cheap. Blacks, both men, and women were becoming heroin addicts.

Street wars were being fought over the city street territories to sell the drugs. While the blacks blamed the white man for bringing drugs into the country, and the poor white people blamed the politicians—the rich white folks for being responsible for the drug coming into America. Pharaoh had participated in a beautiful relationship with Maria, and Pharaoh had learned how to watch her back. At the same time, Maria carried drugs for her father-in-law even though Maria's father-in-law had once sent out a hit on Pharaoh, even though the hit was squashed. Maria's father-in-law disliked Pharaoh. Maria's father-in-law hated all black people, while Pharaoh even more. Maria convinced him to allow Pharaoh to show the skills that Maria had shown him in delivering drugs.

Even though Pharaoh had never given drugs, he was always there to back Maria up. Pharaoh had learned the customers, the cities, and the procedures and the ins and outs of Maria's drug business. Pharaoh would be taking over Maria's husband's job because Maria had sold her fa-ther-in-law in on this deal. She would pay Pharaoh a quar-ter of the salary that her husband was receiving, and Maria would pay Pharaoh herself so that her father-in-law would agree to the deal. Maria knew that her father-in-law loved her and trusted in Maria's ability to make responsible deci-sions and decisions of integrity. Even if sometimes Maria's father-in-law didn't agree. Maria always came out true to her choices and options about all matters that she involved herself, in which only a few times Maria was got herself involved personally. But when she did, then she was always right. Pharaoh was confused about what was happening between YaYa and his ties to Stokes' mother. Pharaoh knew that Stokes' mother was turning YaYa towards God in his heart. When Pharaoh found out that YaYa would give ev-eryone that he was sent to kill a knife to protect themselves against him, so that YaYa would feel that his opponent would have a decent chance to fight for their lives. At the same time, Yaya would always, since lately, come face to face with all his opponents instead of surprise attacks and out-of-the-blue procedures of violence and death strategies against his opponents.

Beyond all doubt, something is happening in Yaya's life to create a significant change. Pharaoh knows that in some way, Stokes' mother is bringing YaYa closer to God by introducing YaYa to her God. To bring change to Yaya's way of life and Yaya's way of living, it would be years later before Pharaoh would be introduced to the absolute truth ANNOUNCEMENT...INTRODUCING THE BIRTH OF YAYA'S SON. WHO WAS BORN DURING THE

TIME THAT STOKES WAS JUST COMING OUT OF
THE STATE MENTAL HOSPITAL IN NEW YORK,
JUST BEFORE STOKES' MOTHER DIED, INCRED-
IBLE WAS HIS NAME, WITH ONLY THAT NAME
AS HIS COMPLETE NAME. Now! It was sixty days after
Stokes' mother's funeral, which was one day for each of
her years on Earth before God called her home to be with
him and heaven's hosts. Pharaoh had kept his promise and
vowed to her that he would not retaliate on The Brother's
Three in any way until the day came that God would send
for her.

During the two years that Stokes' mother continued to
live and recuperate from the drama that the Brothers Three
had sent her through, Pharaoh did not. He could not forget, sit down, rest, or forgive the terrible things that the
Brothers Three had done. Nor could Pharaoh forgive, sit
down, or let rest the Brothers Three's threats towards him
and his family. While Pharaoh constantly prayed, asking
God to give him strength, to uphold Stokes' mother's request and vowed not to lay hands on or bring harm to the
Brothers Three. Pharaoh did lay regards to that vow by saying that until the day came that God called Stokes' mother
home to be with Him, Pharaoh would not abuse his vow.
He constantly prayed for strength and guidance from God
to fulfill his vow to Stokes' mother. Which he did until the
day Stokes' mother died. Pharaoh had upheld his vow to
Stokes' mother. It was almost every day of Pharaoh's life
that Pharaoh did plan the payback to the Brothers Three
for what they had done to Stokes, Stokes' mother, Stokes'
wife, and the threats they had made on Pharaoh and his

family. Early in the morning, Pharaoh left Baltimore after gambling all night at Mr. Robinson's crap house, which Pharaoh enjoyed constantly.

Pharaoh was going to New York to fulfill something that had been on his mind and in his heart for a long time. This trip to New York was different from the so many trips to New York. Back and forth, week after week, month after month, year after year, Pharaoh had made in the past. Because this day, Pharaoh was going to New York to kill the Brothers Three.

Pharaoh had kept his vow to Stokes' mother, and Pharaoh had prayed for the souls of the Brothers Three. But this day is the day of redemption for the Brothers Three.

Now Pharaoh had planned this occasion for eighteen months, ever since he had first gone to YaYa and asked YaYa to take out the Brothers Three. YaYa explained that Pharaoh's beef was a beef that involved a vendetta. To get total results, Pharaoh had to do the murders himself or orchestrate the plan to be followed for murders. It is the only way to set free your heart, soul, and sense of responsibility for the vast cloud that covers the shadow of your life forever and to be free of such a massive responsibility of human love, honor, and respect.

It was still early when Pharaoh pulled into New York City. No one knew Pharaoh was coming but Maria. Not only did Maria know Pharaoh was coming to New York, but Maria also knew why Pharaoh was coming to New York, which was primarily to kill the Brothers Three.

Now Pharaoh had never feared the Brothers Three even when they had first met him through Stokes and had threatened his life if seeing him again. Nor was Pharaoh afraid of the consequences of getting caught concerning the murder of the Brothers Three, but Pharaoh feared God's punishment towards him for murdering the Brothers Three.

God had not given Pharaoh the right to take the lives of the Brothers Three. Even though in man's eyesight, the Brothers Three surely deserved not just to die but deserved to die a death of pain and humiliation, like the Brothers Three had poured out on Stokes and his family. Like the threat that was made on Pharaoh's family. It was given to Pharaoh to take any way he saw fit to deal with men like the Brothers Three.

As Pharaoh prayed for a sign from God to justify him killing the Brothers Three, there came none. As Pharaoh got closer and closer to completing his plan of murder, still there came no justification or sign from God.

The Brothers Three had been buying drugs from Maria for eighteen months. They had stretched out their drug buying purchases from small to big and large. They were now buying extra-large quantities of heroin. It just so happened that night that the Brothers Three was supposed to meet with Maria to accept another big shipment of heroin. While setting up a time and place, the Brothers Three mentioned to Maria that their performance in buying heroin from her had been overwhelming, and they knew it.

They believed it was time for them to meet the people in Africa as an even more significant connection than Maria could provide. It was something that had been promised to the Brothers Three after two years of proving themselves as drug dealers.

The Brothers Three were telling Maria that they knew they had proven themselves over the last eighteen months, and they now wanted to be given a chance to deal directly with the Africans as they had been promised. To be set up in Africa as a citizen, or at least set up so that they could constantly run back and forth in and out of that country purchasing drugs.

Now Maria had corresponded with Pharaoh over the phone and let Pharaoh know what the Brothers Three had said to her concerning them wanting to meet the African connection. That they had proved themselves long enough and now wanted the chance to move up more in the drug game to becoming international drug dealers.

Even though Pharaoh was not a part of the Brothers Three's drug connection they were talking about wanting to become a part of, he knew who was. Only Maria's father-in-law could take on that responsibility. Maria was letting Pharaoh know some of the things the Brothers Three were on the verge of doing ahead of time. Hoping that any information concerning them might help Pharaoh better plan against the Brothers Three.

CHAPTER 7

Lemonade for the Brothers Three

Maria was now much more versed in acting, feeling, and being more like a Christian than Pharaoh knew. Until Maria told Pharaoh that if he was going to kill the Brothers Three, he should pray and ask God to forgive what the Brothers Three did sinfully. To ask God if it is possible, God would send back the Brothers Three to the earth later to rectify the sinful lives they have lived upon the face of the earth.

"But be careful warned Maria, as not to let your anger towards the Brothers Three destroy your Godliness or teach you to live with severe rebellion in your heart towards anything or anyone. For there is no room for hatred, vendettas, dislike or any other thing that would come between our Lord God Almighty and us or His Son who is our Lord and Savior Jesus Christ."

When Maria talked, Pharaoh realized how much Maria had grown in the faith. And of course, why not, after being taught by one as good and righteous as Stokes' mother, who was Maria's Bible study buddy, teacher, and friend.

Even though Pharaoh was the first to turn Maria's thoughts to the Word of God. And who is The Word? Jesus is the Word, Jesus indeed speaks the Words of His Father, God who is in heaven, and indeed, Jesus is the Word. The Word of God in human form, but who continuously tells us, *"My Father sent me, so you will know that they are different even though they are the same."*

Even though Maria told Pharaoh what the Brothers Three talked about, she dared not tell him that the Brothers Three had also threatened her life.

By this time tomorrow, she could depend on taking her deposit ticket to the bank for her life. The Brothers Three threat made Maria hostile towards the Brothers Three and in high hopes that Pharaoh would kill them all.

It was like clockwork when Pharaoh called the train station to find out when the train would be arriving from Chicago, which was the home state of the Brothers Three, and the train station announced that the train from Chicago to New York would be on time.

It was a hot day; the temperature was in the low 100's. The limousine to pick up the Brothers Three had pretended air condition problems, but with iced cold laced lemonade, ice-cold laced bottled water, laced chocolate chip cookies, even the potato chips were laced. They had enough strong medication strong enough to knock out an elephant for three hours.

Maria was on time to pick up the Brothers Three at the train station. Immediately and as soon as the Brothers Three entered the limousine, they began to drink the lemonade without even asking could they have any. "Drink it all," Maria said in a smart-like gesture. "I'm not even going to ask you to save me any."

Now the Brothers Three knew nothing about Maria's father-in-law. Or his power or his statue of a man in which he was able to release all types of forces of death, destruction, and incredible negativity that one could not begin to imagine in two lifetimes upon the planet earth if and when he so desired.

Maria's father-in-law knew nothing about the relationship between the Brothers Three, Pharaoh, or even Maria and Pharaoh's plans towards the Brothers Three.

Nor did Maria's father-in-law know about the relationship between Maria and Pharaoh or the physical internment relationship Maria and Pharaoh were having.

Now true be it that the Brothers Three were ignorant, sloppy, and unorthodox in the field of manners, politeness, and respect. All this showed techniques that the Brothers Three betrayed as they dug into the cookies and lemonade without even asking if they could have any or saying thanks afterward.

Pharaoh wanted Maria to have no part in what he had planned for the Brothers Three, especially after Maria had proven her Christianity and her reason to forgive.

Being the Christian way, Pharaoh pulled off and left Maria after asking Maria to get out of the car and get a bottle of cold water out of the store. When Maria got out of the vehicle, Pharaoh pulled off, leaving Maria behind.

Pharaoh looked behind him in the mirror of the limousine. And saw that the Brothers Three were knocked out from the drugs in the cookies and lemonade.

Pharaoh knew that he had three hours to do whatever he wanted to do to the Brothers Three before they would even attempt trying to gain their consciousness.

The barn where Pharaoh had brought them was cemented all the way around. You entered a square to create a wall around the outer entrance. Pharaoh had a gate built right there in front of the door, but the gate only led up to the cement wall built around the barn. Pharaoh had the whole cement wall cushioned inside the wall to keep the sound inside while the wall kept everybody outside.

Three carts of steel with wheels provided transportation for the Brothers Three. To be rolled on from the limo to inside the barn. There, the Brothers Three were handcuffed to each other.

And chained to a cinder block. On each of The Brothers Three hands and feet, With a chain around their waist.

It was three days and three nights before Pharaoh returned after the evening that Pharaoh had brought the Brothers Three there. The Brothers Three had handkerchiefs tied around their faces to not scream loud.

After Pharaoh had gone and taken off all their handkerchiefs, the oldest of the three brothers screamed out that he knew that Pharaoh had something to do with this.

He swore on his aging mother and the grave of his dead father that he would kill Pharaoh and Pharaoh's whole family.

"And even your God will not be allowed to help you." When the oldest of the Brothers Three said that, Pharaoh held up his hand in the face of the oldest of the Brothers Three and said, "This day or the next, before you take your last breath, you will surely do as we all do when there is no hope. You shall call on the name of God."

Pharaoh was talking to the oldest of the Brothers Three, Pharaoh was standing directly in front of the Brothers

Three. The oldest brother was chained and shackled so that he was lying on his stomach, while the other two brothers were chained sitting in an upright position, but still, they were chained and handcuffed to each other and the wall.

"I know where you live, Pharaoh, and I have pissed and shit on myself three times already. But I will make your mother eat it after I stick a broom up her ass!"

"How?" asked Pharaoh.

"What the fuck do you mean" shouted the oldest of the Brothers Three? Pharaoh said, "How? How can you do these things to my family and me with no hands?"

"What do you mean by that" the oldest said.

It was then that the oldest of the Brothers Three looked up, and Pharaoh had appeared with a hatchet in his hand.

Pharaoh proceeded to chop off one of the hands of the oldest of the Brothers Three. It was three times that the hatchet had to come down upon his hand before it came completely off and the oldest of the Brothers Three became handicapped with only one hand.

The oldest of the Brothers Three was so petrified and horrified until no words were coming from his mouth, only blood where he had bit into his tongue, trying not to scream.

When Pharaoh came down on the other hand of the oldest of the Brothers Three with the hatchet. "Oh God, Help Me! Oh God, What Have You Done to Me!" cried out the oldest of the Brothers Three as the tears, snout, and spit running down his face.

While the frightful ordeal that had just happened to him left him speechless besides the words, he kept repeating, "Oh God, Oh God Help Me!" trying to wipe his face off only blooded his face up more because he had no hands. Only the beginning of his wrists was there for him to wipe his face with.

The screams and cries of the other two brothers were that of crucified and petrified souls of fright beyond this world. As they screamed and hollered until the second oldest of the Brothers, Three realized that Pharaoh had hit him with the first stroke of the hatchet to cause his hand to peel loose from his wrist until the second stroke of the hatchet took off his hand completely from his wrist.

"Mama! Mama! OH God! OH God! Forgive Me for My Sins!" was the worded cry of the second oldest of the Brothers Three as he pleaded to God to please show compassion towards him and touch Pharaoh's heart by letting him keep his other hand.

He said, "I never threatened you or your family Pharaoh, plus, my older brother made me have sex with Stokes' mother, and it was something that I didn't want to do!"

Pharaoh said, "Falsehoods and lies back your words. They fall deaf, mean less, and are not accepted, heard, nor remembered."

"Stokes' mother only cried out for forgiveness for all of you that hurt, humiliated, and made fun of her suffering. But I will show you some form of compassion for Stokes' mother's sake and only for her will I not stick this broomstick completely up your ass, but I will shove it up to your ass only so far, and you can keep the change."

It was thirty-six hours before Pharaoh returned to the barn where the Brothers Three still chained to themselves plus the barn wall. Before he left, Pharaoh poured a bottle of alcohol on each of the Brothers Three, who had nubs on the end of their wrists, meaning the two oldest brothers.

To cause pain but to clean the wounds of the two oldest brothers to help stop the bleeding and clean the nubs of diseases so they would not die yet.

Pharaoh stuck their snubbed wrists into potholders used in the kitchen that he had brought from the dollar store for bandages and numbed all their mouths with lots of Novocain to keep the Brothers Three awake. After Pharaoh had poured a can of chicken broth down the throats of all of the Brothers Three. About keeping them alive and strong enough to keep living, realizing their pain, being strong enough to continue living, but not yet dying.

Pharaoh entered the barn and started in the direction of the youngest and last of the Brothers Three that Pharaoh had not punished or cut off his hands yet. But this third and final brother of the Brothers Three noticed Pharaoh coming in his direction, performing rather cowardly. By crying like a baby and blaming all faults on his other two brothers, swearing that he had always hated both of his other brothers but did all the bad things his brother told him to do because he was afraid of them.

That he would go to church every Sunday, and he would believe in God if Pharaoh would not cut off his hands but would just kill him first.

Pharaoh was tying up the hands of the youngest of the Brothers Three to a pistol. Then Pharaoh tied a string around the trigger of the gun that Pharaoh then wrapped the string around a pencil that Pharaoh placed directly above the head of the youngest of the Brothers Three.

Pharaoh gave the youngest of the Brothers five minutes to pull the pencil on the string, which would then pull the gun's trigger and blow the head off the youngest of the Brothers Three. The youngest of the three did complete his task in two minutes, and his soul was no more upon the face of the earth.

The oldest of the Brothers Three was truly a Viking in all the sense of the word, and he did not moan or groan or even complain about anything.

He cursed the birth date of both his brothers and denied them to be a part of his family, and called them fagot, sissy, and other words of denouncement.

"Fuck you, Pharaoh, for I am the better man than you could ever be. I am a bully of alive and dreaded gangsters because I kill their children."

"Cut off the heads of their grandmothers and then fuck their wives in front of their faces. I also bully governors, councilors, mayors, and big-shot rich men. They all fear me and tremble when they hear my name, and because all these things are true is the reason why I know that I am better than you."

"I know that even with me having no hands, you are still afraid of me, Pharaoh, and I know that what has happened to me is a miracle because you don't qualify to do these things to me."

Stooping down to be equal to the face of the oldest of the Brothers Three, Pharaoh spoke very quietly to the oldest of the Brothers Three in his ear, saying, "You are a fool,

an idiot, and a dummy, and you walk blindly through life
thinking that people are afraid of you and fear the actual
hearing of your name, but you only frighten the men you
deal with and work with in sin and corruption. But Godly
people have no use for you, and they deal with you not at
all and have no fear of you.

But watch you walking into hell with your eyes wide
open because you are too dumb and stupid to know you
are but a fool that knows not the name of Almighty God.

Or how to call him when everything else has failed, and
there is no hope or another way in which you could carry
on in dignity, and all hope and mercy has deceived you
then because you know not God.

"The only living, breathing, Almighty God, besides
His Son Jesus who is also God" cutting Pharaoh off in the
conversation and asking, "Does Your God have a name?"
asked the oldest of the Brothers Three to Pharaoh. "I would
never call His name even if I knew the name of your God,
and I wouldn't even write Him a letter if I wanted to get in
touch with Him, Ha! Ha!" echoed the oldest of the Brothers Three as he smirked the name of God in laughter. But
bringing the oldest of the Brothers Three back to reality,
and wiping away the smirk of laughter from his lips as
Pharaoh reminded the oldest of the Brothers Three, you
have no hands to write God a letter, and you're too stupid
to realize your misfortune of not knowing God Almighty
in heaven. Who gives mercy, forgiveness, and understanding. Even to those who are undeserving and of your caliber in understanding faith, wisdom, and knowledge of
God Almighty.

"But you shall call out his name in agony and pain as though you knew him well before you walk the underworld of hell where you will learn some of the histories of the only living God, besides God's Son Jesus, who is also God. For your surroundings will be only those who also are fools, idiots, and dummies. Who know of God but refuse to follow in righteousness, and who believe not in the name of God nor the name of the Son of God.

"But before you leave this world, you shall call out the name of God and His Son Jesus for mercy. But I don't think that God Almighty will come to your rescue."

"As God comes in the midnight hour, the sunset, the middle of the day, or at any time to those who are witnesses to His answer of miracles. Whether it be mentally, physically, the paying of bills, the miracle performed on a loved one, or *whatever* miracle it may be to the millions and billions of people and to people's situation that God Almighty answers to when called upon."

"When there is no way, but God provides a way to so many who have come to the end of their road. And there is no place else to turn. God creates a miracle to give back to that recipient cures, healing, and blessings of restoration of whatever the case may be for.

"They have surely called out His name in mercy, desperation, hope, and faith that He will come to do whatever it is His will to do to bring about a miracle."

Pharaoh was talking to the next to the oldest of the Brothers Three, but the second of the oldest of the Brothers Three did not hear Pharaoh because the angel of death had already visited him, and he breathed no more the breath of life.

Pharaoh did not know that the second oldest of the Brothers Three was dead. Pharaoh was still talking to the oldest, and the next to the oldest of the Brothers Three as he exited out the barn door, not knowing that now there were two of the brothers dead and leaving only one of them still alive, the oldest.

Pharaoh had been in New York for a while now, and even Maria didn't know when Pharaoh came or left New York because Pharaoh didn't like involving Maria concerning what was happening in the barn with the Brothers Three.

Nor did Pharaoh want Maria to know that he was beginning to feel sorry for the Brothers Three. That he admired somewhat how the oldest of the Brothers Three stuck to his tough-guy guns, and image even when he had no hands. Pharaoh thought how strong this oldest brother of the Brothers Three was and how important he could have fought for God Almighty. And yes, Pharaoh was beginning to feel a soft spot in his heart for the oldest of the Brothers Three. He knew that he had to go back and end the suffering for the last two brothers even though one of the last two of them was already dead unbeknownst to Pharaoh. Time was obsolete, unimaginable, unreal, and as a fantasy to the oldest of the Brothers Three, for he had no idea now, not by accident, but by circumstances, whether it was day or night, morning or evening, one day or the next day.

But he vaguely remembers hearing the echoes of noise from the different surrounding gangs of tough guys, who practiced making firebombs, dynamite sticks, and other means of exploding devices used in scare tactics to provoke fear to those before the emotional act of violence to the fullest extent was applied. And then it appeared to be very hot in the barn, and then that's when the oldest of the Brothers Three heard the next explosion, which lit up the barn in a series of red, orange, and yellow flames that burst the entire barn into nothing but flames that followed smoke that choked everything with life inside it.

The oldest of the Brothers Three smelled the stench of his two brother's bodies burning as he all of a sudden did feel the pain of his own body being burnt in the fire, and he screamed o"OH MY GOD! I CANNOT TAKE THIS PAIN ANYMORE!" And turning over on his stomach while bawling up in a knot, the oldest of the Brothers Three closed his eyes. He silently asked God to take away his pain and forgive him for guiding his brothers in the wrong direction. If he could be forgiven for taking his brothers down the wrong path, then take his life so he could duck this terrible physical pain.

Because all his life, he has worshiped Satan, but he has found out that God is greater. So, he asked forgiveness of his two brothers, smiled, and found peace before he breathed no more the breath of life and died peacefully in the middle of a miracle.

To not feel pain as his body burned, he died peacefully, even in a dreadful situation.

Now, not by chance but by circumstance, true will, and the desire to do as one sees fit, Pharaoh never spoke a word about the Brothers Three, the barn, or the capture or torture of the Brothers Three again to Maria or anyone.

It was a random thing that YaYa saw Pharaoh coming into Maria's apartment one night over a year after the

Brothers Three had been killed. YaYa cut Pharaoh off by going through the parking garage and met up with Pharaoh just as Pharaoh took an unknown shortcut to Maria's apartment that no one knew except Maria, Pharaoh, and YaYa. One had to sit in the back seat of the car and could enter through the floor of the back of the limousine. It led to a small tunnel that the vehicle sat over to take you to a secret iron door that could open into Maria's apartment. If Maria was to open her apartment door from the inside, one could enter.

Now Pharaoh had been mistreated by Maria's father-in-law, who disliked black people, apparently just because they were black. He had had previous run-ins and arguments concerning Pharaoh having a relationship with Maria.

At one time, Maria even tried to get Pharaoh to be her appointed backup person to deliver heroin, while once Maria's father-in-law threatened to kill Pharaoh. Suppose it had not been for YaYa, who spoke up on Pharaoh's behalf. He asked for permission not to have to kill Pharaoh. Which YaYa had never before done. But because Pharaoh, who was just a boy, was fascinated over Maria, who was such a beautiful girl, *that's what YaYa explained to all that would listen*. But YaYa also summed up his advice by telling Maria's father-in-law that if the command were to come to him to kill Pharaoh, then Pharaoh would be dead before the next sunrise.

It was quite a coincidence when YaYa met up with Pharaoh after cutting him off by coming through the parking lot, where the Lincoln limousine was sitting and had been sitting in that very spot for over two years.

The entrance to Maria's apartment was built so that the limousine would cover up the grate in the garage floor where the limousine sat over top of it, where one had to sit in the limousine and go through the bottom of the limousine to open the grate and go through the gate.

If Maria opened the gate from the inside to enter Maria's apartment, coincidently, that limousine sort of marked the beginning of the relationship between Pharaoh and Maria back when Pharaoh had won Maria's money by dealing the cards for her.

To give Maria the card hands that Pharaoh chooses to give her, only asking for Maria in return to be his supplier of heroin in heroin.

Speaking to Pharaoh YaYa startled him, and when YaYa waved to Pharaoh for Pharaoh to follow him, Pharaoh was surprised because YaYa never said too much to anyone.

Pharaoh had never got the chance to tell YaYa that he was sorry for asking YaYa to kill the Brothers Three. After Maria had explained to Pharaoh that YaYa was not just some hired assassin, but one that was designated, trained, and profiled from birth to protect Maria's father-in-law for the entirety of YaYa's life.

With the lives of Yaya's whole complete blood family back in the country where they all were born, to pay the price for any type of disloyalty that would ever be shown to Maria's father-in-law.

The penalty of death was by fire to all, including any pets or other animals that were a part of Yaya's blood family, from the newest addition of Yaya's family to the oldest of YaYa's family. Such a terrible thing would happen to Yaya's family caused by YaYa's disloyalty, then Yaya's whole complete blood family, from the newest addition to the oldest member of YaYa's family, back in the old country in which YaYa was from.

To any new location that any part of Yaya's family may have relocated would be treated like royalty, to want or need for nothing that could possibly be given to a family that was known forever, to be members of the family that was the right hand of the father in law to Maria. One of the most influential men on the planet earth.

He could at any given time come up with incredible amounts of cash, power, or influence in order to tear down, build up, or destroy, satisfy or maintain whatever was his desire to do so on earth. With the help, ingenuity, wisdom, knowledge, and power of (Satan), who was the all and all in the life of the father-in-law of Maria.

Suddenly, Pharaoh looked at YaYa, not for the first time, but the first time looking at YaYa directly or starring at YaYa, who asked the question to Pharaoh, "How much money have you ever had at one time?"

"Have you ever had fifty thousand dollars? Have you ever had one hundred thousand dollars or better still, have you ever had five hundred thousand dollars?" Sitting back in the limousine while getting more relaxed to relate to the questions YaYa had just asked Pharaoh.

With an odd but severe look on his face, Pharaoh answered YaYa and said, "Maybe fifty thousand, or if not, then I'm sure I've choked the shit out of almost having that much. We are talking about money, aren't we? "Yes," answered YaYa, "we are talking about money."

"Then for what reason are we talking about money because I apologize for asking you to take out the Brothers Three for me, but that has already been done. I know now that you are into Maria's father-in-law for the rest of your life and the rest of the lives of your family."

Silence sat in and ruled the room for a moment. Then YaYa asked Pharaoh, "What would you do with five hundred thousand dollars?"

"I don't know for sure, but I think that first I would find a way to help hungry people and people that don't have a place to stay. Then I would go back to school and take business classes for a year to be taught how to make my money *make* money.

But before I did anything, I would first thank God for the money and ask Him to guide me and show me the right things to do.

I would ask God not to let me become selfish, or harmful, or ruin myself in partying, drinking, or taking drugs in any way. Because sometimes money helps to turn a good person wrong if God isn't there to guide them along the way."

Unbeknownst to anyone, YaYa had a deep dark secret: for the first time in Yaya's life, YaYa had sex.

Which, had given him a thrill and climax like no other. YaYa did go back for seconds later, which had made him join the parental segment of life that second-time YaYa performed in sex while Yaya's first performance in sex was done to him orally, and YaYa had fallen in love.

For the first time in his life of being forty-some years old, YaYa had felt the feeling of loving someone other than Maria's father-in-law. Because at a very young age, before school, YaYa was taken away from his family and taught to do everything and anything that he could for Maria's father-in-law.

Because of Maria, YaYa had become the hospital orderly for Stokes' mother and took responsibility for taking Stokes' mother wherever she had to go.

Which was back and forth to the hospital, and up and down the steps in his arms, would he take the frail body of Stokes' mother. And of course, Stokes' mother continuously talked to YaYa of the only living God. While Stokes' mother told YaYa these stories and facts about her God and the Son of God, Jesus Christ, Stokes' mother grew stronger and prettier. Her frail older body developed weight, and during the first year, Stokes' mother told YaYa not just about her God, but she also told YaYa about her life and her son how her son's father raped her. Who was a man sick with two diseases and mental problems drenched with syphilis in his blood and brain, making him a very sick and disturbed man?

The hospital wanted to take her son and experiment on him to find out how bad the syphilis blood in him was.

The hospital had even told Stokes' mother how her son would never be normal because he would always have murderous intentions while being mentally disturbed. How she had refused, kept her son, nourished him, and taught him of her God. While in return, YaYa told Stokes' mother of the nonexperiences he had never had.

His obligations to his family back in his country, his never having a friend or lover, and YaYa told Stokes' mother of his relationship with Maria's father-in-law and Yaya's job, duties, and responsibilities to Maria's father-in-law. Which Stokes' mother semi scolded YaYa of the murderous and homewrecking tasks he was performing for Maria's father-in-law.

YAYA had to start turning his life around to be a candidate for the hereafter, life with God, Jesus Christ, and all of heaven's hosts.

Now in the coming days and weeks and months after the acquaintance between YaYa and Stokes' mother, YaYa began to change his life around to glorify God.

By doing all his negative duties for Maria's father-in-law, in a whole new different way. This included never killing anyone without first giving them an equal opportunity to kill him first by giving his prey a weapon to kill him. While he had only his bare hands to kill with, he prayed for each of his victim's souls before the battle began and asked forgiveness for his victim's death in case YaYa would be the survivor of the competition.

It was then helping his opponents' families that had no way of survival after YaYa killed their spouse. These are how YaYa changed some of his habits and routines for his assassination duties.

YaYa changed how he was carrying out his orders from Maria's father-in-law until he could find a way to do differently to protect his family still back in his country. By being constantly obedient to Maria's father-in-law and showing God that his heart had changed, and he was no longer the YaYa that he used to be before Stokes' mother had introduced him to God, sanctified him, and saved him his soul.

YaYa now prayed constantly and continuously. While in his prayers to God, YaYa always thanked God for sending Stokes' mother into his life. YaYa now prayed for forgiveness of the lives he had taken and the lives that he still had to endure. YaYa thanked God most of all, and more than anything, for the chance to have a son like other men in the world.

YaYa thanked God for the introduction to love and the wonderful feeling of sex, climaxing, and the warmth of the true sense of love for your family and your mate. Which love honestly had to be a blessing from God and a part of God's personality.

YaYa was still talking to Pharaoh concerning how much money Pharaoh had ever had of his own or even in his possession.

It was then that YaYa offered Pharaoh five hundred thousand dollars to enter Maria's father in laws apartment and kill him while Maria's father-in-law was in bed asleep.

YaYa would then leave the front entrance open to make it look like someone came in the front. True, Pharaoh was surprised that YaYa had asked Pharaoh to do something like that.

Pharaoh knew that Yaya's whole blood family would be destroyed if it was ever to be revealed that YaYa, the old trusted right-hand man of the powerful but unknown man of such power and influence in the world. Would set up and play out a scene as violent and disloyal as YaYa was trying to do. To one that held a position and worthiness as Maria's father-in-law, to the dark world controlled by (Satan).

From way back in their mother country with vows, rules, and regulations set up between them before their actual birth by their parents. Who then played the role that they would be born to play, as one who looked and thought of himself as the one and only human that looked at himself as the number two ruler, and only human of that status of the dark and ungodly part of the world of the planet earth.

Now Pharaoh was surprised that YaYa would ask him something like that. Pharaoh knew that YaYa would have to take Pharaoh's life if Pharaoh said yes or if Pharaoh said no.

YaYa could not let anyone live with a secret on him like that, but at the same time, Pharaoh wondered why YaYa would ask him to kill Maria's father-in-law.

Pharaoh's question was soon answered when YaYa told Pharaoh that his conscience would violate a tradition that had been functioning with his people for over a thousand years. And would not let YaYa kill Maria's father-in-law. That he loved Maria's father-in-law and to harm him would be like harming himself because YaYa could not let Maria's father-in-law's blood be on his hand. He felt like he would burn in hell forever, and all his blood family would be cast out of the town in which they live, with their names on the council as traitors in the tent of the elders forever.

While each of Yaya's blood relatives would be hunted down and killed until no blood relative of Yaya's would be upon the face of the earth, and his family seed would be demolished and withdrawn from planet earth forever.

Maria startled both YaYa and Pharaoh as she was banging on the limousine window, trying to get the attention of YaYa or Pharaoh.

Now Maria had been waiting for Pharaoh for quite a while and decided to come out and backtrack Pharaoh's route he had taken that made him take so long. Because Pharaoh had already called Maria and told her he was getting ready to enter the garage and to be looking out for him.

Maria had something that she was very desperate to talk with Pharaoh about. Maria's anxiousness to speak to Pharaoh made her come looking for him, and that is how she happened to see Pharaoh sitting in the car talking to YaYa. But after seeing Maria, Pharaoh knew he had to leave YaYa.

Before Pharaoh got out of the car with YaYa, Pharaoh said to YaYa, "I swear on the name of Almighty God with all my Christian beliefs that the conversation we just had will never again be spoken of, not even with you."

Now Pharaoh saw how close YaYa and Stokes' mother had become. Pharaoh knew that anyone who communicated with Stokes' mother also had to be involved in Almighty God and Jesus Christ without a doubt.

Pharaoh hoped that by him telling YaYa that he would never again even speak about the conversation he and Yaya had about assassinating Maria's father-in-law. {Which Pharaoh swore to his God in heaven} Pharaoh had never sworn on the name of his God before} that would in some way help ensure Pharaoh's life continuance. Which it did, for Yaya's belief in God now, YaYa did believe Pharaoh's sworn statement to Almighty God. It reframed him from the usual evil, which would have beyond a doubt been the death sentence for Pharaoh.

Entering Maria's apartment, Maria broke down in tears and told Pharaoh about this frightful dream. She had never before had a dream in her life.

She dreamed that her father-in-law had given Pharaoh the job that she and Pharaoh had begged her father-in-law to give to Pharaoh, concerning taking over Maria's job, delivering drugs to different cities. Maria's father-in-law had been instructed by a much higher authority than himself to deal with black people and drugs. To destroy black families, black organizations, black colleges and universities, black freedom fighters, and all, to destroy the black race.

In reality, Maria had overheard this conversation with her father-in-law in her sleep. Pharaoh was Maria's father-in-law's choice to develop contacts with black people.

Even though Maria's father-in-law disliked Pharaoh and all black people, Pharaoh was the only black man that Maria's father-in-law knew right then.

He thought black people were ignorant, dumb, unable to understand or relate, and not honest or trustworthy.

Now black people were not presently into drugs as though white people were because black people didn't have the money to spend on drugs, Besides the Musicians and the men that made money off making their girlfriends sell their bodies in the street for money.

She continued with Maria's dream concerning Pharaoh and Maria's father-in-law the night before. Maria explained to Pharaoh that she had seen that Pharaoh had gone to jail for selling drugs in the dream. She had come to visit Pharaoh in jail and had to sit across from Pharaoh with this great long counter between them.

They were not allowed to touch each other while she wanted so much, not just to touch Pharaoh, but she wanted so badly to hug and kiss Pharaoh. Which awakened Maria from that dream in tears, and the dream was so real.

Pharaoh stood there looking at Maria in amazement. The only thing that Pharaoh and Maria wanted more than anything was for Maria's father-in-law to give the right for Pharaoh to learn Maria's job. Distributing drugs to different cities. Now, Maria is telling Pharaoh that is the one thing she *doesn't* want now is for Pharaoh to get that job.

Pharaoh had learned a lot concerning the customers, the meeting places and hotels, layouts of the different hotels in different cities. Even some of the customers that Maria dealt with personally. He was only known as a bodyguard to Maria because neither Maria nor Pharaoh wanted Maria's father-in-law to know that Maria was including Pharaoh in some of her travels and meetings. She would never allow him to make drug deals or even see a drug transaction. In reality, Maria could keep her reliable, respectful, and dependable relationship with her father-in-law to not disappoint him in any way. Maria had asked her father-in-law's permission to bring Pharaoh on the team as a standby or one that could help her or back her up or take her place if need be. But Maria's father-in-law stuck firmly to his position of not liking Pharaoh or black people at all until he was told by one of much greater authority other than himself to begin to fit in black people into his drug-infested operations.

The purpose was to bring down the black race who were so much in love and worship with their God. If possible, try to destroy them as a race because Satan already had the plan in motion. Let heroin, cocaine, reefer, and crack cocaine be introductory to all who would allow these drugs to destroy their lives and ruin their children's chances of having everyday lives.

Alcohol was beginning not to have the power as drugs had with the younger generations, who seemed to love indulging in drugs much more than alcohol. Even though alcohol is a drug, his super plan was to elevate the drugs with more poison each coming generation.

So, sex, drugs, pills, and alcohol seemed to destroy lives and families. Drugs as a whole caused chaos and tragedy. They seemed to be doing an excellent job of killing millions of people, families, and generations throughout other countries as well as our country of America.

The introduction of crack cocaine, artificial heroin, and the new additives in drugs made these additives caused these old drugs to make people have no control over their drug use. They started losing themselves, their families, hopes, dreams, and futures.

It seemed to elevate the caliber of artificial drugs to detrimental stages as each generation became more and more pharmaceutical, and the death tolls rocketed sky-high. The neighborhoods became vacant ghost towns of empty boarded-up houses throughout the different cities of America.

The word homeless became a reality in Baltimore City, which Pharaoh had never heard of before in all his life. He had never heard of a homeless person in Baltimore, a city noted for its cleanliness and its clean white marble steps all over the city.

A city that loved to read and educate its citizens brought drugs into our country because the Vietnam War had started. It caused our young men to come back from the war with their limbs missing off their bodies and heroin habits. To cope with their torn up, scarred up, burnt up, and mentally disturbed minds from the tragedies of war in which they had not only seen but had been a part of.

With the ending of the Vietnam War, tons of high-quality heroin came into our country. Even after the war, it was at the lowest prices. What used to cost ten dollars was now selling for one dollar.

It was to make heroin use so much more affordable to the poor. To create more drug users, even those who could not afford drugs, the black people and minority people could join the spread of drug users, which soon made thieves and homewreckers out of men and women. It would divide the families when some people would rather pay for drugs than pay their rent or mortgages.

There would be people living in boarded-up and vacant houses, and it provided homeless people that had lost themselves and their homes and families. To the rivers of homeless people, drugs were continually creating a flow of people who satisfied themselves with the cover of a vacant house because the high satisfaction from the drugs best fit their fancy.

Along with the few people who just fell on bad luck and lost whatever place they had to stay, the younger generation also relied on the state to care for them and their babies.

To wait for state or government provisions that provided them with housing, food stamps to buy their food, and medical assistance for them and their children.

While the real needy of the housing, food programs, and housing which were the elderly, the disabled, and the Veterans of the Armed Forces of America that were mentally or physically disabled, were left fighting for the right to be acknowledged.

"ONLY IN AMERICA" was such foolishness tolerated even though some assistance was necessary to help provide food, shelter, and medical aid for the elderly and to allow for a while to those who fell on hard times.

At the same time, the government was taking away recreation centers for the kids to play safely and degrading the schools in the city by closing them down and preparing a lesser potency of needed uplifting and educational teaching from qualified, dedicated educators who were ready and waiting to teach.

Indeed you can read between the lines and understand, know, and believe who it was that orchestrated this downside of negativity and especially when the Lord's Prayer was banned from the public schools. Daily morning exercise and, of course, this was how some children learned the Lord's Prayer. Those who didn't want to participate in saying the Lord's Prayer could easily sit in another room while the prayer was being said.

Even though the Lord's Prayer was said in only minutes, not hours, of course, it was (Satan) who caused a disturbance in heaven and was kicked out of heaven.

The one who sleeps at a zero-tolerance yet is still too busy finding ways, avenues, and schemes to hold back, stagnate, and cripple the minds, hearts, and souls of those that love and worship God Almighty and those who are righteous in their hearts and willing to help their fellow man.

While all people usually blame the white man for the cause of negativity, that happens to them and their people. True, the light-skinned man was the first slave ever for (Satan) to be sent to America to bring forth much evil.

But really, the white man is only a phrase that originated in early America to describe the human being that had never before been seen in America by the natives.

They were the original Americans here that populated the country. Still, that same label afterward was then labeled *the white man* for the wrongdoing and evil that the white man brought with him to America.

But it is wrong to blame others for people not being understood by others. Or to create indifference in humans by others, or to create a reason to sin because it is a sin for one human to hate another.

There is no difference in the different colors of people's skin, and humanity has no choice in what color his skin brings to Earth. There are only righteous and evil people, and it is your choice to be either good and honest or evil. There are good people of all colors and sinful people, but the light-skinned man was the first slave to (Satan) to be sent to America.

Some light-skinned people turned their backs on the belief in God and served (Satan). In hopes of earthly fame and fortune, advancement, and riches abundantly by lies and schemes that had been promised them by (Satan).

In this world that God created, only those who are good and those who are evil by their own choice, and it is God's Son, Jesus Christ. He came to the planet earth to give his life through suffering and pain for those of us who believe in God and that Jesus Christ is the only begotten Son of the only living God, besides our Lord and Savior Jesus Christ, who also is God. He promises all who believe in God eternal life and peace in heaven. Even then, when God created the world

So was God's begotten Son there even then, because God tells you so in the Christian Bible *John:* 1st Chapter 1st Verse 1: *"In the beginning was the Word. The Word was with God, and the Word was God"* Jesus is the Word, for he speaks the Word of God, His Father, Creator of all that is good, righteous and worthy Lord God Almighty. And because Jesus is the begotten Son of God, then Jesus also is God.

Man is accountable by God for his actions, activities, and deeds while on Earth. Even though man makes many mistakes and wishes he could do some things over if he had the chance. So he would do them a different way. Man is responsible for all his decisions. Even though God forgives him for his many sins when asked to be exonerated from his heart, But (Satan) is much more intelligent, conniving, and shrewder. (Satan) plays on the weaknesses that man has by putting in front of man the things that man so desires and shows man a way that these things can be obtained if man follows the deeds and practices of (Satan).

While drugs, alcohol, and pharmaceutical pills and drugs are just some of the many ways used to entice a man.

Money, power, and lust are the most used enticements that (Satan) uses to lure man into doing evil and wrong things that (Satan) wants man to do.

(Satan) now has also found that it is fair game to include the righteous man into the trap of using drugs to get the honest man started on becoming a man of doing wrong things.

Even though (Satan) does not turn the righteous man into an evil man, but (Satan) can help to turn the honest man into a sinner and a wrong man who loses himself into worldly deeds and actions, but who finally, after terrible ideals and sinful acts. He will return to God, who forgives him and gives him strength, courage, and a new way to continue on his path in peace without turmoil.

After realizing how lucky and fortunate, he is to have been blessed by God. Who gave him the right to testify by healing him spiritually, mentally and giving him back to himself at the most crucial time in his life. By leading him to hold to faith in the Lord, for all else has vanished.

A man stands there holding a mind full of broken promises of or about riches, fame, power, and glory. To only see his life in ruin, his dreams, hopes, fame, and future vanishing away from (Satan)'s possession as he rocks back and forth in the arms of Jesus after calling out His name, *Jesus*, the Son, the only begotten Son of God.

When everything else has failed, man's salvation is once again in the hands of God. The only one who will not forget him, refuse him, nor turn his back on him. Indeed, that was the purpose of Jesus Christ, the begotten Son of God.

That was the purpose of Jesus coming to earth and giving his life, to bring salvation to all humanity that believes in God, and that Jesus is the begotten Son of God. For those are the ones that salvation awaits, and they are the ones that will receive salvation, peace, and eternal life with God, so believe the Christian religion.

Through the passing years, YaYa and Pharaoh had established a very tight bond between the two of them, and Stokes' mother was one of the significant reasons why YaYa and Pharaoh's bond was so close. Even though she had now passed on to be with her God, Stokes mother had enlightened YaYa with stories about Pharaoh and his faith, belief, and love and worship of Almighty God, and God's Son Jesus, God's only begotten Son who also is God. But besides that, Stokes' mother had enlightened YaYa with the knowledge of telling YaYa that she had seen in Pharaoh's eyes. That he was one that God was with, one that had been chosen by God to do God's work and to glorify God to those that knew God not. She also told YaYa that Pharaoh had no idea of God's deeds for Pharaoh to do. That Almighty God protected Pharaoh.

Now it came to pass when YaYa found out about a meeting that would come to order concerning Pharaoh, Maria, and (123). Concerning Pharaoh being delegated the right to be on the team with Maria, even though unbeknownst to (123). Maria no longer wanted Pharaoh to be a part of her team anymore because of a dream Maria had had which made Maria see in her heart that Pharaoh would be going to jail if he became a part of Maria's team.

Now Yaya knew that (123) hated Pharaoh, mainly because he was a black man, but the fact that Pharaoh could be sleeping with his godson's wife made (123) hate him even more.

YaYa had forewarned Pharaoh before the time that if he could make (123) believe that he would not be working with Maria but would be working with someone else instead.

Then (123) might even consider letting Pharaoh on a team of his own.

(123) needed a black man on his team to get into the black neighborhoods. YaYa didn't know that (123) planned to kill Pharaoh at this meeting in front of Maria. YaYa had also explained to Pharaoh that there was something between Pharaoh and Maria. That (123) would never accept Pharaoh as a team player on any team that (123) had something to do with. But because (123) had been instructed by a higher power than himself to bring a black man on their team. Even though (123) hated Pharaoh there, was still a chance that (123) would accept Pharaoh as a team player if only to make good of what he was supposed to do, and he was told to do so by a greater authority than himself.

Now Pharaoh had no intentions of selling drugs in the black communities, and not just that Pharaoh didn't want to hurt black people. Pharaoh had no idea of the harm he could bring to the black communities by helping to bring drugs into the communities. There was no sign of the harm that drugs would do because there were hardly any black drug users in the City of Baltimore. Nor were there crucial signs of any destruction caused by drugs to the communities, houses, the population, and morals and principles of the people or communities.

Pharaoh had focused his mind on finding a white girl to take to New York so he could introduce her to (123). To prove that he no longer wanted to be on the team with Maria. After Maria told Pharaoh of the frightening dream, she let him know that she was now against him bringing drugs in and out of different cities (123).

Pharaoh realized that as long as he and Maria were having a relationship of any kind, his life would always be in jeopardy. Pharaoh had well searched his mind for a white female that could be the woman to play this part that he needed, and his first thought was of a friend of his named Elizabeth, nicknamed {Cakes}, only by Pharaoh. He gave her that name because she had a big pretty round ass that looked like two Cakes to Pharaoh. Cakes was white, intelligent, pretty, and intelligent, but Cakes had one weakness: she liked to use heroin.

Cakes was a part-time heroin user, and even though Pharaoh trusted her, Pharaoh knew not when the day might come when she might sell him out. Pharaoh felt that Cakes would not be untrustworthy anytime soon, and Pharaoh knew that Cakes always had a crush on him and that she would do almost anything to help him.

Pharaoh explained to Cakes the proposition he was about to introduce her to concerning (123), and Pharaoh asked Cakes if she would be interested? Cake's reply was, "If I will have time to be with you, and if that is what you want me to do, then consider it not only done but consider it my pleasure to do it for you with no questions asked."

Not wanting to be late for the meeting that (123) had arranged, Pharaoh was going over everything in his mind to try and make sure that he had everything in its proper perspective and ready to present to (123). He would unveil his surprise strategies to Maria and her father-in-law in hopes that he could improve the situation enough for (123) to let Pharaoh have the job. Not being on Maria's team, but being on a team of his own to distribute drugs in different cities for (123). Unknowing to Pharaoh, once again, God would step in and not let Pharaoh become a drug deliverer.

Pharaoh had arranged to have Cakes on the corner in New York City waiting for him to send a message of where to go and who to trust; when someone showed her his hat and watch, then they would be trustworthy. In the evening, just before dark, Pharaoh came to the apartment that he was told to come to for the meeting between (123) Maria and Pharaoh. Even though Pharaoh wasn't late, he was still the last to show up.

Pharaoh knocked on the apartment door, and immediately someone opened the door.

"Come in, Pharaoh" (123) said in terrible English, "This is the day for which I have been waiting for." One of (123)'s bodyguards then locked the door, and then Maria screamed out, "No! No! (123) Don't do this!"

And for some unknown reason, Maria knew that (123) was planning to kill Pharaoh. Falling on her knees and hugging around the legs of (123), Maria pleaded to him.

"Please! Please don't kill him, for if I have wronged you, disrespected you, or angered you in any way, then let me pay for my faults!"

This type of behavior coming from Maria made (123) even angrier because (123) had only known Maria as a vicious, wild jungle tiger who would tear off her enemies' heads and burn down their houses. She would eliminate their whole family to prove a point if that is what it took, but (123) had never known Maria to be this begging bitch that seemed to be as weak as a pussycat. (123) did not know that Maria now had God in her life and was not that rowdy bitch she used to be, and Maria knew that (123) loved to be begged to flex his power by making someone that he considered to be powerful, fall on their knees and beg him.

"Why are you not on your knees begging for your life Pharaoh? Why aren't you pleading for me to give you mercy and your life?"

"I came here today to offer you a proposition that could be of great help to you, and there is no use in me begging you for my life because you have no control over my life. Because when my God sent me to this planet of earth, he gave me a time to arrive and a time to leave, and if I die here today, then this is the time that my God has arranged for me to die years ago. He gave you also a time to arrive here on earth and a time to leave. I have come of my own free will today to bring you a proposition that will not only increase your authority and bring much more finance to your organization but will provide you with a way to reach the many ethical groups in America that you have not reached yet." Repeating what (YAYA) had told him to say.

Now, the things that Pharaoh told and said to (123) were things YaYa knew concerning (123). YaYa knew that (123) had been given orders to reach out more into the different ethical groups of the various races of people.

Especially black people to try and destroy or at least turn millions of humans from worshiping God to worshiping (Satan) through drugs, money, power, cars, and all sorts of material things in which to catch the eye of those that were righteous.

And try desperately to turn them to evil, or at least turn righteous people into bad people. Neither (YaYa) nor Pharaoh knew the actual damage to the cities, towns, communities, and states that drugs would bring through murder, lying, stealing, and cheating, nor the many other bad things that would come from the bringing of drugs into our country. Only (123) and (Satan) knew the results that drugs would bring, but (123) feared nothing or no one like he feared (Satan), and (123) knew that Satan had demanded him to find a way to communicate and negotiate with black people. All the people that worshiped God, but especially black people, and (123) knew how (Satan) had punished his father, who was the first (123).

The present (123) knew how all his forefathers feared the wrath of (Satan) for not being able to fulfill the obligations that (Satan) placed upon their heads.

All the while, Maria was constantly pulling on Pharaoh's hand and leg. Trying to pull Pharaoh to his knees, to beg (123) for his life, but after a while.

Maria realized for the second time that Pharaoh was not the little hustler that she thought he was, but instead, Pharaoh was a true warrior for God Almighty. Beginning to feel ashamed and small, covered with anger and disbelief that Pharaoh would still stand and buck (123). He was all the power and glory at that particular time. Not understanding Pharaoh's faith in his God. (123) hollered out the words in plain aggravation, confusion, and embarrassment

"Shoot that motherfucker!" as (123) pointed to YaYa screaming out Yaya's name, but YaYa had already taken the bullet out the first chamber, so the gun would misfire because YaYa didn't want to have to be the one that killed Pharaoh. Now YaYa had never before interfered in any of

(123)'s business or never even uttered a word but simply did as he was told.

YaYa looked at (123) and said, "Maybe you should just listen to what he has to say before you kill him." (123). He looked at YaYa strangely as if he was surprised that YaYa said something.

Then (123) said to Pharaoh, "What is it that you think you can bargain with me or proposition me into even listening too?"

Now Pharaoh had rehearsed in his mind what advice YaYa had already given him and the first point that YaYa told Pharaoh to get across to (123). Which was that Maria would not be working with Pharaoh, or Pharaoh would not be working with Maria.

Instead, Pharaoh had put together his team, which involved a beautiful white lady that would help Pharaoh get into all the new territories that involved blacks and whites that would not be suspicious-looking.

YaYa had already explained to Pharaoh to concentrate on the new areas that Pharaoh would bring to the blacks. Even though at that particular time, Pharaoh had no idea in his wildest imagination how much trouble and disaster that drugs would bring to the City of Baltimore. Presently, the drug problem in Baltimore was not a real problem, and there was not even a drug or narcotic squad, even though there was drug participation and use in Baltimore.

On a microscopic level was the sale and use of drugs in Baltimore, even though drug use and drug sales would have eventually risen much higher with the participation in the Vietnam War, which was the purpose and plan of

(Satan) from the very beginning. Even after it ended, so many high-quality drugs could flow into the United States of America at the lowest prices imaginable. The neighborhoods of black people would deteriorate unbeknownst to Pharaoh.

Nor did Pharaoh know then how much trouble drugs would bring to so many cities throughout the country and land of America.

Presently Pharaoh had no black customers in his drug business, but only whites. There was little drug use in the black communities at this particular time of the late 1950s and early 1960s.

Pharaoh also remembered to explain to (123) how much more money he would be bringing in as opposed to how much money (123) was getting, which almost doubled the amount (123) was presently getting. Still, what interested (123) the most was when Pharaoh said he would be getting some black business with drugs.

That's when (123) saw the damage in his mind that could be done to black people through black people using and selling drugs on a much higher level than at present. The satisfaction that (123) would bring to the face of (Satan) when he would see and realize the disaster and casualties that black people and people who loved and worshipped God would receive, experience, and die from after destroying themselves. And if they didn't kill themselves, then they would at least do a lot of wrong in the eyes of their God, who will indeed judge them when they stand before Almighty God, so believe the Christian religion on judgment day.

Now, (Satan) most graciously would be overwhelmed in joy or achievement when he learned the news that blacks and other people that worshiped God would soon be using drugs. Using them in their kitchen on Sunday morning instead of giving worship to God and the Son of God. Even though there will never be peace or happiness on earth for Satan, Satan's every minute on earth is spent bringing harm, misery, or some pain or sorrow to the human race, especially those who worship Almighty God. And even though Satan's mischief, problems, and disasters are planned generations before they occur, it is the reason why the babies belonging to the era of the sixties were so prominent in adult body size. (Satan) had made preparation for the babies of that generation to be born much more mature than their parents were. The drugs were already planned a generation ahead of time so that the men would have sex with the children to bring confusion, chaos, pregnancies, and havoc through drugs. They would create party time, sexual involvement, and babies having babies through young adolescent girls with the maturity in their bodies as if there were women. Experiments in the baby's milk created such mature bodies for the oncoming generation (Satan) had prepared a whole generation or two before these events happened.

Along with dividing the senior citizens as they are now called, from the young by putting them in old citizen homes. Those who moved were our grandmothers and grandfathers and our great-great-grandmothers and great-great-grandfathers. So, we would never even hear of and about our great-great-great-grandparents, their parents, and their great grandparents. Presently, the average American, especially the black Americans, can usually only relate as far back as his grandparents. Maybe some people can even relate back to their grandparents' parents or great grandparents as planned by (Satan) many generations ago. But the real reason for the separation for the old and the young is that the senior cannot teach the young the truth and not give worship and praise to Almighty God, which would be taught to the young by the old. The old generation was introduced and taught to worship Almighty God from their old when they were young. There is no one to teach the truth because our old has been separated from our young, and our family bonds are weak, and we sometimes know not who our blood relatives are, nor their achievements. They cannot reach out their hand or voices to help us, for they know us not, or they have been misplaced in the shuffle, rearranged, or relocated so that we are not aware of who is in our elderly family tree. This scenario includes almost all people and families in America, especially black people.

It was the fall of 1968, which was Pharaoh's most favorable time of the year. But while Pharaoh also loved the wintertime of the year. He didn't like the summertime too much because the weather was too hot for him, and he dreaded the heat. Pharaoh's drug business back in Baltimore was going well besides the fact that Pharaoh did not have not one single black customer to buy drugs from his small but welcomed and needed drug business. It wasn't because Pharaoh couldn't have any black customers, nor was it that Pharaoh was trying to save his race from using drugs. The drug-using and drug selling thing was becoming more and more popular. There was an increase in the drug game of both using and selling. The authorities had put together a drug force team to operate in Baltimore. The leaders were smart enough to use neighborhood black and white men as the police or drug agents. To catch and lock up their one-time neighbors or people that had lived in the same neighborhood as they had at one particular time, and it worked. The old neighborhood guys that became drug agents did do their duties, and they did lock up the drug dealers. Drugs were becoming big business for Baltimore's lawyers because they and the judges and lawmakers were making big bucks and changing the laws so they could increase the bails for drug dealers and users to unimaginable prices. The authorities gave Little Caesar the blues by locking up many of his dealers and constantly harassing him by stopping him, searching him, and abusing his rights. They were even taking some of his exotic cars to ride around in themselves and be able to brag that they were in a Bentley or whatever other exotic cars that they were able to take from Little Caesar. Even if it was just for a day, but during all this, Pharaoh dreaded selling drugs to the neighborhood people, both male and female. It seemed as if Pharaoh was doing wrong by selling neighborhood people drugs even though Pharaoh did sometimes give drugs to the neighborhood people.

Even though he would not take any money for the drugs, West Baltimore was different from East Baltimore, way behind in the hustling world. West Baltimore was more organized, wealthy, united, and intelligent about the hustling world than East Baltimore, which was behind in the hustling world. West Baltimoreans Who would supply many East Baltimoreans with drugs? Who would open the frontier for East Baltimore to become as intelligent, united, competent, and competitive as West Baltimore concerning the sales and distribution of drugs? Even though West Baltimore will always be where it all started for the original, rich, and flamboyant lifestyle of hustling in Baltimore in Pharaoh's day and time. Pharaoh did not like selling drugs to the neighborhood people. Pharaoh did try to enter into the big boy status of selling drugs on Pennsylvania Avenue to the retail drug supplies of the wholesale drug dealers.

Even though Pharaoh had broken the barrier and had indeed entered into the big boy arena with the big-time West Baltimoreans, he was still not allowed to penetrate through the faithful, united, and original players who had put together this loyal organization. An organization that allowed no outsiders to penetrate their sanctuary of loyalty, trust, and allegiance to their cause of sticking together. Even though the big eighth of raw heroin that Pharaoh received once a month from Maria through Stokes was top-notch rated, Pharaoh tried very hard to sell some of his heroin to the West Baltimoreans who were heavyweights. Still, they refused to buy from Pharaoh because he wasn't one of them. Pharaoh was allowed to gamble shoulder to shoulder with the West Baltimorean heavyweights. Pharaoh had started in the drug world with and from the big names of the West Baltimorean heavyweights, but the West Baltimorean heavyweights refused to buy drugs outside their circle. Pharaoh didn't know it then, but God Almighty stopped

Pharaoh's advancement into the West Baltimore family. Pharaoh tried so hard to penetrate but couldn't. Pharaoh's God would save him many more times from destruction, adversity, and even self-destruction before Pharaoh realized it was God who was denying Pharaoh all these opportunities to advance himself in the drug world.

Pharaoh loved the fall season of the year, and Pharaoh loved to watch the rainfall from the sky as God cleaned the earth and watered all the plants and green and trees. At the same time, he grew all the food, green vegetation, trees, and everything from the earth that needed water to grow. Pharaoh's imagination of the pouring down rain upon the rough open sea was terrifying and exciting. He had never seen that site before but felt God watches it quite often since God was the only force to create such dynamic places to be performed or seen by the human eye. It was 1969, around six years before the Vietnam War would end. The drugs were coming into America from the war in Vietnam plentiful, money was plentiful in the streets, and life was good for those left back in America who did not participate in the involvement in the war. But our young American soldiers were returning home from the war without legs, arms, and mentally disturbed from the horrible sights they had seen and been a part of during the war. Pharaoh was a married man with a child, and therefore he was excluded from having to enlist in the Service.

Pharaoh's favorite place was still Robinson's crap house. Pharaoh was every night, all night, seven nights a week gambler who had accomplished quite a name for himself as an East Baltimorean in Mr. Robinson's crap house. He was

accepted and respected by the heavyweights of West Baltimore and the professional people that owned and operated
businesses properties up and down the great Pennsylvania
Avenue. Shark Skin and Little Caesar both were excluded from the Vietnam War. Even though Pharaoh never
thought about asking them why they were excluded from
the Vietnam War, he sure was glad that they did not have
to go regardless of their reasons why they were also excluded. Pharaoh's brother Frank was killed in the Vietnam War
in a helicopter crash which devastated Pharaoh's life with
pain and grief. Pharaoh would miss him and think of him
all his life. He would only stay in his brother's daughter's
life until she started college as a little girl. Even though
Pharaoh had promised his brother {Frank} before his death
that he would look after {Lisa} which was his little niece's
name, all her life.

Pharaoh would carry that shame to his grave because
Pharaoh saw her no more after Lisa went to college. Nor
did Pharaoh stay in touch with her or her mother. Even
though Pharaoh had gotten incarcerated when Lisa started
college, and prolonged Pharaoh's life to confinement for
a few years. He still had no excuse for not being back in
touch with Lisa and her mother after Pharaoh was free.
Time and time again, throughout Pharaoh's life, he would
continue to carry this grief of disappointment for his lack
of communication with Lisa and her mother. In not keeping his promise to his brother, whom he loved with all his
heart. Pharaoh lost the beauty of being a part of his niece's
and her children's and children's lives. {Pharaoh, thinking
back to when first Pharaoh did accept the job of working

for (123) Since Pharaoh had taken the job working for Maria's father in law (123), Pharaoh and Maria's relationship had changed quite drastically. They both cared for one another very much so, but it was like they were now on two different missions. Maria was into Christianity while even though Pharaoh still loved and worshipped God and Jesus the Son of God, Pharaoh seemed very much interested in the activities of the world and trying hard to please (123). (123) was the prince of darkness, the number one slave. While Pharaoh seemed to be growing further and further away from God, Maria seemed to be growing ever more and more close to God and the study of Christianity. It was late in the midnight hour when Pharaoh was coming in from Robinson's crap house. A place that Pharaoh loved to be a part of and enjoy the action of gambling with the best of West Baltimore's most prominent of the "Who is Who" of the Pennsylvania Ave business owners. When on his way up the steps to his room Mama Grace quietly said "Good morning" to Pharaoh, and she smiled at him. She quietly said to him once again," It is impossible to serve two masters, for you will spite one to give to the other. But even though Pharaoh never wholly understood the parable because Pharaoh could think of no one he loved more than God. Even though Pharaoh showed that he loved money and the worldly life more than God, Pharaoh did not mean to do so. He was beginning to do just that. Now Maria and Pharaoh still studied the Bible together, and Pharaoh still told Maria Bible stories which Maria loved to hear from Pharaoh. Maria had never asked Pharaoh any biblical questions or questions related to God that Pharaoh couldn't answer, so it was surprising when Maria called Pharaoh one early morning about 5:30 am. She asked Pharaoh if the black slaves brought from Africa adopted the white American belief in Christianity for their religion. They named their little black babies all the Christian biblical names like Mary, John, Peter, Sarah, Phillip, Moses, Peter, Ester, etc. Would the black slaves have been Muslims and named their children after African culture and African names? With names in the holy Quran, if the black slaves of America would not have been taken from their homeland of Africa? This was a difficult question for Pharaoh because the Holy Bible that Americans read from has most of the same characters that the Muslims Holy Quran have with the same names. The characters' names are pronounced differently, even though they say or mean the same word but only in a different language. The Holy Bible says that one particular character did or said something, while the Quran says that a different character did the same thing. The Holy Bible and the Holy Quran both tell the same story and have the same characters, but the two Holy books differ on the character's name that performed the deeds. So the two Holy Books used the same characters but let different representations of the same characters perform the same acts. {So, believe the author of this book}

Pharaoh was indeed happy that Maria had turned out to be such a scholar at becoming so interested in Christianity, the Lord God Almighty, and His Son Jesus Christ. There was still a great amount of love in Pharaoh's heart for Maria, but the love for Maria was different now. It was not like lust or a person's outer beauty, but it was a love guided by respect, understanding, strength, and faith mixed. Most of all. Maria and Pharaoh's relationship was built on trust in each other for who and what they both were. And the faith they both had in God Almighty, Jesus Christ, and their faith in the religion of Christianity. Maria never spoke of her feelings toward Pharaoh working for her father-in-law (123). She let Pharaoh know with her eyes and avoided the subject always of Pharaoh working with her father-in-law. Pharaoh had been working for (123) now for over a year. On a particular night in Baltimore on 25th St. and Howard Street in East Baltimore, Pharaoh met (123) at a nice and popular restaurant, Wymond Parker of Maryland. He was to give (123) a lot of money that Pharaoh had in his possession that belonged to (123). At the same time, they both could enjoy a good and filling meal. This was the second time that Pharaoh and (123) had met at this restaurant and eaten. (123) did very much enjoy the food there, but most of all, he enjoyed not being known like he was known in Baltimore like he was in New York, Washington, California, Miami, and many other places. He was a known target for being a very influential, powerful man who could bring down great establishments in those places. Or he could build up little nothings to become a powerful business if he chose to do so. Now Pharaoh was sitting in his car in front of the restaurant. Waiting for (123) to arrive so they both could enter simultaneously. Suddenly, Pharaoh noticed that (123) was sitting across the street from an Oldsmobile car dealership. In the showroom window sat a 1968 convertible top-of-the-line ninety-eight Oldsmobile that Pharaoh had to go and look at, feel, touch, and inquire about. Pharaoh got out of his car to cross the street and look at this ninety-eight Oldsmobile. What caught his eye first was that the antennae was operated inside the car to make the antennae go up and down. This car had an FM radio station and an AM station and while the average car only had am stations. Pharaoh had seen only a few cars with an FM Station and an am station, which was the station that the whole city was listening to. More at least the east, west, and south parts of town listened to the AM radio station. The car even had a big comfortable armrest In the middle of the front seat to rest your arm while driving along, with wooden paneling inside. It had push button seats to move up and down, forward and backward which was unheard of at that particular day and time, while the outer body of the car was blood red with a white convertible top and all-white leather inside. Now, it was sixty days later when Pharaoh was called to meet (123) at the corner of 25th Street and Howard Street in East Baltimore to pick up a package that was unbeknownst to Pharaoh. Pharaoh respected him because he knew that he and (123) had met before and had even had lunch, breakfast, and dinner There before at different times, so Pharaoh started on his journey to meet (123). There at a time that only the two would know according to what time it was in the day, evening, or night. That the message was received. The next morning, Pharaoh reached the restaurant on 25thand Howard Street in East Baltimore in front of the Wymond Park Diner. After getting out of the car and entering the restaurant, Pharaoh noticed that the waitress that usually waits on him or takes his order smiled at him sort of unusual as she came closer to him to take his order for breakfast. Upon her arrival at his table, she told him that his breakfast had already been paid for regardless of what he ordered. She gave him a note and told him that he was supposed to take the note across the street to the Oldsmobile car dealership and pick up a package from Mister Abraham. Now, not being aware of any of this, Pharaoh was sort of confused about what to do, and he wondered if this package was drugs or money or whatever and who was Mr. Abraham? But Pharaoh did do as he was instructed to by taking the note across the street to the Oldsmobile car dealership. They had no knowledge of (123) or anything to do with any kind of illegal doings. Rather, they had just sold a car to a customer for cash and held the car for pick up by Pharaoh once he showed his ID and asked for Mr. Abraham, who was introduced to Pharaoh by another car dealership employee. Meeting Mr. Abraham, who shook Pharaoh's hand and smiled at Pharaoh as he handed Pharaoh a set of keys and told Pharaoh that he could drive the car off the showroom floor and exit the side entrance of the building. Tags and titles were both handed to Pharaoh, and the car was all registered to Pharaoh in his name. Pharaoh was overjoyed concerning the purchase and gift of the car; still, something seemed missing or out of place. It did not make sense because Pharaoh knew that (123) did not like him. A few hours later, it was only a few hours later that (123) called Pharaoh at his home and thanked him for saving his life during a robbery in which (123) was mistaken for a mark, which a hit was out on. (123) could have possibly killed the two hitmen that threatened (123)'s life with his high advancement of self-defense and life-taking expertise as opposed to the amateur hitman qualifications. The two hitmen whom Pharaoh knew personally and had immediately recognized both walked up to (123)'s car door and opened it with their guns drawn as one entered the back door. One entered the front seat while Pharaoh came running and screaming down the street to the two hitmen saying, "No, No, that's my blood, and my friend, you have made a big mistake." Pharaoh jumped on top of the car's hood, calling the two hitmen by their names. "That's my blood! That's my blood!"

At the same time, a black Lincoln Continental limousine pulled up across the street with the original marks inside, Which the two amateur assassins did kill immediately. After nodding their heads and hunching their shoulders to Pharaoh, to show they acknowledged their mistake. And to say, "I'm sorry...what the fuck... shit happens. Were The last words uttered from the mouth of one of the hitmen? Before they both jumped into the car that immediately pulled up for them to get into. And in a New York second was gone like the wind? Now, (123) was not known to everyone. But, many people had heard of him because of the supernatural authority that being a part of (Satan) gave him. He had the authority, knowledge, and expertise to do what was not heard of being done by a lone human being. But because (Satan) was behind and with (123) in everything he did, and especially wrong and evil things that were done by (123) to so many people who had done no wrong to him. (123) was a bragger of the things that he could do. And a bragger about the things that he had already done. (123) loved to brag about his power and authority over humanity upon the earth. While he bragged about the money that he could get any and every time he needed it or wanted it, he bragged to Pharaoh about the car he had just given him. Then Pharaoh understood and realized what Mama Grace meant when she told Pharaoh that no man could serve two masters. Because he would spite one to satisfy the other, Pharaoh realized that his God did not want Pharaoh to take that car from (123), but Pharaoh loved the car and did not want to hurt (123)'s feelings by not taking the car. Pharaoh did realize that he was spiteing his God to satisfy the God of material things even though he knew that his God disapproved of Pharaoh taking the car from the god of material things, which in all reality was (Satan). He was not a god but at one time did have power and authority over some of God's angels. But Satan was kicked out of heaven by God.

(Satan) wanted to be worshiped like God was worshiped, and he had gotten some of the angels to follow him by misleading them. (Satan) Who was once a part of the heavens population, even then, he was not God because there is but one God besides God's only begotten Son who also is God.

Pharaoh did accept the car, and Pharaoh did like the car very, very much. Pharaoh also realized that he was not pleasing God by taking the vehicle from (123), especially when Pharaoh found out that the car had a secret place for Pharaoh to hide his gun right in the driver's door of the vehicle. And another hiding place in the passenger's side of the door so Pharaoh could hide his eighth of heroin that Pharaoh still received every month from Maria. These things fascinated Pharaoh, especially the car and the hiding places in the car, while the new technology in the car was a dream for Pharaoh to be a part of and use. Now Pharaoh was turning his back on God to be so thrilled concerning these worldly things. Pharaoh's interest in worldly life and worldly activities was at the top of Pharaoh's priorities. Now Pharaoh did not thank God for the car. Pharaoh knew that God disapproved of Pharaoh accepting the vehicle. While Pharaoh took everything he ever received to God first, to give thanks upon all things he received, even worldly accomplishments that brought Pharaoh beneficial endings and positive learnings were brought to Pharaoh's God as thanking him for that privilege. Even a crust of bread had to be given thanks to God before being eaten by Pharaoh so that Pharaoh was letting God know that everything he received was in any way good.

Then Pharaoh wanted God to know that he thanked him for it and knew that it came from God and not himself or (Satan). No one nowhere can give the gifts of need and lifelike God can, while forgetting none and serving all who cries out to him. Even those who cry out or speak not, but whose trials and tribulations cry out to a God known to be the only one for the sure healing process. In one way or another, while always knowing best to present himself at the right time and never being late or early but always at the perfect time.

Now Pharaoh's friends and even his neighborhood loved Pharaoh's new blood red car with its convertible white top and pure white all leather seats, and with its push-button windows, locks, AM and FM radio. Its eight-track tape system, push-button seats, and comfortable armrest in the middle of the front seat. It put a shame on the older cars of that day and time that did not have any of the Pharaoh's car's features—not even counting Pharaoh's hiding places built into the driver's door and the passenger's door, for his gun and the narcotics. The car's antenna that raised from the inside anytime Pharaoh wanted to extend it for purposes of being able to bring in remote radio stations to be heard clearly by simply pushing a button.

It was early 1969, and the Vietnam War was still in full blast, and the young American soldiers, both black and white, along with other nationalities, cultures, and religions. All being Americans of which America was built upon. From present-day Americans' great grandmothers and great grandfathers, who were once immigrants from other countries. They dedicated their all to becoming Children of Jourmajesty. They carried the weight of being the backbone of America; now, their children who were born here in America, and were the first real Americans besides the American Indians, were the first authentic and original Americans. They were returning home from the Vietnam War with half their bodies missing and their brains burnt out. This was because of the terribleness that they had encountered and seen during this so uncalled-for war, which was the start of our communities and neighborhoods becoming ghettos and our children, young men, and women becoming junkies. Homeless people became a reality in the vacant buildings, leaving the areas an eyesore. Those who then gazed upon it without knowing it was meaningful and once home for the surrounding communities before drugs.

(Satan) took God out of our schools and stole love, unity, togetherness, faith from ourselves and our communities while selling our souls for the choice of drugs that one desired the most.

Now, it was not long before the time came for Pharaoh to go to New York to once again get his big eighth of heroin from none other than Maria. Though Pharaoh and Maria weren't being intimate, it was a fact that they both felt the very same way towards each other as their first love started.

They were more intelligent than to let their feelings for one another be seen or thought about by others. They both knew that their lives depended upon their intelligence concerning their relationship and their love for one another.

The faith, worship, and praise they both shared in worshiping Almighty God. Sometimes together, and sometimes apart, but always they both worshiped God. Mama Grace and Maria were both telling Pharaoh and trying to show Pharaoh that he was becoming more and more interested in the worldly life of drugs, women, and money. Then he was interested in his children and the God he showed one time that he loved and worshiped. He included his God in all the things he did.

No evil was in Pharaoh's heart. Even in the worldly things that Pharaoh did, he always found a way by doing them outside in the open where his soul was free to explain to God his true intentions. His joy was always helping those who needed help as he talked and taught about his God, whom he loved and worshiped so much. As Mama Grace and Maria both tried to show him, his focus now was on worldly things and people more than on his God.

Even though his activities were always on the street, his accomplishments, even on the street, were taken to God in thanks and appreciation that he was safe. Understanding that once again, his God was there for him, blessing him and protecting him, even as he performed in the world and joined in with worldly people, doing material things. Even then, Pharaoh's heart and soul were pumping for the pleasure of performing for God and his teachings of the Word of God. Pharaoh's enjoyment now was his shiny new car and entitlement to the funds he now made with (123). Not to mention the street fame that was becoming and meant a great deal to Pharaoh, instead of giving credit to all Pharaoh's accomplishments to Almighty God as he had always done. He was always the first to give all credit of all his achievements to God Almighty, but now Pharaoh seemed to wallow in the glory that he was all that he wasn't.

Pharaoh's every night's closing activity was always the same: gambling at Mr. Robinson's crap house where the thrills for gamblers were always and forever to be at its best. The thrills and enjoyment of this so addictive game were beyond all that its players and participants could ever imagine it could be. Even though they had no clue how bad off their addiction to this gambling or how little control they had over how much money they could lose or win before quitting that night's episode.

Now, it was one of those nights that Pharaoh was leaving the crap house and had won forty-two hundred dollars and decided to go to New York to purchase heroin. It was the first time that he would take his shiny new car on the New Jersey Turnpike on his way to New York, but he first had to get someone to drive for him because he knew that he could not go to New York after gambling all night. He was tired and sleepy as tired and weary could be. It was a fact that {Star} didn't drive and was more of a housewife scenario than anything, but raising her sons was the only real life that she was interested in, and of course, satisfying Pharaoh at all and any cost. In contrast, Pharaoh did not look at her as a street woman or a female of the world. Still, instead, Pharaoh knew that taking Star to the movies, taking her out to eat breakfast, lunch, or dinner, and to some occasional out-of-town activities were a world of happiness for her, and she asked for no more. When Pharaoh would keep a hotel room over from when he had conducted business for (123), all the kids, Star, and Pharaoh would all stay in an expensive hotel for days watching videos that hotels had but had not become mainstream for the public.

Chapter 8

Speed, Cigarettes, Alcohol and God's Blessing

Now it wasn't hard for Pharaoh to get one of his female friends to drive him to New York. So many females would be glad to just take a trip to New York and see and feel the city's heartbeat. Come back home and tell their friends that they had been to New York and just because Pharaoh would choose a female to go with him didn't mean that he would be intimate with her, but even Pharaoh had many female friends, he only had a few male friends and a lot of male associates. Pharaoh never let anyone know what he was going to New York for besides to have a little fun, but he never spoke or talked to anyone about drugs being a reason for him to go to New York. It was after 4 am when Pharaoh was coming down North Avenue from West Baltimore, going home to East Baltimore when he was passing {L&N}. It was a famous after hour eating place in the city to eat if you considered yourself *somebody Special* and wanted to be around other people *special* or people that mattered concerning the nightlife scene. Pharaoh gazed upon {Katie}, who was a barmaid at Steve's Cocktail Lounge, which was Pharaoh's most favorite place that Pharaoh leisurely hung out. Where Mr. Torrain, who was one of the most significant number backers in the whole city, ran his nightclub and loved Pharaoh dearly. He also owned the pool room upstairs, where Pharaoh entertained his gambling buddies and directed the daily crap games. Pulling over to the curb and also blowing his horn, letting down his window, Pharaoh called to Katie, and as she came over to the car, the first thing said out her mouth was "MY, MY, MY. You certainly have a nice car."

Now Katie was a young school teacher from Ohio who came down to Baltimore occasionally to spend time with her father, who was a professor at {Morgan State University}. Katie and Pharaoh always had a little fling, so I thought everyone knew that. Still, this time Katie had come to stay awhile, and each time she came to Baltimore, she came straight to Pharaoh to let him know that she was in the city. As Katie got closer to the car, Pharaoh saw that she had been crying, and she explained to Pharaoh that her car wouldn't start.

"Leave it!" Pharaoh was yelling to Katie, "Come back and get it tomorrow. Come ride with me, and I will bring you home later today or maybe even tomorrow, but I will not keep you forever, and I will be taking care of you.

It was the fall of the year in 1969 that Pharaoh could pay less than twenty dollars to fill his nineteen sixty-eight, ninety-eight Oldsmobile full of gas, and it was then that Pharaoh told Katie to get in the driver's seat and drive on to New York. The smile on Katie's face told the story of how happy she was to be going to New York. Still, Katie asked Pharaoh if she could stop in the liquor store and get a pack of cigarettes, and while Pharaoh offered to get out and get the cigarettes, Katie refused.

Katie told Pharaoh that he was doing enough by letting her drive to New York and that he was exhausted, and all Pharaoh had to do was lay back and enjoy the ride. Sleep was beginning to fall upon Pharaoh as he tried to keep his eyes open, but it seemed as if his body knew that he had been relieved of the tremendous pressure of having to stay awake. Now that Katie was there, Pharaoh remembered seeing Katie come out of the liquor store, and he remembered thinking, why did she have a big bag for a pack of cigarettes? But that was Pharaoh's last thought as he pushed the button and laid the chair back to a comfortable position that suited him. Pharaoh's eyes were closing as he watched the white marble steps passed on Orleans Street that took Katie to 95 north, leading to the New Jersey Turnpike and straight into New York. Then, Pharaoh lifted his head and told Katie, don't be afraid, get in her left lane, and drive. Even though the speed limit was 65 miles an hour, it was alright to go 80 and 85 miles an hour.

There were no cars out there on the highway at that time of the morning, except for trucks and the state troopers, which didn't bother you too much. Katie then reassured Pharaoh that she was an excellent driver that rode the highways and byways going back and forward to Baltimore from Ohio, and Pharaoh could just lay back, get some sleep, and leave the driving to her. Of course, Pharaoh had been telling Katie about his God, but Katie was not interested in that conversation and said that God had not heard her prayers when she had begged Him for her grandmother to get well from constant pain and suffering. She had been witnessing her grandmother suffering for years, but God had deceived her by not letting her grandmother get well and had let her die. Katie explained to Pharaoh that she did not want to talk about God and told Pharaoh that God is not with you when times get hard, and you beg for his help and presence in your life and when you need God. He won't be there for you, but God would forsake you. "Have you ever been, really, down with hard times kicking your ass? Or have You ever needed or wanted God so very, very bad while going through monstrous times concerning sickness, death, confusion, physical, or even some form of mental sickness? Lying on your deathbed or watching someone you love lying on their deathbed, and God showed up to give aid? Then and only then can you tell me about God, and what He will do for you or what He will do to help you or bring you through all that is of trouble and disaster to you." After thinking about the questions, Katie had asked him, shaking his head no while trying to put himself in that situation of needing God that bad and asking and begging for God's help and being turned down had not yet ever happened to Pharaoh. God had always been there for Pharaoh every time Pharaoh had asked God for help or just downright guidance through different situations and stressful times. Pharaoh had not been tested for his loyalty, trust, and faith in God. God has always been right there to answer, protect, and guide Pharaoh through all his immature fears, troubles, and minor occurrences of trust and faith in his God. But there were times in Pharaoh's life where he would bear witness to God's ever-loving and forgiving companionship without end or tiring. Pharaoh's nineteen sixty-eight, ninety-eight Oldsmobile gave a luxurious, comfortable, and smooth ride as it quickly sped up to sixty-five, then seventy, seventy-five,

And eighty as it glided over the highway of 95 North New York-bound highway.

As Pharaoh closed his eyes to give rest to his body, soul, and his mind, he then saw his brother {Jonny} coming towards him {in a dream} with a hooded jacket that covered his head and half his face. "Why are you wearing a hood?" Pharaoh asked his brother Jonny, {in Pharaoh's dream} who answered, "We all wear hoods to hide our faces while we do the work of Satan. Satan is why all the buildings are boarded up and vacant. And drug use has taken over our cities in America, which has brought violence, murder, and unconcern about all our people concerning one another. Who are those little girls standing over there in the corner by the vacant building?"

Pharaoh asked his brother, Jonny (while still in Pharaoh's dream). They are the little girls taught to think that they are grown women because they have bodies like full-grown women.

"To supply sexual favors for the men that supply them with drugs, money, tennis shoes, clothes, and even needs for their children."

"Though they are but babies with babies, when they are supposed to still be in school. But the school system itself has failed the young girls and boys of our cities by closing up or shutting down because of the misuse of the funds dedicated to the school's system.

"Everyone is blaming each other but overlooking the real reason, which is Satan being the real cause of all the negativity done to the school system. And the backwardness being done to our children to keep them out of school. And to take God out of their lives, by separating the youth from the elders."

"Which, the elders are living in senior citizen buildings so the old that loves the Lord cannot testify, they cannot teach the young the Word of God, and the young without guidance from the elders start to believe that wrong is right after following in the footsteps of Satan."

"Doing the will of Satan and being taught that wrong is the right way because of the negative rewards are given by Satan to those who know not right and that the rewards are sinful and evil."

"Where is Mama Jonny?" Pharaoh asked. After a some-what pause, Pharaoh's brother answered.

"Mama died a long time ago before the neighborhood was destroyed by drugs, murder, and people without honorable intentions. But with devilish deeds and Satan's leadership, has turned our whole country upside downwards."

"God in the lives of a lot of people are but a lost cause and without God in our lives or God's Word not being taught to our children brings on confusion and lost souls in a sea of damnation. There is "Righteousness in *America*."

America has not been noted for worshiping substitute gods and other fake gods like so many other countries have. For there is but one God besides Jesus Christ, who is the Son of God."

"To all my knowledge found about the early original American Indians. They have always mainly been known to worship the Creator of life and death who resides in the heavens above.

"Who is the creator of the wind, rain, snow, mountains, trees, and so many, many, other fantastic and unbelievable creations of Almighty God. Such as the moon, the sun, summer, winter, spring, and fall, while let's not forget that God Almighty is also the Creator of man, woman, and both life and death."

"We are only juices of our parent's bodies. We have turned into sperm from their bodies to become living people that will grow into adult humans. Almighty God has given us all a certain date to come to the planet earth. He has also given us a certain time to leave the planet earth.

{Pharaoh's brother was still talking to Pharaoh in the dream} "The work of Satan has made some image shadows of evil that shows Satan has been trying to take over America for centuries. However, he has not yet found a way to bring America down to its knees in evilness.

"And yes, there is *Something About America.* Which is that righteousness is in America. "

"Since the Stone Age, Satan has been watching America. Satan has been watching even during the time of the American Indian."

"In the recent years compared to the past years, one can tell that some sort of dent has been made to bring evil to America through Satan's great efforts. There is but little progress made through the centuries, with much of Satan's evilness being overturned. There is still some lasting progress made." "Yes, there has been some progress made to hurt America by bringing evilness to America in the last four centuries much more than ever before, but in the previous seventy years, much progress has been made in America through (righteousness) to undo a lot of evilness that was done to America

It was then that the car swerved. Pharaoh was immediately up and aware of what was going on, and Katie assured Pharaoh that all was well and that she had everything under control.

"Thank God," Pharaoh said sort of quietly, but Pharaoh's words were heard by Katie, who responded by saying, "God is never there when you need him, and he is not reliable. So one day, you too will bear witness."

Pharaoh had laid back down in a comfortable position as he quietly and silently asked God to forgive Katie for her unfaithfulness and disbelief towards Him. Pharaoh reassured God that he would never doubt Him.

Even after forty years of trouble and problems, "I still will never doubt you, Father, because I know that you will still be there with me. Nothing could happen in my life to make me believe, not in you, God. I will always and forever trust and believe in you, Father," was the words of Pharaoh before he laid back down in a comfortable position, in the front seat of the 1968 ninety-eight Oldsmobile, with Katie as the driver.

Almost immediately, Pharaoh went back to the dream that he was having about his brother Jonny. The dream took him and Jonny to a very narrow hallway that was very slippery to walk down. It kept them both sliding from one side of the hallway to the other side. But as long as they kept their hands on the wall, then they would not slide from one side to the other, but they would stay stationary to one side of the hall.

"Why is this hall so slippery, and why do we keep sliding from one side to the other" Pharaoh asked his brother Jonny in the dream.

"The halls are the paths of Satan in which you will have to walk down while you hold onto the wall. Which symbolizes faith, faith in your God as He unbeknownst to you constantly protects you and carries you when you become too weak to continue on in your extreme effort to not give in to Satan."

"Even though God has willed you to let Satan take you through some of his travels in trying to win you over to him completely by interesting you into some sinful situations. Situations that will prove fun and exciting to you but are dreadfully sinful. And for two decades, you shall be faced with this monstrous thing that you will describe as *The best worst thing that ever happened to you.*"

"Why should I have to be a part of this for two decades? Why so long?"

"Because you vowed to not give up your faith and trust in God for forty years, so said you in your vows. In not giving up the sanctuary, trust, and faith in your God, the time will pass so fast, and you shall make plenty of advancement. You shall accomplish a lot while continuing with your normal lifestyle."

"Most of all, everything that you do and accomplish, besides what God will give you while protecting you, will be but bait to hide the real purpose and outcome, which is trying to be made of you from Satan, who knows that God is with you. Satan hates you because he knows that God loves you."

"God remembers your prayer to him as a little boy sitting on the church bench when you were so small that your feet could not reach the floor from the church bench. Public school, you were not of age to attend yet, but poured out your heart to God in trust, faith, and love, and asked God to come and go with you throughout the rest of your life."

"God has been with you not just from that day to this day, but God was with you before you came on the planet. He protected you from the things your mother put in her body to rid herself of you trying to hide her sinful actions of adultery."

"The two decades will pass so fast while Satan tempts you to become one of his many followers. They are tricked and fooled by Satan's lies, promises, and ways of presenting a situation to look good and tempting. Only it is dreadfully sinful, bad, and disgusting."

"During your two decades, Satan will keep tempting you to become one of his many lost souls. So your nights will be short, long will be the days that you will mostly spend sleeping."

"The entire outcome of the whole two-decade ordeal will be judged by the outcome and severity of the car accident in which you will be involved when you wake from this dream."

While Pharaoh was having this dream, he continuously kept hearing this siren interrupting his dream. Pharaoh kept ignoring the siren noise, throwing the noise out of his mind and continued with his dream.

Until the car just missed hitting a tree. Pharaoh opened his eyes, and that's when Pharaoh saw all these trees coming right at him! It was as if the trees were all running towards him. By a miracle or rather, the will of God, the car seemed to have eyes of its own because the car did not hit one tree as the car had gone off the highway and into a wooded area with nothing in it but trees, traveling through the trees, the car did not hit any and came to rest on a downhill slope. It rested with the car hanging or instead dangling off an embankment. Pharaoh awoke and said to Katie, "What happened? Are you alright?"

By this time, people were coming through the thick of trees, trying to find out how bad anyone was hurt. Was it anything anyone could do to help the survivors in the two cars that had run into each other and, how bad was anyone hurt?

Before Pharaoh and Katie exited the car, Pharaoh asked Katie to explain to him what had just happened. Whether or not she was right or wrong in the cause of the accident. These are the questions that Pharaoh asked Katie as they both were exiting the car hanging over the barrier.

Before Katie could even answer, a State Trooper was just reaching the car as another trooper came running down through the wooded area to meet them.

The State Trooper heard Pharaoh ask Katie what had happened. Before Katie could answer, the state trooper responded to the question saying, "I have been chasing this lady that was driving this car for the last twelve minutes with my siren on and my red and blue lights just flashing. Katie was clocked at traveling 105 miles an hour. She ran in the back of the car in front of her who was slowing down because of my siren, and my blue and red flashing lights.

Then, Katie looked at Pharaoh and said, "Fuck the Trooper Pharaoh He's lying!"

She stumbled up the hill and through the wooded area leading back to the highway. Then Pharaoh put together Katie's slurred speech and the empty fifth liquor bottle that the state trooper held up. The trooper had taken it off the floor of the driver's side of the car. Katie was pickle pissy drunk!

After locking Katie and Pharaoh up, it was found that Katie had a history of drunk driving. She was not supposed to be driving because her license was suspended. The courts in New Jersey, where they had an accident, held her without bond until she had had a court hearing.

Katie's father would also have to appear with her because she was released to and in the custody of the last three times of this same offense. It had been determined that whenever alcohol entered Katie's system, the alcohol changed Katie's brain and the mental state that made her "not responsible" for her actions.

Nor would she remember anything that she did while she was intoxicated. She would deny all actions charged to her believing that people were lying to her.

Pharaoh was released with the understanding that he had to come back to court on the trial date. Pharaoh was charged with allowing Katie to drive with such a problem and the courts decided that it was Pharaoh's fault somewhat, that he couldn't have been in the car with Katie that long from Baltimore to New York without knowing that Katie was drinking.

Even if Pharaoh just had smelled the alcohol, he had to know that Katie was drinking alcohol at some particular time. Pharaoh was heavily fined, and his case was then pending

As Pharaoh left the courtroom, he did not see Katie or her father. It was because Katie was ashamed of all the trouble she had caused Pharaoh. She had utterly totaled the 1968 Oldsmobile with all its extras. With all of its comforts.

The state trooper at the accident and chased Katie stopped Pharaoh in the hallway. He told Pharaoh that he had never seen an accident that bad where both cars were totaled, but no one was hurt. The trooper also said that he knew that whoever Pharaoh was, that it was a *fact* that God was with him that night of the accident.

The trooper then asked Pharaoh if he was hurt in any way, and Pharaoh answered and said that his new diamond ring had cut or instead scratched his index finger.

The trooper just dropped his head and said, "Unbelievable! So the sum of this whole accident was that you scratched your index finger with a new diamond ring you were wearing. And that's the sum of this so terrible accident."

Early in the morning, Mama Grace woke Pharaoh up and told him she sent Maria to his room. Pharaoh could not believe his ears because Mama Grace was a Christian woman, and she didn't believe in letting women go up to Pharaoh's room unless she was not aware of it.

Mama Grace trusted Maria, and Mama Grace knew that Maria knew Mama Grace was a Christian woman and wouldn't commit open sin in Mama Grace's house by being sexual towards Pharaoh in any way. Maria hurried up the stairs to Pharaoh's room, where Pharaoh stood in the doorway waiting for Maria. Upon entering his room, she said to Pharaoh, "Something's wrong, Pharaoh! Something's wrong! YaYa is in hiding, and no one can find him. He has been disloyal to my father-in-law, which puts disrespect, humiliation, and death on Yaya's family! Including their pet dog, goat, rodents, bugs, or insects found refuge in their homes. How could YaYa allow this to happen? What has happened to YaYa, and why is this happening to YaYa?"

Now Pharaoh felt as though he knew most of Maria's questions about YaYa. Even though Pharaoh would be just guessing, he remembered something YaYa had said to him. He said that Stokes' mother was as small as a doll baby, but her faith was strong and significant as a mountain. He said that he would protect her from harm and any force against her. That her God was now also his God

Stokes' mother told Pharaoh that she saw YaYa as a tower of pure muscle and blunt force. While Stokes' mother had only had sex once in her life, YaYa had *never* had sex in his life. God did let them both meet and enjoy one another's company in a very unusual way that they both did become attracted and companions to one another.

While the whole world looked on by paying them no mind, God blessed their relationship towards one another. It was a day that made up for a year for them both in happiness, peace, and love.

God did bless them with an infant baby boy to share, love, and have, to the end of both their lives in secrecy and devotion. They were devoted to their threesome in secrecy, love, companionship, the three of them together in unity. Until the end of each of their lives, in remembrance of one another. They were broken apart by no one, or nothing, or anything while worshiping God and the Son of God. Forgiving such a gift to the threesome as only God could give to an unusual Christian couple. A couple truly believed, trusted, and had faith in Almighty God.

Now to explain the situation, cause, and actual happenings of the events of Yaya's whole family's assassination thoroughly.

It all started when YaYa conversed with Pharaoh and asked Pharaoh to kill (123) for 500 thousand dollars. Being that Pharaoh was in the position to be in the house with (123). while dating and having a relationship with Maria.

Even though (123) might not know of Pharaoh being in the house, Pharaoh did turn down the offer of killing (123) for 500 thousand dollars. Though Pharaoh was allowed to keep his life also because of Stokes' mother, who had a secret relationship with YaYa, she taught YaYa of her God and the Son of God.

Stokes' mother did beg for the life of Pharaoh not to be taken by YaYa. To trust Pharaoh to hold forever the secret concerning the offer Pharaoh had refused about killing (123).

More than six years later, that (123) did hear that conversation while sitting in Maria's limousine. There YaYa did ask Pharaoh to kill (123). But unknowing to everybody and anybody, the tape player in the limousine was on and recorded the whole conversation of YaYa asking Pharaoh to kill (123) for 500 thousand dollars.

The limousine had been in the garage for over six years due to some major faults, which caused Maria's father-in-law to get a new limousine and not use the old one for over six years.

After hearing the tape, Maria's father-in-law investigated the situation concerning Yaya's loyalty. He found out that YaYa even had a woman that he was seeing. That is why Maria's father-in-law assassinated YaYa, the Assassinator.

True it was that nothing could have stopped the mighty hand of destruction that came down upon the family of YaYa for his disloyalty. True it came to be that Yaya's whole family was destroyed, counting his brothers, sisters, mother, and father.

Even though YaYa was never allowed to meet his parents. Nor his cousins, aunts, uncles, or any of his family members. True it was that they all knew him. True, even their pet goat and dog were also killed. And their three houses all burnt to the ground. The rodents and insects living in the three houses also died.

The three houses that belonged to Yaya's family were burnt down and were replaced with a barn that sold hay or rather horseshit. It was all so odd because, through the passing years, YaYa's family had begun to see YaYa as a prisoner to (123) instead of a loyal and loving servant.

His family knew that Yaya's life had been taken away from him so that his family could enjoy the riches in life in their country. While YaYa had not once felt the feeling of love, passion, or sexual satisfaction for YaYa was as a slave to (123) from the time he was born to the time surpassingly to the day of his death, even never having a childhood.

Yaya's family saw him differently. They saw YaYa as a hero. He is full of strength and loyalty to his family and people but not to (123). YaYa looked forward to the day that he might become free of his slavery (123) when he could enjoy even the simple things of life like love and happiness, peace, and the art of growing old and having children.

When the time of death came for Yaya's family, they all accepted the conclusion and hailed YaYa as a hero to his family. Forgiving all his life to slavery to (123) so his family could live in luxury, peace, and freedom while living the lives of celebrities and royalty.

YaYa was taken from his parents and family when weaned from his mother's breast. So that YaYa shows no love or concern for no one. Even though this was cruel, it was the way of their country. So some say and believe that that is the same way that (123) was introduced to (Satan) that started (123)'s slavery to (Satan).

It happens that when YaYa met Stokes' mother, the day that she first put her mouth upon the private area of YaYa, that he gave his soul to Stokes' mother. For such a wonderfully warm and sloppy wet feeling that he had never before felt. He did confide in her and told her things about his life that no one else knew. Stokes' mother also confided in YaYa and told him something about her life that no one could ever imagine.

And because YaYa did know his family's name and passed that knowledge to Stokes' mother.

Stokes' mother began a secret writing pattern to Yaya's mother and family. The first letter to Yaya's mother was delivered and accepted. YaYa also wrote one letter to his mother using the code that Stokes' mother had developed.

YaYa explained the goodness and righteousness in Stokes' mother he had never before known because his life was full of death and destruction. YaYa also told his mother of this wonderful, powerful, and righteous God that Stokes' mother worshiped.

He, too, now believed in this great God that lived in the sky in a kingdom unseen by man. That this God had provided him with a happiness that he was afraid to tell anyone about, this God had shown him the meaning of mercy, love, and obedience far above the loyalty and obedience he was taught to give to (123

Now both YaYa and his family knew that it was taboo for them to communicate, so only two letters were written to Yaya's family from YaYa, in Yaya's second and last letter to his mother and family. YaYa told his mother how Stokes' mother had taught him to pray. It is so easy to pray because you have to believe in God. Talk to him like you are talking to someone that knows all your secrets. Come to Him with your heart and soul through the words you speak to Him, and He will most definitely hear your prayer.

He will give you comfort even if you don't see it right away, and His way is the best way and the only way. In Yaya's mother's second and final letter to YaYa, she told YaYa that she too had heard of this great God, and she didn't know whether to believe in him or not. This God was the correspondent between YaYa, Stokes' mother, and herself, which was enough to make her get the entire family together.

While they all held hands, she asked this great God to please hear her prayer and continue giving her son peace and happiness. Yaya's mother called out His name as she said, "I THANK YOU Almighty GOD, and so what I have heard of you and your greatness be true, and I pray this prayer in hopes that you will forgive my family and me for our faults and injustices. While you will remember us all when the time comes for us to pay our debts."

One year later, the wind blew the hay outside the barn that used to be the direct spot that the three houses of Yaya's family in his country occupied as their homes.

It was turned into a large barn after Yaya's entire family was murdered. For Yaya's seek and find a role that YaYa played in giving peace and love to himself at the expense of his whole family's head.

YaYa had not been seen for over a year, and Yaya's whereabouts were vacant in the minds of all but one, which was Stokes' mother's twin sister.

Who was hiding YaYa with the son of YaYa, whom many, many people were looking for? And all with malice in their hearts against YaYa? Who never came outside of the comfort zone of Stokes' mother's twin sister? That had provided for them while hiding right there under the noses of (123). Within twenty minutes, driving distance of each other even though the communities were different.

(123)'s search for YaYa did not include Yaya's son because (123) knew not of Yaya's son. Nor do they have (123) anywhere to look for YaYa except in their old country, where (123) believed YaYa would receive help, guidance, and aid. Or To escape to another surrounding country other than their own country.

For (123) even with all his power and glory, authority, and connections, had no room or authority, strength or say so in the field of good, righteousness, and love. Those forces (123) knew nothing off and had no power or authority. Because they were things of righteousness and goodness and truth, things created by God and things that represented God's goodness.

It was surprising when (123) came to Pharaoh and told Pharaoh that he knew about the killings of the Brothers Three. He knew who was responsible because Pharaoh was young and still able to learn. If Pharaoh were interested, (123) would like to offer him some parts of Yaya's job here in America. Since YaYa would no longer be able to carry out his duties for (123) never again.

True it was that Pharaoh had begun to be one that had proven himself to (123) as honorable, strong, dependable, wise, and intelligent. Once, (123) thought black people were lazy, stupid, unintelligent thieves. Pharaoh had shown (123) a different view of the black man and a different opinion about the black man's ways, habits, loyalty, and intelligence.

(123) had become to trust Pharaoh, believe in Pharaoh, and place a high value on Pharaoh as a trustworthy, intelligent black man with principal, honesty, and integrity. Most of all (123) saw Pharaoh as a leader and wanted Pharaoh on his team with a more high ranking position than Pharaoh had now.

(123) asked Pharaoh his opinion on giving his loyalty to (123) and about having a higher position. And what did Pharaoh think about YaYa's disloyalty to (123)?

Pharaoh did offend him with his answer by asking (123), would you like me to tell you the truth?" (123) you were wrong to have taken away all YaYa's privileges as a man and a human being by depriving YaYa of the feelings of sex, love, motivation, and self-esteem. The feelings of having a child, whether male or female. Most of all, taking away the privilege of having a mate, someone to talk to, be with, and love, was wrong. It had to come to a different conclusion, other than what had been expected. YaYa still loved you as he hoped for a way out of the life imprisonment that you had given him. YaYa himself didn't know how he disliked his life even at that particular time. He was too much trying to please you. And be the bodyguard to you that he was supposed to be, by the laws and bylaws of his country."

"And as he found out little by little how lonely and sad he was after starting to feel what God began to show him. He encountered situations that provided love, sorrow, peace, and care. YaYa ventured outside the box of the life of you. Which taking care of you was the only responsibility of Yaya's life."

"Get out of my sight!" screamed (123) to Pharaoh. "You have no idea what loyalty is to one that deserves it!"

"You are out of place by speaking on the ways and beliefs of my country and my people, so shut your mouth and be gone from my sight. "If I have offended you (123), and if that is what it took to make you see the truth, then God has blessed my intentions."

"Before I leave, I ask you only to put yourself in YaYa's situation for a lifetime and take away from yourself all the things that you have taken away from YaYa. Yaya never knew his mother, father, sister, or brother because of you. Nor how it feels to love anything or anyone. Do that to you, and tell me how you would feel."

Pharaoh was in a huge hurry to get away from (123) because fear had run through Pharaoh's heart for his life somewhat. Pharaoh quickly left the presence of (123) and the city.

Pharaoh was stopped at the corner of Ninth Avenue and 31ST Street while trying to leave New York by (123) himself. Who demanded that Pharaoh get out of his car and get in the limo with (123), which Pharaoh did.

Pharaoh sat in the limo with (123) and closed the limo door. Immediately (123) said, "You have no idea of my age. Because I'm not like you and can double your life expectancy with my life expectancy."

"Before me was my father, and before him was my grandfather. While we all have had the same goal, neither of us fulfilled this goal of holding back, abusing, misusing, and trying to destroy the Children of Jourmajesty, which are the people who see good in others. Who believes in justice, freedom, and love for all people regardless of color, race, culture, or religion, and who gives up their lives fighting for the rights of others? I must know, what is wrong with the people in America?"

"Pharaoh spoke quietly, trying not to upset (123), and answered and said, *"God is in America."* (123) said, "I have heard something like that before. And I have looked all over America! So where is this God?"

Pharaoh said, "God is in the hearts and souls of most of the American people."

(123) said, "I don't understand that, nor does it make any sense to me. I have been looking in trees and bushes and expecting to see a dead person sitting or standing

around. And now you tell me that this God is in the hearts, souls, and minds of people of America!"

Pharaoh said, "No, not just American people that believe in my God, but people all around the world who are of the Christian faith believe in my God, or the same God as I do because there is only one God, besides God's Son who is also God."

(123) said, "That is crazy and unbelievable, now you are telling me that this God that has given my family so much trouble for over two hundred years is in America, and is in the hearts, souls, and minds of people that believe in Him! AND has a Son that is also God?"

"Pharaoh! I called you back because you are different; you're intelligent, trustworthy, bold, and many other things. But I find now that your beliefs are foolish, impossible, and unimaginable to me. I just want you to immediately get away from me before I forget your good worth and demand your death which is in my power and authority any time I want, and your God has no said so concerning the matter."

Pharaoh loved Baltimore, and for him, there was no other city in the world like his home City of Baltimore. Every time Pharaoh returned to Baltimore from different cities, especially New York {which was a second home to Pharaoh} it was always a pleasure to be back home.

Even though some cities had a lot more to offer and were much more exciting, it was time to go home to Baltimore after a while.

Back in Baltimore, the Vietnam War had provided so much quality heroin that even poor people could become junkies. Homemakers were sneaking off getting high on heroin. It had become a problem for almost all the cities in the United States, especially some major cities like New York, Chicago, Boston, Baltimore, New Jersey, California, San Francisco, and Philadelphia.

It was hard for Pharaoh to adjust to the new coming drug users, the young men and women he had grown up with and knew all his life. Even the professional gamblers and bank robbers, pickpockets, and people of academic backgrounds and high potential educators, lawyers, and doctors were all using heroin whether they were injecting it with a needle or sniffing it up to their nose, for sure. Without a doubt, it was an epidemic, even if it had not yet gotten out of hand.

Shark Skin had gotten shot in the leg by one of the officers he had made fun of for having a cheap car, and a Ford was opposed to having a Cadillac. Sharkskin had gotten five years in prison. But within a year had made his way to a {Camp Center}, to get work release then, To be on his way home within another year. And Little Caesar had been harassed so severely by the new narcotic squad that had been put together. For the growing drug problems.

It seemed like everyone and their mother was now selling heroin because there were so many users. Which meant there was so much money to be made in the drug business.

The Feds had come down on Little Caesar and caught him with a machine gun. They had continuously locked up his dealers, and it cost ten times the usual amount to get them out of jail.

While Pharaoh's drug business was steady blooming, Pharaoh's gambling habits were costing him tens of thousands of dollars for the first time. Because losing was what Pharaoh was doing a lot of now, Maria didn't see Pharaoh like she used to. And Maria and Pharaoh's prayer sessions weren't so many now but now so few.

Pharaoh's year of 1969 had made him a lot of money even though he couldn't see it, for his gambling losses were significant. But, he had had a fantastic year being with the kids because Linda, Pharaoh's first child, was in grade school, and she was doing exceptionally well each year. Gerard, Pharaoh's second and oldest, started his first year in kindergarten. While Avis, the third oldest and baby boy, was to start school six months later. The youngest child, the baby girl, and her little sister were Pharaoh's baby girls with a beautiful young female who worked in an ice cream place where Pharaoh sometimes hung out.

After a few dates, he became quite fond of the young and delicate female. She told Pharaoh she was pregnant but that she could not have a baby because her mother would kill her, and so she was going to get rid of the baby. Pharaoh did not protest nor see her again for six months to find out that she was still pregnant and big as a house.

Now for whatever reason, the baby girl of Pharaoh's upcoming family of Gail Lee Gold, whose mother {Delores} had expressed to Pharaoh that she was now married, which made Pharaoh not be as close to this baby girl Gail Lee Gold as he should have been.

Even though Pharaoh's love for the baby girl was just as much as it was for the rest of his children

It would be well over twenty years before Pharaoh found out that Gail Lee Gold's mother wasn't married. She thought that Pharaoh did not want the child and that unknowing to Pharaoh, he had hurt Delores' heart. That is why Delores told Pharaoh that she was married. Besides having fun with the children, Pharaoh had met even another fine young lady that he admired more than anything or anyone.

After Pharaoh got her back in school, he dated her every day and night. {Paula} was her name, and she began to be Pharaoh's girl along with his sons {Tony} and {Gerard's} mother, who was his girl also. So those three had a threesome for many years.

While in college, Paula was at Pharaoh's house every day and every night until her uncle got off from work at the Baltimore Post Office at seven in the morning.

Pharaoh's life was especially good, rewarding, and filled with peace, love, devotion, and faithful in his worship to Almighty God. Pharaoh always wondered which one of the two women between Star, his son's mother, and Paula, whom everyone believed to be his heart, would Pharaoh end up with in life, or would they always be a threesome.

Pharaoh did not know that one of the two would betray him while the other would ask him to marry her immediately or leave their twenty-year relationship.

Christmas and New Year's were always the most challenging times for Pharaoh because both of his girls would put in their request to be with Pharaoh for the Christmas and New Year's holidays in June.

Pharaoh had to eat dinner with his mother in New York and Mama Grace in Baltimore. He had to stop by and kiss his grandmother. Both girls were his day, and both girls were his night. At the same time, one was his joy and the other his jewel. One would give her all, and the other would give everything she had.

Now Pharaoh would talk with both girls for hours, but their conversations would be about money, business, other multiple subjects, advancements in life, and the modern-day world. All its faults and its advantages.

On the other hand, the other would listen to conversations carefully because she had a speech problem, so she didn't talk much. She would always be able to build on whatever Pharaoh had said, and their conversations would last for hours. They would be about any and everything possible you could think of, including Almighty God and the subject of other religions. The holidays came and left each year, and Pharaoh made it through another year with the holiday. Satisfying and respecting two girlfriends, two mothers, and a grandmother with love, appreciation, and care.

The (123) Family was always steady at work. Building and doing whatever it took to be done to hold back, stagnate, cripple and try and break the spirit of the Children of Journajesty of that present generation, and the next two generations to come.

The (123) Family had already set the pace for the next two generations. Front-lined by the children of the Children of Journajesty, who dealt with negativity, led down a path of misguidance. It would lead to the destruction of the older Children of Journajesty. They dealt with so much negativity directed by the younger Children of Journajesty.

They were looking for advancement in life, even if it meant killing their kind in a race for material things.

Some of their senior citizens died in poverty, confusion, destruction, and the loss of themselves and their souls. They turned away from God and got caught in the trap (123) Family laid.

Trying hard to destroy the Children of Journajesty, some of the younger Children of Journajesty were turning their backs on the older or senior ones, and they had gone astray in the world of drugs and caring not for themselves. The younger Children of Journajesty, who had like some of the older, were the more foolish Children of Journajesty.

They followed the wrong path with selling and using drugs to maintain their material needs by selling drugs to their seniors after being put in a position to do those negative things. Using the (123) Family as a mechanism to help hold back, abuse, and misuse the Children of Journajesty.

They put God on the back burner of their lives because the older Children of Journajesty had taught the younger generation of the Children of Journajesty. They were sealed with faith in Almighty God as their proper way of life, and their secret source of power, authority, and their primary source of survival. They were now turning a deaf ear to the old way of life and their faith in God, while their righteousness seemed to be declining.

Now it was terrific when Maria called Pharaoh, who had just come home four-thirty in the morning from gambling at Robinson's crap house. It was not strange for Pharaoh to get calls this time of morning because everyone that knew Pharaoh knew that this was the time in which one could catch Pharaoh home, as long as he had not taken the phone off the hook

Pharaoh and Maria had distanced themselves somewhat even though they still stayed in touch.

Pharaoh was glorified to work with Maria's father-in-law, while Maria wanted only Pharaoh to discontinue his relationship with her father-in-law. Maria feared for the safety and wellbeing of Pharaoh and had continuous dreams of Pharaoh going to jail for working with her father-in-law.

When Pharaoh answered the phone and found out that it was Maria, his whole face lit up with a smile, and his heartbeat was not normal but happier.

Now Pharaoh and Maria still had lengthy conversations concerning God's word, which they both still loved to converse on, and it was then that Maria told Pharaoh that in the Bible. God told Samuel to tell the Israelite people that he would be their king, giving them an advantage over all people and armies of the entire universe, including planet earth. But the Israelites people told Samuel, who was the interpreter between God and the Israelites, that they wanted a man for their king. A man like the Egyptians had for a king, but then God told Samuel to tell the Israelite's that if they choose a man for a king, then they would have to sooner or later fight wars and send their men off to war. And hundreds of thousands of their people would die on the battlefield, but the Israelites still preferred to have a man as their king other than God Almighty being their king.

"Is this true, Pharaoh?"

After pausing for a moment then Pharaoh answered, "Yes, it's true, but I never thought of it the way that you're looking at it because I see already what you are looking at."

Maria continued by saying the war-torn country that Israel has been through for a thousand years would not have been so if the Israelites had accepted God as their king. The disputes and arguing over the homeland God gave to the Israelites would not have been. Things would have turned out much better for Israel if the Israelites had accepted God instead of a mere man as their king.

Who ended up disobeying God and becoming lost in the heart of God and not deemed honorable or trusted by Almighty God.

Maria went on, saying, "I wonder would the frightening Holocaust horrors that happen to the Jewish people? Would it have still happened, or would it have been prevented if the Israelites would have chosen God to be their king?"

Silence had found Pharaoh very, very quiet and without comment for a moment, soon saying, "I had never thought of that situation like that before or with those specifications or turned around facts that could make such a difference in the past, present, and future lives of the Israelite people. Concerning if they would have just accepted Almighty God as their king thousands of years ago. But wanting to follow the identical ways of their then oppressors. The people that had their foot on the necks of the Israelite people and people that God had just freed from slavery."

"They choose to want what their oppressors had, and follow the ways and traditions of being identified as their oppressors by having a mere man as their king when they were allowed to have Almighty God as their king."

Now Pharaoh was indeed still tired and sleepy from the activities he had just been a part of at Robinson's crap house. Even though he had won thousands of dollars that night, he was still exhausted. Pharaoh was very much indeed happy to have had the conversation that he had just had with Maria, which had quieted him down and brought peace and rest to his body, mind, and soul.

After the conversation with Maria, it was much that Pharaoh realized how much he missed her. But they both knew that their separation was for the best and the only way in which they both could satisfy Maria's father-in-law but yet still be able to continue with their lives. And continue to have some communication, understanding, truth, and Bible study.

It was doubtful but faithful when Pharaoh received a notification from a runner of (123)'s. Who found Pharaoh to deliver the message, asking Pharaoh to immediately see (123) on essential business that could not wait another minute. It will be put off until tonight at 9 pm at the exact location where the message was brought to him concerning his ninety-eight Oldsmobile.

Now right away, Pharaoh thought that this meeting with (123) would be about Pharaoh's court date in New Jersey he was having in the morning.

(123) had provided Pharaoh twice to meet with the judge, hearing Pharaoh's case for lunch. The judge hearing Pharaoh's case decided that Pharaoh would get one thousand-dollar fine and a time limit of sixty days on probation

without having to report to a probation officer. This was for the charge of letting Katie drive without a license and for having a piece of a reefer cigarette in the ashtray of Pharaoh's car.

It was nine o'clock pm on the dot when (123) came walking through the door of the Howard Street restaurant to meet with Pharaoh. Pharaoh was already seated at one of the booths eating pancakes, eggs, and bacon. Which was not yet a meal that Baltimore had adopted late at night but was a meal that New Yorkers ate 24/7 because their night-life went straight through from sundown to sunrise, making day and night as one. {So thought the out of towners}. Who was used to a certain kind of food for the night and a different type for breakfast?

Not just for the followers of (Satan), but also for (Satan). (123) was much like (Satan), whom he worshiped as some people worshiped Almighty God. (Satan) tried to follow the rule of Almighty God of never having to apologize. Because God does no wrong, but (Satan) does no right. Because his concept is always to bring pain, conflict, disaster, misery, evil, and death to all except to his followers, who will be judged sooner or later by Almighty God, sentenced and condemned to whatever punishment so desires Almighty God.

Now (123) did not apologize for anything concerning the death sentence of Yaya's family, nor did he mention news concerning YaYa.

He told Pharaoh that when Pharaoh went to court the following day, he did not have to worry about the trial's outcome. It had already been understood that Pharaoh would get a thousand-dollar fine and sixty days of unreported probation.

Pharaoh was to hand the man dressed in all black the briefcase in which (123) was then handing over to Pharaoh. (123) told Pharaoh that the contents of the case were one million and a half dollars. That because YaYa had deceived him, his daughter-in-law was now believing in a God that she had never seen or talked to, and he was on a mission from his overseer and trusted no one else besides Pharaoh.

(123) said at some point in time, the receiver of the briefcase will say to you, "I'm the man in all black." That will be your key to hand over the briefcase, and fear not.

It was about six o'clock in the morning when Pharaoh and Paula left Baltimore to attend Pharaoh's court hearing in New York. While Shorty Oscar was Pharaoh's lieutenant, Paula was his second command. She did everything legal and illegitimate with Pharaoh. She was indeed intelligent, wise, and one hundred percent for Pharaoh regardless of what, when, and how. Paula was the one who went with Pharaoh that day to his court hearing in New York.

It was eight o'clock in the morning when Paula and Pharaoh reached the courthouse in New York to await trial scheduled for nine o'clock that morning. Within the next twenty minutes, the courtroom filled up very fast. When the judge came out, everyone had to stand, and when Pharaoh turned around. He then saw two armed troopers standing in the back of the room, and it looked as if the troopers were looking straight at Pharaoh.

Pharaoh wondered how armed troopers could be allowed in the courtroom. After hearing some court cases that were called before Pharaoh's case. Pharaoh's case was called before the court, and he was given a twenty-five hundred dollar fine and sixty days unsupervised probation. The judge then explained to Pharaoh that he now had a federal detainer against him. The detainer was charging him with a federal narcotics offense of association with a known international drug dealer, voter registration fixer, and association with a starter of wars in other countries that had ties to the USA.

Now on the indictment with Pharaoh were at least ten other names in which he had never seen, heard of, nor associated before ever. Because Pharaoh had a federal detainer or a federal charge, this new federal charge detained Pharaoh from being released in New York. The new federal detainer charge took away Pharaoh's eligibility to be free and made sure for Pharaoh to be arrested on another charge. The government wanted Pharaoh concerning this new federal charge was hope and a wish that Pharaoh could give them a name to tack onto (123) so they could arrest him.

Not only did the federal authorities not know (123)'s name, but they also had no idea how he looked. So, it made sense to Pharaoh that out of the three or four times that Pharaoh had seen (123), that he had never looked the same or not even sounded the same. He was usually identified by a saying, "This be me."

Now unbeknownst to the federal authorities, Pharaoh could not help to identify (123), nor did Pharaoh know anything about (123)'s business.

Pharaoh was then ordered to await custody of the state of New York, which was the state that was turning Pharaoh over to the Federal Marshals. Pharaoh's only fear was what he was supposed to do with the briefcase that (123) had given him with the 1.5 million dollars in it.

It was then like the judge was reading Pharaoh's mind and demanded that Pharaoh not touch anyone until the judge talked with him first. Pharaoh had asked the judge whether he could have a word with him. When the judge said no one was to take custody of Pharaoh until the judge had first given Pharaoh a chance to speak with him.

"Approach the bench, young man," the judge said to Pharaoh. "And bring all your belongings because I will have to turn you over to the Federal Marshals that are waiting for you after I give you a chance to be heard."

After approaching the bench in the courtroom. Pharaoh then asked the judge could he give his belongings and his briefcase to Paula, and the judge answered, "You may give everything to me, and I will decide what I will give to your female friend because I am the authority in this court, and I am the man in black."

It was late that night when Pharaoh walked into the federal institution called West Street, which was reserved for federal prisoners, but Pharaoh was feeling a tremendous headache when he arrived in the jail because he was thinking back to how he had been playing games with the FBI because Pharaoh had caught them following him.

It had been brought to the attention of Star because everywhere that Star and Pharaoh would go, then Pharaoh would see the Feds following them. But Star said she did not notice it and not to worry. But Pharaoh kept describing the car's color, and it was the same model car as his ninety-eight Oldsmobile but blue.

The night before Pharaoh had left to go to New York to court, he dropped off a big eighth of heroin and asked Star to keep it for him because the Feds were following him.

He had no place else to go right then, so Pharaoh left the heroin with Star and took the Feds to Washington on a wild goose chase.

The next day while he was in New York in court, The Feds raided Star's house while Star happened to be in the window looking at the kids playing.

When The Feds pulled up and jumped out of their cars, Star was afraid. She then realized that the same car-like Pharaoh's car that Pharaoh had told her about was following him.

Star ran into her room, took the heroin, and threw it in the crib where Pharaoh's youngest son was sleeping. The officer in charge told the other officers searching the room not to touch or tamper with that crib as long as that baby stayed asleep. And that baby stayed asleep during the whole raid. The Feds never touched that crib, and they found nothing, and Pharaoh smiled to himself as he thanked God for the blessing.

As soon as he was shown where he was to sleep and which bunk was his, Pharaoh went right to bed with a terrible headache and right to sleep. Trying hard to end the so awful day that he had just overcome.

The following day, Pharaoh was awakened to start his trip back to Baltimore, where his federal charge was created.

Unbeknownst to Pharaoh, he was then dressed in a white jumpsuit, showered down, and stripped of all his hair off his head and face. After being shackled hands and feet to a chain through the floor, he finally reached Baltimore driving ninety-five and a hundred miles an hour.

After traveling for three hours at ninety-five miles an hour from New York to Baltimore, he finally reached Baltimore with just one forty-five-minute break stopping for lunch. After reaching the prison there.

At that particular time, there was no room on the federal side of the jail, so Pharaoh had to wait for space on the national side of the prison.

It was sort of funny to him to see all the hustlers he knew all dressed in white jumpsuits with bald heads and humble-looking expressions on their faces. Even the most famous and well-known hustlers were among the inmates who wore these ball heads and white jumpsuits. Little Caesar was still known, loved, and treated, especially even in these conditions. So were most of the hustlers that were *in the know*. They got special treatment, including Pharaoh.

It was a week later before they moved Pharaoh into the House of Correction, nicknamed {The Cut}. That was because there was so much stabbing and being cut up going on there. When Pharaoh first entered the cut, he was brought up through the stairs that led him to the center of the jail, which was called {Center Hall}.

All the inmates could walk around Center Hall, but no one could enter unless one was to leave the jail or downstairs, where visiting privileges were allowed.

Standing there in Center Hall, the men started to call Pharaoh by name jokingly. Just letting him know that he was home for the time being with the rest of all that had gotten caught breaking the law, but not to worry because his friends were there to take care of him.

Hollering the loudest was Black Butch, or {Woody Stroll} which we had named Black Butch after the black movie star, Woody Stroll. There was also {Alvin Fields} and his codefendant {Nathan Right} who would at a later date after also qualify for the Camp Center. He would become very tight with Little Caesar, and Little Caesar and Nathan Right both would make their way to the Camp Center. But Nathan Right would be the one that snitched on Little Caesar at a later date when they both were free.

When he snitched on him, it put a black mark on all East Baltimore hustlers for some time. Then Nathan Right would go in hiding and never again be seen by the East Baltimoreans that loved him, believed in him, and respected him as a man, a hustler.

There was {Little Casey} and the {Notorious Ellsworth Douglas} who would make one of the top wanted men on the FBI list for Christmas of nineteen sixty-eight. And one that could up and take his weight. He would see the street one more time only to have another shoot out with the police, be captured, and then die in jail while trying to regain his freedom again.

There were Pharaoh's friends and colleagues, {Bobby Lucas} and Chicago, who were both parts of the notorious bank robbers; Bobby Lucas and Chicago would both be associates of Pharaoh well after they were all old and gray. Even though they sometimes only saw one another on the fly, they always had time to say special hellos and goodbyes.

There was {Big Ned} who was the brother of Jessie, who both were personal friends of Pharaoh. Jessie and Pharaoh prospered much during the later years working with one another, while Big Ned's favor would cause Pharaoh to break his promise to God. It would cost the life of Big Ned in the future, and there was the Notorious {Ladies Man Sonny Smooth}, there was {Rollo} the stickup man, who would soon be murdered, and there was {Mr. Gentleman} and his brother {Splobie}, who were bank robbers and drug dealers. There was also {Pimp Time} who was also a lady's man and a fighter, and there was {Little Edward Lawrence} and the Harvey Brothers, who both were pool champions.

There were many more associates of Pharaoh's, but the book would be filled while just trying to name them.

Pharaoh only named some of East Baltimore's best for those incarcerated with him, not the many greats of East Baltimore that were not in the Cut. These were some of East Baltimore's finest in the fields of gangsters, hustlers, pimps, and stick-up men, all who Pharaoh knew well and rubbed shoulders with and gambled with on an everyday basis when they were free.

The iron gates of the {Center Hall} slowly began to open, and for the first time in his life, Pharaoh was actually in jail doing time, but besides a different scenery. Pharaoh was with the very same people that he usually was with on the street because they were all in jail with him.

Pharaoh's whole neighborhood was in jail. The people from Robinson's crap house were in prison, many drug dealers and drug users were all in jail together with the pimps, thieves, and nightlife people that filled the night spots with their fancy clothes and pockets of money as they used to walk with a swagger in their steps.

Burglars, and murders and men with natural life sentences, and men that had been in jail for the last twenty years of their lives, were all there together.

Pharaoh's friends brought him soap, toothpaste, hair grease, cookies, candy, cigarettes, and soda. Pharaoh was even taken to the jailhouse commissaries and bought ice cream, cakes, and pies.

Finally, Pharaoh was taken and shown where his cell was. Pharaoh's cell buddy also showed Pharaoh the tier that housed homosexuals. They were all dressed like real women, with all sorts of fancy women's underwear, dresses, skirts, and bras.

Now Pharaoh was not one to dabble in homosexuality in any way, but there were men there that would kill you for just looking at their homosexual friend or wife, as the man would call it.

Pharaoh was surprised that the Cut had Utz Potato Chips, Tastykake pies, and cakes. He loved the sour cream new addition of Utz, already the best of the best in potato chips, and the best in cakes and pies was Tastykake. At the same time, Utz would add sour cream potato chips to their list of different flavors of potato chips, and the Tastykake people would count on chocolate éclairs and peach to their flavors of butterscotch, jelly crumpets, and apple pies.

Who now had added chocolate eclairs and peach pie to their menu of cakes and pastries, and it was privileged to Pharaoh to sit back and enjoy a cold can of Coca-Cola, with a bag of sour cream and onion potato chips and a chocolate eclair pie, and Pharaoh's saying was that anyone who came to Baltimore had to taste Utz potato chips and a Tastykake or Tasty pie before they die.

It was nineteen-seventy, and the jail at the House of Correction was wide open, and the cell doors opened six in the morning. The inmates were free to come out and roam all over the jail because, at that particular time, the inmates ran the jail and talked to the officers as if they were dogs. There would come a time that Pharaoh would witness the change of control in prison go over to the officers to be in control and run the jail while demanding respect and for all inmates to follow orders.

Pharaoh's first night in the rec room was unique because he was in a vast space that held hundreds of men, all doing different things at one time.

Like, three or four TVs made it possible for hundreds of men to watch three or four different shows at one time, while another couple hundred exercised inside. At the same time, many men played various card games for fun, while many gambled for high stakes card games for cigarettes and cash. Many other men sat at tables and wrote letters while other men just walked up and down the room; some were walking alone while some were walking in groups or individually. Everyone was interested in what they were doing and not concerned with all the noise and other activities that were going on presently, but had tuned everyone else out to relate to whatever one was doing.

Now the activities in the rec room at night lasted from 6 pm until 10 pm, and different sides of the jail had different nights and days to participate in the activities. The first night that Pharaoh decided to participate in the rec room activities after the rec room time was over, Pharaoh returned to his cell, and the cell doors opened back up for the inmates to go back in their cells.

Then Pharaoh's cell buddy, a Muslim brother, asked Pharaoh whether he would like to have a piece of his sandwich. Pharaoh knew that it was a no-no to accept any gifts in jail from anyone unless they were friends from home, relatives, or best friends.

Pharaoh said, "No, thank you," even though the sandwich that Pharaoh's cell buddy had just taken off the light bulb in the ceiling smelled delicious. It was a steak and egg sandwich that Pharaoh's cell buddy's {sandwich man} left him. Like he did every night.

When Pharaoh's cell buddy came back from the rec room, the sandwich was smoking hot, smelling good, and tasting delicious from the light bulb's heat. Even though there was a little burnt spot in the middle of the bread from the light bulb's heat, Pharaoh explained that his cell buddy's sandwich man who worked in the kitchen did deliver Pharaoh's cell buddy a different kind of sandwich every night. It was not a week later when Pharaoh also had a sandwich man from the kitchen bring Pharaoh a sandwich every night for a total of five packs of cigarettes a week, which Pharaoh made daily by operating a store in the Cut.

Pharaoh was amazed when his cell buddy made a cup of tea in the toilet. By rolling a lot of toilet tissue around his hand and cupping it in a cup-like form, then set the paper on fire in the toilet, then holding a tin cup over the fire with a pair of tweezers until the water boils. The tea bag is put into the cup to make tea.

All these things were unique to Pharaoh at first, but soon they were just jail house everyday methods to survive in jail at a somewhat comfortable effort of survival. In the Cut, stabbings were daily. Other methods of violence were used daily also. Such as throwing lighter fluid in another person's cell and setting him on fire or a gang of men jumping on just one individual and beating him to a pulp. Butt stabbings were the most used form of daily violence.

The Muslims were an organization that wasn't feared. But inmates did walk around the Muslims, trying not to cause an uncalled situation. Many inmates joined the Muslims, so they could be protected from other inmates who would prey on them if they weren't under the protection of the Muslims organization.

Time was passing pretty fast. On those nights, one would call on God as they asked how much longer they had before going home.

There were the sleepless nights where it seemed as if you would never be free. There were times that Pharaoh had to show that he could hold his own when he had to beat his new cell buddy with a baseball bat for stealing the watch that Paula had given him.

Pharaoh only had four visits a month. Pharaoh's mother was now living in New York. Mama Grace was a starch Christian and did not believe in visiting jails. Even though Mama Grace wrote Pharaoh daily, his grandmother was current and regular with her visits to Pharaoh. He had to divide his visits up to know which day each person was coming. Pharaoh needed to see Paula most of all because she took care of all his business for him and kept charge of all his money coming in and going out.

Star was his children's mother and his number two girl, so Pharaoh saw Paula twice a month, Star once a month, his grandmother once a month, and that was a total of four visits a month. Star wrote Pharaoh every day, and Pharaoh received a letter from Star every day except Sundays because the mail did not run-on Sundays. Star's letters were needed. To help Pharaoh get through his day every day.

Mama Grace wrote every two weeks, and Pharaoh's grandmother wrote seldom, but she never missed any of her visiting privileges. Paula's letters were daily also but not like Star's everyday letters, and nothing or no one matched Star's every day letters.

Even though Star's letters all said the same thing over and over and over, which was "I Love You!" "I Love You" "I Love You!"

Pharaoh was always happy to hear from Paula and how much money he had. Pharaoh always leaned a little more toward Paula than Star, even though Pharaoh never showed it or never let anyone disrespect Star, including Paula.

Pharaoh leaned more towards Paula; Pharaoh stopped anyone in their tracks that put Paula before Star because no one was allowed to do that.

Now Pharaoh's lawyer was a personal friend of {Proposition Joe} who was an excellent friend of Pharaoh's. He was the one that Pharaoh studied under before becoming not just a hustler but a "Hustler's Hustler."

Which hustled hustlers by bringing to them whatever they needed, including connections, experience, knowledge of specific needs, and necessities in the hustling world.

Proposition Joe was the person who had introduced Pharaoh to Mr. Murdock. Mr. Murdock was the lawyer's name that was representing Pharaoh. Mr. Murdock was an outstanding and upcoming lawyer who knew the law.

He had been a federal prosecutor, and even though he did not have a lot of shortcuts by knowing judges or making it possible that one could go directly to the Camp Center like many white lawyers, Mr. Murdock knew the law. He knew the law very well, and it made up for the shortcuts that he could not provide to his clients by being one of the best at what he did know concerning the knowledge of the law. Especially federal law, after Proposition Joe, introduced Pharaoh and Mr. Murdock to one another, so Mr. Murdock could represent Pharaoh in the federal case against Pharaoh and the three other state charges against Pharaoh that had been placed on Pharaoh's head.

Mr. Murdock was introduced to Paula being Pharaoh's number one girl. And Mr. Murdock fell in love with Paula the first time he laid eyes upon Paula. It was secret admiration and physical attraction because Paula was indeed a beautiful, intelligent, and smart female. But Pharaoh peeped at Mr. Murdock's personal attraction towards Paula right away.

And even though Pharaoh came with the seal of approval, when introduced to Mr. Murdock, Mr. Murdock still saw Pharaoh as a hothead young boy living with his mother while trying to be a superior hustler.

In return, Pharaoh saw Mr. Murdock as a great educated lawyer who had proved himself as a qualified lawyer able to compete with any other lawyer on the planet when it came to knowing the law.

Mr. Murdock had one weakness; Mr. Murdock loved to drink alcohol. He wore the look and smell of alcohol. Even though Mr. Murdock was a professional person, Pharaoh felt that Mr. Murdock had nothing on him besides that Pharaoh respected Mr. Murdock and trusted his freedom with him in the courtroom.

CHAPTER 9

Forsaken By One Trusted

Now Star did not like that she could only see Pharaoh once a month, and on her next monthly visit to see Pharaoh. Star looked into Pharaoh's eyes while tears ran down her face. Star told Pharaoh that she knew that she wasn't as pretty as Paula. She knew that she wasn't attending college like Paula. But if Pharaoh would just give her a chance to prove herself to Pharaoh, and how much she loved him and would do anything for him, if he would just give her a chance and let her see Pharaoh more than once a month. Then she would be happy. But if Pharaoh felt it was best just to see her once a month, she would accept that because all she wanted to do was satisfy Pharaoh and support Pharaoh in any way that she could.

Now it was Paula's time to visit Pharaoh, and Pharaoh had asked Paula for a radio. Paula was dragging her feet about getting the radio for Pharaoh. When Paula came on her next visit,

Pharaoh told Paula that he had a friend that could get out of jail for a three hundred dollar fine. Pharaoh wanted Paula to pay the fine, but Paula's response was sort of smart and semi disrespectful. Pharaoh told Paula that he would stand up in that visiting room and slap her fucking head off her shoulders.

It was then that Paula surprised Pharaoh by saying, "You won't do anything to me because the white man has got you now. And you can't do anything but what he says."

Hearing these words from Paula, Pharaoh knew that he had lost control over Paula, which was a lost cause in his life. Pharaoh knew that someone had been telling Paula all the shit that she was now talking and the bad part was that she had to be holding still and listening to that shit.

Pharaoh knew that, in a sense that Paula was right. The white man (or the system} did have Pharaoh in their grip. Pharaoh knew that he did not have the necessary tools, nor was he in a position to handle a disobedient bitch that chose to listen to another man concerning her man's credentials, His situation, or abilities to maneuver. Pharaoh got up, walked out of the visiting room, and left Paula sitting there in the chair.

It was late that evening when Pharaoh removed Paula's name from his visiting list, and it was only a week that Pharaoh missed {Paula} so intensely, but Star moved right in place.

Pharaoh did remember what Star had said when she only begged, not asked, but had begged for just a chance to let her perform for him and prove her love for him. And that there was nothing that she wouldn't do for Pharaoh.

By the grace of God, Pharaoh only stayed in the Cut for eleven months before he was warranted the opportunity to move on forward to a minimum-security prison. He was also able to obtain work release status.

Now Mr. Murdock had beat the federal charge that was hanging over Pharaoh's head. Pharaoh had gotten one year for a pistol charge and beat the other two state charges. So, Pharaoh ended up with the five-year sentence that he had first received, and one year for the pistol charge added on to his original five-year sentence, which gave Pharaoh a total of six years.

Pharaoh paid Mr. Murdock and was well satisfied with the legal services from Mr. Murdock.

In the eleven months that Pharaoh spent in the Cut, he refused to see Paula many times. He never added her name back on his visiting list. It was there in the Cut that God displayed the truth about selling drugs and the harm that drugs did not just to a person, but the drug user's whole family, friends, and associates.

God showed Pharaoh the true damage that drugs did to people. Their communities, their future, and the future of their children's dreams, goals, and righteousness all go astray.

When Pharaoh's little brother Jonny started using drugs and then Cakes, Pharaoh promised God that after God had shown him how drugs ruined people's lives and destroyed their neighborhoods, and stole the righteousness right from their souls.

Pharaoh knew that he would never again sell heroin, which was the promise he made to his God. He would never again sell heroin.

Pharaoh first started selling drugs to feed his own little family while he also helped Mama Grace survive and pay her bills. Not once did Pharaoh think about the harm and tragedy he was bringing to people he was selling drugs to.

Pharaoh was under the impression that he was helping the addicts he was selling to by bringing them safety in buying drugs. Bringing them security, not being cheated or robbed, and a backup plan to make sure that not even the ones selling them drugs could hurt them, cheat them, or rob them. Without being caught and disciplined to the extent that they had to repay whatever was taken unfairly and apologize for face-to-face to the one wronged by the one that did the wrong. All Pharaoh's drugs customers were white people. Only a few blacks were using drugs in Pharaoh's community because most blacks were too poor to buy drugs at that day and time.

Pharaoh was not on the level to know the few blacks who were using drugs because they were mainly pimps, Musicians, doctors, lawyers, and blacks in some professions. He had not yet climbed the ladder to reach those types of black people. He was just being taught about drugs and what not to do with drugs. Who not to sell drugs to, and how to do what you need to sell drugs without getting caught.

In the early stages of the introductory to drugs in the ghetto for users and sellers, the saying was called "pulling one's coat," usually from one older hustler to one younger hustler and a user. There was then loyalty, character, understanding, and downright sympathy for those caught up in using drugs, and it was just one's character or principle to not take advantage of one caught up in using drugs.

It didn't take long before Satan had taken all the little bit of good that was once in drugs out, so everyone acted doggish, and sympathy, love, and care soon turned to greed and selfishness.

Little Caesar had first invested in Pharaoh by giving Pharaoh drugs to take to Pharaoh's part of town to sell drugs or try and find the few black drug users in 1963.

Pharaoh's first lesson and rule of the drug was that drug use was for fools. Two, it was never to be used by the dealer. Three never to sell drugs to a pregnant woman. And last, four, never take a life because of drugs, in any way at all. Pharaoh was turned on with the lifestyle of the then Pennsylvania Avenue, and Pharaoh weighed its value. What benefits that selling drugs could bring him and his family instead of its destruction.

Pharaoh took the plunge, and that's how Pharaoh had first begun, but from the second day that Pharaoh had taken the bundles of heroin from Little Caesar. Pharaoh rejoiced, but even better than that, Mama Grace told him after he had contributed to the responsibilities of the household that there was no mortgage on the house. The house was paid off after the death of {Daddy Grace}.

Mama Grace had no idea what drugs were because there were no drugs in the neighborhood. Mama Grace nor Pharaoh knew anything about what drugs did to people or the communities, or people's souls, their worldly possessions, or their character.

Pharaoh found out immediately that he could take care of his wife and daughter and child on the way. He could also help pay Mama Grace's bills and treat her to oysters, crabs, and all the good food that she could not afford to buy, like treats and goodies that Mama Grace used to look in the window and wished she could buy.

The time in {the Cut} went past pretty fast for Pharaoh because he opened up a store that sold Tastykakes and Tasty pies, which was Pharaoh's favorite. He gambled all evening until the cell doors closed, and then he would come in his single cell and fall out exhausted.

Pharaoh also became Vice President of one of the five organizations in the Cut. In which Pharaoh's organization brought in outside people to the functions that were given. {Star} and Pharaoh's grandmother did not miss one, and they were always there and on time. Pharaoh did get to touch Star and hug and kiss Star and his grandmother.

Now it was amazing how heroin had spread in the ghetto; when there were but a few heroin addicts, it was now many.

The visitors coming to {the Cut} was now bringing heroin on their person so as to slide it into the inmate's mouth or just sneak it to the inmate across the counter. But Pharaoh loved steak, and {Star} was always sneaking Pharaoh a steak sandwich into the prison. Pharaoh had to sneak the sandwich upstairs, and all the inmates that knew Pharaoh knew that he would have a steak sandwich when he came up from his visit with Star.

Star never gave Pharaoh a chance to mourn over the loss of Paula because Star performed for Pharaoh. Star never missed a visit, never was late, got a job, and helped to provide for Pharaoh. Most of all, Star wanted to have some money saved up to help Pharaoh do whatever he wanted to do.

One day after Pharaoh had had a visit with Star, Star had brought him a steak sandwich, and Pharaoh had taken the steak sandwich back up into the jail. He was called back downstairs to the visiting room, and Pharaoh knew that Star had not come right back. He knew that it was not his grandmother.

Pharaoh had already put in writing not to call him for Paula. So, Pharaoh thought the jail was calling him back downstairs for the steak sandwich he had gotten from Star, but he had already eaten the sandwich.

Pharaoh wondered if they had pictures of him taking the sandwich he had done many times before in the visiting room. But right away, he was led to a different room that they strip search you in. He was seated in a chair behind a great long desk, and before Pharaoh could prepare himself, in walked Maria.

When she saw Pharaoh sitting behind the desk, Maria ran towards Pharaoh and jumped over the desk and into the arms of Pharaoh. The guards had to come and pull Maria back across the table while Pharaoh explained to Maria that they were not supposed to touch. But Maria never paid any attention to the words Pharaoh was saying, or the guards motioning to Maria to come back across the table and stop kissing him and touching him all over him.

Now unbeknownst to Pharaoh, Maria had come to see him the day before and paid the guard three hundred dollars to let Maria come back the next day when that guard would be working in the strip search room.

That guard assigned that strip search room to Maria and Pharaoh. The guards were telling Maria what to do and what not to do. Maria already knew that that strip search room belonged to Maria and Pharaoh for the next three hours. Maria was still as beautiful as ever. And even a blind man could see Maria's love and affection for Pharaoh and how glad she was to see him.

"This is the room that I kept seeing in my dreams when I kept telling you that I kept having this dream about you being locked up for working with my father-in-law."

It was a good day, a perfect day that Maria had brought into the life of Pharaoh while he was incarcerated.

After about two hours, Maria asked Pharaoh, "Why does the Catholic religion pray to Mary, the mother of Jesus, instead of sending their prayers straight to God? And why aren't their prayers straight to God?"

"The Catholic religion prays to Mary, the mother of Jesus is like in my opinion, you asking your preacher, your mother, father or a good friend of yours that is a righteous person to pray for you or someone that you know or love. If you can understand that, you should realize asking someone already in heaven to speak with God on your behalf. And if you are a true Christian and believe that {The Virgin Mary}, the mother of Jesus, who is also God, then you must believe that The Virgin Mary is now present in heaven.

Since she is in heaven with God, the Son Jesus, she is much closer to God the Father. She has played such a magnificent role in the life of Jesus Christ, our Lord and Savior. Which has made her worthy of such great potential off heavenly matters than you are here on earth. Then it is understandable that the Virgin Mary, mother of Jesus, who is also God, could bring your prayers to God the Father, or God the Son, much sooner, better, and more precise than you. That you are just human and stained with sin down here on earth, that is my opinion about that situation and how I see it and how I relate to it, and I approve of it even though I'm not Catholic. I have never used that theory, but not to say that I will never use it. Still, the integrity, belief, caliber, and criteria of such a matter must be chosen by only you from the understanding of your heart and soul of such delicate and righteous concerns. One must realize that Mary, the mother of Jesus, was not made or forced to bring her child Jesus into the world. One of God's top angels, {Gabriel}, was sent to ask Mary if she would agree to be the mother of Jesus Christ. To participate in the birth of Jesus Christ, Through her pregnancy with Jesus after being chosen by Almighty God. To be blessed by Almighty God. To bring the Son of Almighty God into the world without the conception of a human man, but by the {Immaculate Conception}."

Pharaoh said, "First of all, Mary, the mother of Jesus Christ who is also God, was born into the world from birth without sin. She kept her body pure and clean to bring forth from her body into the world, a sinless baby Jesus, who entered into the world sinless. Because Mary, Jesus's mother, was born unto the world innocent, which is the meaning of {Immaculate Conception} from my understanding, which means that Jesus' birth into the world without the contribution of a man was the meaning of the {Immaculate Concept {Immaculate Conception} is the birth of Jesus without the contribution from a man.

But that is not true because the {Immaculate Conception} is the birth of Mary, the mother of Jesus, entering into the world from birth without sin so she could have a sinless body in which to bring forth her son. Jesus, from an innocent body."(so believe the author of this book)

It was a beautiful, wonderful, and righteous day in the life of Pharaoh. For his stomach had tasted the flavor of the steak. At the same time, his heart had been soothed with the visit of Star. And the news of his sons. And while Maria had filled his soul with the conversation of righteousness. And his earthly desires of lust had been aroused and taunted. With the sexual and human touches towards Maria and Maria towards him. WOW! What a good day for an inmate.

It had been only nine months when Pharaoh was called to his classification officer and told that he would be going to a minimum-security institution known as the Camp Center.

It was a place that Pharaoh had been to before when he was a free man and had visited Shark Skin twice before.

Not once did Pharaoh think that he would be in this same Camp Center serving time. Pharaoh did not have a lot of buddies to say goodbye to because even though Pharaoh ran a store in the Cut. He did a lot of gambling with the big-timers of the jail. Or the inmates are known to have some weight in the jail. Pharaoh was still quite a quiet and low-profile type of individual.

Shorty Oscar was Pharaoh's lieutenant when Pharaoh was a free man. Pharaoh started off his narcotic business with Shorty Oscar. He was Pharaoh's loyal and trusted friend and associate,f and they did everything together and were always together.

Even though Paula was second in command but Paula had proved herself worthy of being second in command. There was no animosity between Shorty Oscar and Paula.

Shorty Oscar was at that present time when Pharaoh was about to leave the Cut, and Shorty Oscar was still sort of angry with Pharaoh. When Pharaoh made bail for fifty thousand dollars, Shorty Oscar felt Paula was supposed to get him out on bail.

Shorty Oscar had, at the last moment, and unbeknownst to anyone, pleaded guilty to all the charges to try to save Pharaoh from going to jail. The judge saw through what Shorty Oscar was trying to do. Since Shorty Oscar had not done this at the beginning of the trial but had waited until the end of the trial. The judge found both Shorty Oscar and Pharaoh guilty of the same charge.

Then Shorty Oscar tried to save Pharaoh, but he had not attempted to do this at first. Since Shorty Oscar then, later on, came back and pleaded guilty, then he lost his right to an appeal bail, but at the time, Shorty Oscar thought that Pharaoh had not given Paula the okay to bail him out and had just left him in jail.

Shorty Oscar also was in the Cut when Pharaoh was ready to leave. Pharaoh came to Shorty Oscar and told him that he was leaving and going to the Camp Center and would like to have Shorty Oscar's blessings and in return.

Shorty Oscar gave Pharaoh his blessings and wished Pharaoh the best, but Pharaoh carried a slight grudge in his heart. Because Pharaoh felt as though Shorty Oscar had not been fair towards him by thinking that Pharaoh would have left him in jail, Pharaoh felt as though Shorty Oscar should have never listened to the guys trying to turn Shorty Oscar against Pharaoh.

In due time Shorty Oscar and Pharaoh would soon be as they were in the hearts of each other; though they both had different things they both shared against each other, friendship, dedication, and love for each other would prevail over everything else.

Now Shark Skin was the best of friends with Pharaoh, and they both loved and respected one another as friends, buddies, associate's neighborhood pals, and the best of respect from one hustler to the other.

In later life, {Dapping Slim} who was Shark Skin's brother, would also share the privilege of being Pharaoh's best friend. But Pharaoh would always love, honor, and respect Shark Skin.

Now! The day before, Pharaoh was to leave the Cut and go to the Camp Center. He was approached by three men who threatened to rob or take from Pharaoh all his belongings from his store, which were his cookies, potato chips, sodas, toothpaste, and Tastykakes and Tastykake pies. Because the three thought that it would probably be an easy task. They felt as though Pharaoh would not want any trouble because it would stop him from going to camp, and nobody would do anything wrong to have to stay in the Cut when they had a chance to get out.

But to the surprise of the three men that tried to rob Pharaoh. He bucked on them by hitting one of the three men, the closest one to him, across the front of his legs right below his shin bone with a baseball bat. It bent the man over, grabbing the front of both his legs in pain and agony. Pharaoh smashed the second man in the face with the steel bat, but the third man pulled out his homemade shank and stabbed Pharaoh. That's when Big Ned stepped in front of the knife, he was stabbed in the shoulder, and took the stab wound for Pharaoh.

Now Big Ned was a true homeboy of Pharaoh, and big Ned was also the first black man to whom Pharaoh had ever sold heroin.

Big Ned was an East Baltimore great. He was known to do right, and his word was his bond. His friendship with you was dynamic. If you were ever close enough to him to be his friend, then he would die for you because that is how Big Ned saw and related friendship to the few that he considered his friends.

Big Ned had got a big eighth of heroin from Pharaoh on consignment and had come back and paid Pharaoh thirty-five hundred dollars when he was introduced to his sister {Jessie}. Who would, in turn, be dealing with Pharaoh for the next forty years as best of friends, business, and lifetime associates?

Big Ned pushed Pharaoh into his cell and closed the cell door. Big Ned smashed the third man trying to rob Pharaoh—punched him with his fantastic big fist! For Ned was a giant of a man, incredible, big, powerful, and known not to be fucked with.

His sister Jessie was of the same awesome size and carried the same reputation, and in fact, all of Big Ned's family were huge in size, strength, height, and weight after Big Ned had pushed Pharaoh into his cell, closed the cell door.

Big Ned said to Pharaoh, "Go on to camp, stay out of trouble, and I'll take the weight for the charges of all this shit. Go home and enjoy your life but remember, you owe me one."

Ned then took his foot and kicked the third man that tried to rob Pharaoh down the steps and onto the tier underneath the tier they were just fighting on. Big Ned then called the guard and was taken to an outside hospital where he was stitched up for the stab wound he had received for Pharaoh accidentally.

Big Ned returned to the Cut, where he was later charged, and a one-year sentence was added to the twelve-year sentence that he already had because no one wanted to press charges against Big Ned.

The Camp Center was so very much different than the Cut. One was allowed to sit with, eat with, touch, hug, and kiss on your family, and your family could even bring you food from home or the fast-food industries.

On Pharaoh's second day there, he received a visit from Paula. At Camp Center, you could have a visit every day from seven to nine at night and Sundays and Saturdays from twelve until five?

In the next three months that Pharaoh was there at the Camp Center. He joined the school program and received his G.E.D., which he was proud to achieve, which led him to apply for work release, which he did get and started to work at a factory where the work release bus took him to work and brought him back. Pharaoh's hours of work were four in the evening to midnight.

Now Pharaoh never let Paula come to see him, and in fact, he put her out of the visiting room. He told her to sit on the hot bus she rode down there and let people see that she had done something disrespectful to receive that sort of treatment after she had come down there on the bus to visit Pharaoh.

Pharaoh never let Paula visit him at the Camp Center, and Paula did not do time with Pharaoh, and pretty soon, Paula stopped trying to visit with Pharaoh.

Pharaoh was working then. He had the right to go out on weekends from Friday evening at five until Sunday evening at five. Star was there to pick Pharaoh up for weekends once a month. Pharaoh gave all his weekends to Star because she deserved every weekend that Pharaoh got.

Pharaoh did very much appreciate Star and the performance that she had given Pharaoh while he was helpless and could not do for himself. Star performed for Pharaoh like a soldier at war protecting his country. Sure, enough the time would come that Pharaoh had to try and show Star how much he appreciated her performance and dependability, courage, and sole dedication to him by granting Star a wish that Star dreamed about and hoped to make reality one day.

Little Caesar and Nathan Right worked together on a trash detail and became very friendly towards one another even though Nathan Right was not a drug man and knew nothing about drugs.

He decided to go the route of drugs with Little Caesar and not rob banks anymore. Nathan Right was a church boy like Pharaoh and Pharaoh, and Nathan Right's families were brothers and sisters in the church world.

Pharaoh and Nathan Right were brothers, friends, and worldly associates in the world of hustling. Nathan Right and Pharaoh were men of the world after they were able and old enough to choose their paths.

Nathan Right was a great contender for the hustling world.

Everyone in the Camp Center that was on work release and had a job had a money sheet that hung in the hallway to see it. Most of the Camp Center compared the amounts of money to the name of the individual name to see who in the Camp Center had the most money in their account. Some men had been on the job at work release for years and had as much as twenty thousand dollars in their account.

No one had as much money in their account as Little Caesar, which made him the talk of the Camp Center. Little Caesar was just a regular guy to Pharaoh, one that Pharaoh saw in the street on a regular basis. And one that Pharaoh knew that he had more money than the governor of the state and more prestige and recognition. He was probably connected to half the people of the city in one way or another.

Yes! Little Caesar was a bad mother fucker during his day and time. Pharaoh loved and respected him, for he would have to go to Little Caesar at least three different times in his life, never to be turned down by Little Caesar.

Half the hustling world in Baltimore would sooner or later eventually have to turn to Little Caesar for help. Mainly in the finance world, people would need the help of Little Caesar to pay their car notes, house payments, gambling debts, loans, household bills, and school tuitions.

Little Caesar would help those in the hustling world with him and those who were just plain people trying to make the best of a difficult situation.

Pharaoh stayed in the Cut for almost ten months. He remained in the Camp Center for nearly two years while having at least fourteen weekends of coming home once a month to spend a weekend from Friday evening five o'clock to returning to the camp Sunday evening at five o'clock.

Pharaoh received his high school certificate or G.E.D. from the Camp Center, and later, he would also receive college credits. Pharaoh knew that it was his God who had brought him out of the Cut in just nine months. Pharaoh would have probably had to stay there for the duration of his sentence. Pharaoh knew that God had blessed him to make it to the Camp Center.

Pharaoh thanked his God for protecting him while Pharaoh came through that dreadful and terrible {Cut}. God protected him when Satan tried to keep Pharaoh from coming home when the three guys tried to rob him, and Big Ned stepped in and took the blow that was meant for one of the three guys trying to rob Pharaoh's store.

The blow fractured Big Ned's wrist, and then Big Ned took the charge for Pharaoh so Pharaoh could continue going home. Pharaoh's prayers were continuous to God and Pharaoh's Day finally came for him to leave the Camp Center and go home.

Pharaoh had three thousand and five hundred dollars in his account when he left the Camp Center from working on his work-release job and had received a G.E.D. He had already enrolled in Morgan State College for the following semesters as a business major, which would indeed teach Pharaoh the skills he needed to know to succeed in the business world.

While Pharaoh was in the Cut, he had learned that heroin was a community robber, a stealer of souls, a destroyer of families, and a vital weapon for Satan as he destroyed the hearts, minds, and souls of the soldiers of God.

Even though Pharaoh wasn't sure what he would do, he positively knew that he would never again sell heroin. That was Pharaoh's promise to God that he would never sell heroin again in any way, shape, or form unless to provide food for his family as the last result for survival.

He wished and hoped and prayed that his brother Jonny and Cakes somehow could be redeemed again back to themselves and stop using heroin, which would be a lost cause for his brother Jonny and a possibility for Cakes.

It was a sweet life for Pharaoh because he was now a free man, and Star had gotten a job and saved up money and got a house, where Pharaoh spent all his weekends when he was still locked up. The house that Star had gotten was right across the street from her mother's house, and Star asked Pharaoh if he would come and live with her and Pharaoh's two sons. Pharaoh knew that he was indebted to Star for her performance when he was locked up. Star performed for Pharaoh like a soldier performs for his country in wartime. She was there for everything that Pharaoh could want and have. Except for his freedom because that was the one thing that Star had no control over giving to Pharaoh.

Pharaoh explained to Star that he was not ready for marriage or living together because he was not prepared to settle down, have one woman, and come home every night. Because some nights, he would not even be in this city.

Star told Pharaoh that if he came to live with her and his two sons. She would not put any demands on him; She would not ask him where he was going or when he was coming back. All she would ask for in return was that Pharaoh would take time out now and then and take her for a ride in the car, especially when it was cold, so she could see the people who had no vehicles and had to walk.

Star also told Pharaoh that she would do everything to make him happy and dedicate her life to making her a priority. Making sure Pharaoh was delighted, and there were no limitations of what she would do to make Pharaoh happy twenty-four seven. Pharaoh and Star made the agreement to make living conditions understandably agreed upon and satisfactory accepted.

For twenty years, Star would keep her part of the agreement. Pharaoh and Star, with their two sons, started their living together experience immediately.

Pharaoh and his first wife had divorced after two years, in which Pharaoh's wife Jazzy finally gave consent for Pharaoh to have a divorce. She had asked Pharaoh from the first time of her learning of Pharaoh's son not to be involved with the son he had had with Star, even though Star became pregnant with Pharaoh's son intentionally even though Pharaoh did not intend for Star to get pregnant.

But because Pharaoh had refused to not be a part of his son's life from Star, that was the beginning of Pharaoh's separation from his wife, Jazzy. Fifty years later, Pharaoh and Jazzy would still love one another and help to bear each other's burden with each other every day in every one of the fifty years to come. Jazzy would be there to support and give love and care to Pharaoh's son. It would also be factual that Jazzy would support Pharaoh's second son by Star. They all would love, appreciate, and support one another for a lifetime.

While no one would ever take the place of Jazzy's s parents, who would also be entwined in love, happiness, and contentment for Pharaoh and all Pharaoh's children until the day they both would die.

Pharaoh enrolled in college at Morgan State College in nineteen seventy-five but fought for Morgan State College to become Morgan University.

Pharaoh prided himself for being a part of that struggle to turn Morgan State College into Morgan University.

In Pharaoh's first semester at Morgan, Pharaoh took his daughter Linda to class with him a few times even though she was not yet ten years old.

Pharaoh would have never ever thought that his little daughter or rather his oldest child would one day share the same classroom with him at Morgan University, as they both studied psychology in the same classroom many years later. So, this was done so she could see and feel the college classrooms and the college campus, so in reality and in hopes that this would encourage her to make the same positive choices. In his second semester, Pharaoh took his two young sons to his classroom on the campus of Morgan University. In hopes that his two sons would also, one day, major in business administration, which they both did, and even though Pharaoh did not get all A's in his classes, Pharaoh did learn the field of business very well.

Pharaoh flexed his business learnings by first investing in a little grocery store. Pharaoh did not indulge in the selling of heroin anymore at that time and had no idea to sell heroin ever again. Pharaoh did not have to use any of the money he had brought home from the Camp Center or any money that Star had saved for her and Pharaoh while he was away. His gambling skills with the luck and blessings that God was granting him with enough money to open the grocery store without using money from the Camp Center that he had brought home with him.

Pharaoh never went back to selling heroin, and only a few of his white customers did he see or hear from. Very few people knew where Pharaoh lived, and they only knew how to get in touch with him by the old phone number and the house Pharaoh used to run.

Pharaoh flexed his learning skills from Morgan University when he invested his whole thirty-five hundred dollars that he had brought home from the Camp Center in an apartment building. Which housed three apartments, a beauty salon space, and a downstairs basement turned into a grocery store. After purchasing the apartment building, which was a very good investment, with one stipulation concerning the lady that lived on the third floor that had been there for more than thirty years.

She had never missed a rent payment and was now an old lady. She was still paying the same amount of rent that she had been paying when she first came, which was six-ty-five dollars. The one stipulation in the Pharaoh buying the building for such a low price was that Pharaoh had to let the old lady stay for the same rent that she had been paying for the last thirty years. And to not raise the rent as long as she lived there, which was what Pharaoh did agree upon.

So, he purchased the apartment building for thirty-five hundred dollars and agreed not to raise the old lady's rent for as long as she lived there.

CHAPTER 10

Pharaoh's Self-Superman Image

I t was the first time that Pharaoh had been called {Mr. Gold} when he went to collect His rent for the first time from the apartment building. The three tenants in the building had set up a surprise meeting for Pharaoh. In honor of a young black man becoming the owner of the building which housed them. When they called his name, they put a "Mister" in front of it. He was not only surprised but confused because Pharaoh had not yet been schooled on the position he had now engaged in as a business owner.

All Pharaoh had to do with the apartment building was collect rent and keep the facility in good condition. So, the upkeep of the building is what his brother Jonny did. While Pharaoh then focused onward on the drive and development of the grocery store. Star and Pharaoh's two sons went around to the surrounding stores in the neighborhood and found out the prices that the Korean and Chinese store owners were selling their products and goods. There were very few black store owners, so Pharaoh lowered his prices a few cents lower than his Korean and Chinese competitors. Pharaoh executed all the business skills he had learned at Morgan University.

He made sure he had what everyone needed for breakfast, lunch, and dinner. He made sure he had a variety of sodas, juices, milk, and of course, all the favorite snacks and Tastykakes and pies that Pharaoh himself loved so much.

Cakes was also locked up about the same time Pharaoh was arrested in New York, and Pharaoh had not seen Cakes for over eighteen months since they were together when the riots broke out, in reference to the Martin Luther King assassination.

Pharaoh had to get Cakes back to her section of town, and Pharaoh had to hide Cakes on the floor of the car while he drove through the crowds of rioting black people.

Pharaoh did not agree with all the looting, stealing, robbing, and destroying the stores and properties because the next day after the riots, the people had no stores to go to buy food and essentials. Pharaoh did not see Cakes anymore until he had called for her when he needed her to ride with him again for Maria's father-in-law. Sixty days later, she told Pharaoh that she was pregnant in jail.

The system wanted to take her baby when the child was born, and she didn't know what to do, so Pharaoh told Mama Grace about the situation.

So, the system would not take her baby when the child would be born; Mama Grace wrote Pharaoh and told him that she would take the baby until Cakes came home from jail.

That was almost eighteen months later, and Pharaoh was now looking down on the crib in which the child Cakes had born into the world. And Mama Grace had given a home, was now laying there looking up at Pharaoh.

Smiling while giving all her love and appreciation that an infant baby could provide, even though she was two years old. Now when Pharaoh and Cakes also were incarcerated. They both wrote to one another regularly, but Pharaoh came home first and did not communicate with Cakes at all because Cakes had gotten locked up before Pharaoh. So, they did not communicate until Cakes had gone on the run from jail and called Pharaoh and asked Pharaoh to come and pick her up.

He did even help Cakes get a place to stay in a rented room, and after Cakes went and saw her baby living with Mama Grace. Soon afterward, Cakes was no more.

Pharaoh had not lied to Star when he told Star that Mama Grace was keeping a white baby for a white lady. Keeping children was what Mama Grace loved doing. But he did not tell Star the whole story about the little white baby that Mama Grace knew was Pharaoh's new and youngest child.

Pharaoh did not see his good fortune as going to college, getting his grocery store, and even obtaining the apartment building as blessings from his God. But instead, Pharaoh saw these things as accomplishments of his own doing and his ingenuity.

Pharaoh forgot who was always in charge and from whom all blessings came. Nor did Pharaoh know that this was the start of a new beginning. It was the start of a lost and purposeless journey.

Now the guys on the corners that were hustlers knew Pharaoh and were proud of him. They saw life in advancement and business the same way as Pharaoh saw it. With all promotion and glamour being done by the *individual* whom the glamour seemed to represent.

But they knew not who the only one made these advancements and glamorous things possible.

For they were people of the world, looking in on the hand and world of one that was a believer in God and Jesus Christ. Even if the Godly one himself had forgotten from whence, his blessings have come. (Satan) picked up on the mistake of Pharaoh's misrepresentation of who the leader was and who the follower was in his life. This would be Pharaoh's first lesson of finding out that regardless of how high in life one can go, and regardless of what one may accomplish or what one may gain in life, that without God, one who thinks he has everything has nothing, for there is but one Giver to all that have anything. The same One that gives is the same One that takes away. There are also times when (Satan) will supply one with authority to worldly people. So that you trip over your own feet, thinking that this is something that you have done yourself. Not realizing that this is something that (Satan) has given you to have authority over you. Bringing you back into the realm of worldly people and sin.

Star woke Pharaoh up the next day, telling him that someone was at the door to see him. The person said to tell Pharaoh that it was "The one, who was a one and only one!" That he needed to talk to Pharaoh. Now Fat Ronnie Blackwell and Clyde Stokes {Shark Skin's brother} were the two best friends that Pharaoh had. If it had been either of them, Star would have said so. So, Pharaoh didn't know who was at the door. Now all this new stuff was happening to Pharaoh. He believed that the person at the door had something to do with the purchase of cocaine. Pharaoh was prepared to let them know that he did not have any cocaine in his house and not come to his house looking for cocaine. To call him first and they would set up a meeting place.

When Pharaoh reached the front door and opened it, there leaning against his car with his arms crossed with his great big grin showing his gold teeth stood Big Ned.

Hollering at the top of his voice, "That Be Me!" "I love you, boy! I remember how you helped me get back on my feet when nobody else did!" "I remember when I was ready to rob all those mother fuckers that had money or dope, and you came along and begged me not to do it. You gave me a half key on consignment, and we made money hand over fist ever since."

"That's why I would kill two-three mother fuckers for you, but right now, I need a favor until I can help myself. And I won't let you down unless they kill me. But for no other reason will I let you down or give you any excuse about your money."

Now Pharaoh was really in a bind because he had promised God that he would not never again sell heroin.

Big Ned was the reason why he had gotten out of jail. He had taken the blow meant for those trying to rob Pharaoh, which fractured Big Ned's arm. Big Ned had stayed in prison an extra year for taking Pharaoh's charge.

Looking down at Big Ned with a smile, Pharaoh set everything aside and went to the car where Big Ned was standing. He tried to hug him, but Ned was too big to be embraced.

"Come on in," Pharaoh said to Big Ned. Big Ned refused and told Pharaoh that his house was too small and that he would have a lot of trouble bending down to get in there. He said that he would have to do a lot of bending down while he was in there. So, Pharaoh went back into the house, got a grand, and gave Big Ned. He told him that he would see him in a couple of days and have something for him.

He had given glory to Pharaoh for getting out of jail and going straight to college. And or applying his business learnings to the real world and successfully making them work. For becoming a well-known young, thoughtful, and intelligent businessman. Now Gypsy had approached Pharaoh about buying some cocaine for the high society people uptown. The whores and pimps and professional people indulged in the sniffing of "the fun high" in which the high was called or referred to. Because it was a high used to party, stay awake, and indulge in sexual desires. To enjoy the beauty and temptation of things that are not supposed to be. Pharaoh told Gypsy that he had promised God that he would never sell heroin again. Gypsy told Pharaoh that cocaine was not heroin. It was not addictive like heroin. Instead, it was used to have fun or add another party to the party you already had. Gypsy explained to Pharaoh that cocaine was a "party high" and that you had to have money to indulge in it. Also, it would not harm you in any way besides keeping you awake if you did enough of it. Gypsy told Pharaoh that he had one customer in mind that Pharaoh could make a thousand dollars a day off. And that one customer would bring Pharaoh many more customers.

Now it happened that Pharaoh did follow the advice of his lifetime friend Gypsy. Pharaoh did go back to New York and purchased cocaine from some of the Spanish people that Pharaoh had met through Maria when he was selling heroin.

The Spanish people used to try to give Pharaoh Cocaine for free to bring to Baltimore to start a market for in Baltimore years ago. But Pharaoh always refused but was back in New York doing business with the Spanish people about buying cocaine.

Now Gypsy was right. The first person he brought to Pharaoh to indulge in the sale of cocaine was a number backer. He came to Pharaoh at least three times a day, and each time he came to Pharaoh, he would spend at least five hundred dollars each time.

But the Spanish people who sold Pharaoh the cocaine would continuously try to get Pharaoh to indulge in the buying and selling heroin.

Pharaoh kept turning down their offers, not wanting to break his promise to God. Even when Pharaoh offered to take a couple of keys of heroin and pay for them later, Pharaoh still refused.

Now (Satan) was steady baiting Pharaoh into a trap that would make Pharaoh break his promise to God. Concerning Pharaoh not selling any more heroin again Also for Pharaoh to believe that it was Pharaoh himself who was making all these positive moves and advancements stretching out in the business world.

Pharaoh! Nobody or anyone has even the authority to turn his head in a yes or no gesture unless God Almighty said or approved it. On earth or in heaven, righteousness and God's authority are needed in order to make anything manifest without controversy or negatives to soon be catching up. Pharaoh was well accepted in the Spanish world. Even without Maria or Stokes beside him, Pharaoh was appreciated as one who could hold his own. One of character and balls, one to be respected, and one who was a man of God. Pharaoh did not visit Stokes every time he was in New York. Nor did Pharaoh visit Maria.

When he was in New York, it would come to be that Pharaoh would not answer the phone when Maria called to have their usual Biblical conversations. Instead, Pharaoh would duck Maria's phone calls. He was not allowing himself to be enlightened with biblical discussions that would have given him the strength to sharpen his wisdom and heart. Pharaoh was super proud of the time Maria took learning, and she had taken on a steady flow of knowledge in her continuous search for the Word of God. Maria enlightened Pharaoh so much concerning The Virgin Mary for the second time. This time, Maria's findings were about how once the Virgin Mary was the teacher of Jesus by simply being His mother. Then Jesus began to be the teacher of the Virgin Mary as he taught his mother the Word of God in higher definition. From wince, He had come, what He was here to do, and why. And also who had sent Him. Pharaoh was too busy putting forth a dollar first before his God. Although Pharaoh knew not the trouble, he was heading for. He was not aware of setting God on the back burner while continuing with his life. Not realizing that there is no life without God. Even when one sets God down for a moment to continue with his life, without God and without realizing what he is doing, without God, even for a moment, then there is no life. For that moment without God leaves you vulnerable to be taken over by (Satan). For lack of God's protection, even for that one moment, without the protection from God while setting God on the back burner for even one moment could quickly turn into a day, week, month, year, or years without having God's protection.

They were sitting God on the back burner, which Pharaoh had begun to do. Power, authority, fame, money, women, and still have the privilege of having one's health, strength, mental capacity, and the right to determine right from wrong is genuinely a dangerous combination for some to have. Whether a man is a king, peasant, student, or teacher, authority, money, and power are too much For some to cope with without abusing that combination. They were having too much without knowing what to do with it or using it without abuse.

It would be decades before Pharaoh gave God the complete reigns to guide his life again. True, it would become that Pharaoh would follow some of the devilish ways of (Satan)]. While being led into temptation, the words, patterns of lust, and disobedience would become quite common to Pharaoh. (Satan) would never change Pharaoh's love and worship towards God. Nor would (Satan) ever turn Pharaoh to be evil or let Pharaoh Abuse or misuse anyone like (Satan) would try so hard to get Pharaoh to do.

God would never turn his back on Pharaoh. Nor would God ever leave Pharaoh throughout Pharaoh's trial and error with God and life upon the planet earth.

Now it came to pass that Pharaoh was feeling great about himself because when Pharaoh tried, he was not allowed to cut into the West Baltimoreans territory and sell heroin.

After Pharaoh had taken his friend Gypsy's advice and went and purchased some cocaine. Without even having anyone to sell it to, but taking Gypsy's word that Gypsy's one customer would be all Pharaoh needed for a while. Which all came true, and then the West Baltimorean, big-time hustlers started coming to Pharaoh to buy cocaine for their personal use.

The times changed, and Pharaoh was the leading man for cocaine. Cocaine became a big thing in all the cities, and billions and billions of dollars began to be spent on cocaine. All this and one hundred times more negativity had brought forth destruction and terror like never before ever seen or heard of.

This drug of fun called cocaine would bring to all the cities and towns in America to condemn, ruin and destroy their communities, neighborhoods, and families as no plague has ever done before—leaving behind dead bodies, dead souls, and the death of people's morals and principles and their Godliness. This had been the plan of (Satan) long before this present generation of people was born.

(Satan is the sole cause of all negativity in the world. He plans these destructions long before they happen, like generations ahead of the actual event or happening.

Pharaoh was sad, hurt, and ashamed of himself because Pharaoh had brought back an eighth of heroin for Big Ned. Three hours after Pharaoh gave it to him, the narcotics squad raided his house.

Big Ned was beating the police to a bloody pulp. Until they killed him, shooting him dead. His body was taken out the window because he was too big to be taken down the steps and out the front doors. And because he resided on the second floor of an apartment building, they had to lower his body down on a big machine from the second-floor window to the street.

As the years passed, Pharaoh never forgave himself for being stupid enough to trust Big Ned's life while forsaking his promise to God even though Big Ned knew not God as Pharaoh did.

Pharaoh had no excuse because Pharaoh knew God and had to know better than to taunt God with a broken promise. To be as wrong as to continue selling drugs. Drugs that bring death and violence, and the loss and respect of dignity. The loss of souls wherever drugs are, and the loss of whole families, communities, whole cities, and whole countries.

For drugs are some of the favorite devices used by Satan to destroy large volumes of lives and souls at the same time, compiling evil and perverted thoughts and actions together.

There could have been no other or better woman to serve Pharaoh. To be with him more or do more for him while he was incarcerated other than Star. It had been years since Jazzy had finally given in and divorced Pharaoh.

Even though they had never stopped caring for one another or being a part of each other's lives, through the next sixty years, they would still be for one another to help or do whatever they could for each other whenever they could.

Now Jazzy had refused to give Pharaoh a divorce for years, but finally, the day came that Jazzy did give Pharaoh a divorce.

Pharaoh felt free for the first time since he had married Jazzy. Even though Pharaoh was never sorry that he married Jazzy, Pharaoh truly loved her. They both were only children who stepped out in the world as children and into a world of adults with adult responsibilities without understanding life, love, and family survival.

Pharaoh understood that Jazzy loved him, and if Pharaoh had not been so into himself, he would have tried a little harder and just accepted one woman. The marriage of he and Jazzy would have had a much better chance to be successful, even though they were both young and still children. Pharaoh was about twenty years of age when Jazzy finally divorced. Pharaoh felt free as a bird and vowed that forty years would pass before he would ever get married again.

With Pharaoh's divorce, his life changed because Pharaoh felt free to have sex with as many females as he so chose to that would have him. Pharaoh was and had become a "ghetto celebrity" and had his choice of many females.

But because Pharaoh had a choice of females, he started to withdraw from dealing with many females. He started dealing with a few at a time even though Star was always his number one female. Pharaoh was the first to let everyone know that Star was his main girl now because Paula was no longer in the picture anymore. And he knew that God would not look down on him shamefully because he was not a married man anymore and owed vows to no one anymore.

Pharaoh knew that Paula would put her best foot forward to return to the relationship between Paula, Star, and Pharaoh. He knew that never again would he trust Paula with his heart. Nor his life because she proved to be unworthy of that position in his life. Even if she meant it not to be that way or had made a mistake and put her career in front of Pharaoh, or whatever the case may have meant to be. Pharaoh's recollection of the person and standards that Pharaoh trusted Paula to have towards him, for him, and to him, showed from her heart. To put Pharaoh first above everything, anything, anyone, or any situation.

Which was how Pharaoh *thought* the relationship was between him and Paula, as the same between Pharaoh and Star. While Paula proved not to be that loyal, Star took the reins and the leading position. She proved to be faithful, trustworthy, and reliable to do whatever was in her power to do whatever Pharaoh asked of her to do for her man, no matter what.

So, the time did come for Star to get the chance she asked Pharaoh for. To prove that she would prevail when allowed to prove her allegiance to Pharaoh for his worth, name, and soul. And for his love which she did without a doubt. And for twenty years, so did Star perform for Pharaoh.

It was the year 1975 when Pharaoh met the African girl who looked white. Her name was {Wendy Sundae} She told Pharaoh the story of Journajesty and Rhythm. It was the most exciting story that Pharaoh had ever heard. It was a story only supposed to be still known and kept alive in the memories of Wendy's family tree to be remembered. To be vouched for in any time of need or doubt, concerning any truth of this so magnificent and truly remarkable story. 1975 was also the year in which Pharaoh opened his disco nightclub and met Virginia. Who was a barmaid for Pharaoh and the only employee that Pharaoh ever had a fling with, but who was worthy in every sense of the word and would prove her loyalty to Pharaoh?

Unbeknownst to Pharaoh, this also was the year 1975 in which Pharaoh's wife would be born. Pharaoh would marry this woman twenty-four years after her birth. She would help bring Pharaoh back to his God and live a righteous life after being lost in the world for two decades of doing worldly things and associating himself with people of the world who did material things, not the things of those who love and worship God.

1975 was also the year that Pharaoh had then presently enrolled in Morgan State College. He witnessed the struggle upfront, live, and was personally involved while taking part in the changeover from Morgan as a college to Morgan as a University.

It was also the year that Pharaoh began to learn the skills in which Pharaoh became to be an outstanding and legitimate businessman from the knowledge obtained from Morgan University. Which was applied to all Pharaoh's businesses and proved successful in every way but worthy in the sense that the knowledge was mentally absorbed to become a part of Pharaoh's skills and secrets of his arsenal of expertise.

It was a very unusual hot summer day in 1975 when Pharaoh first saw the African girl Wendy Sundae. She was the teacher, instructor, and coordinator to the wonderful world of Music, peace, and coordination to vibes to heavenly thoughts and feelings.

Pharaoh would soon experience while dealing with and through a hands-on relationship with the African girl Wendy Sundae, which would prove to be rewarding, enjoyable, meaningful, calm, and beautiful—even becoming a learning experience for Pharaoh.

In the late afternoon, Pharaoh was sitting in a car that he had rented while traveling back and forth to New York. And to have while he made his rounds and presence known throughout his business circles. Both legit and illegitimate. Right after the time in which Pharaoh had used his newly learned business knowledge to take the opportunity to go in partners with two brothers. They were nephews to Star {who was the mother to Pharaoh's two sons}.

The business was a family-owned nightclub of the two nephew's fathers that had been shut down, closed, and deemed bankrupt—even owing back taxes for the business that was once functional. Now, these were the business conditions before Pharaoh decided to join forces with the two brothers and bring them back on board with the business. Pharaoh did do along with investing ten thousand dollars with one of the two brothers who also contributed ten thousand dollars. They all three became partners in the nightclub in which they all contributed different skills in making the lounge successful. Pharaoh's job was unmingling all the legal and business transactions. To free the club to be able to function legitimately. To also form a corporation, name the corporation, obtain and maintain a federal ID number. At the same time, he had to also get legitimate contracts with the liquor companies. Get the gas and electricity turned on, get a license for the liquor to be sold, and contact the cigarette companies to bring in their cigarette machines.

In which Pharaoh did do all the things he was supposed to do. Pharaoh saw that he could do these things, and it made him feel important and worthy of being somebody that Morgan University had taught the subject of business administration to.

One of the brothers who went into partnership with Pharaoh built a stage, decorated the whole club downstairs and upstairs, and loaded the club with disco lights. Seats were made into and around the wall for the downstairs club. While creating a vast dance floor in the middle of two seated bars that sold liquor to the customers in the club downstairs.

Decorating the upstairs on the second floor with lights, a fountain with running water in the middle of the floor. And also a bar, decorating the third floor with amusement game machines and a bar.

Now! Pharaoh's business with cocaine grew and grew, especially for the nighttime clientele that provided unity and fun for the nightlife. No one knew that the pleasure provided by the use of cocaine would soon turn to disaster from smoking the pipe and doing what would be known as freebasing.

While Pharaoh only sold cocaine to the hustlers and nightlife people who could afford to spend at least five hundred dollars to party with the cocaine, or a thousand dollars or more. Even though the uptown west side guys did not let Pharaoh into their heroin circle when Pharaoh had tried to indulge in their distribution of heroin circle. They did all come to Pharaoh to buy cocaine to party with.

Pharaoh's cocaine business was with personal friends only and rejected any outside people that were not regular personal friends of Pharaoh.

The business was booming both with the cocaine and with the nightclub. So much until Pharaoh had to hide his car whenever he was in the club. Because there would be from two to ten people waiting at Pharaoh's car when he would sneak out the back door or side door of the club to get to his car that was supposed to be hidden, Pharaoh started renting cars so he could change cars every week. Changing cars every week was a plus to Pharaoh, but a negative for all Pharaoh's friends that use-to-use Pharaoh's car to sleep in. Or the African girl that used to chew up all Pharaoh's chewing gum that Pharaoh left in the vehicle. Along with rolls of quarters, Pharaoh left in the car if people of a long friendship with Pharaoh or neighborhood buddies needed a sandwich, a soda, or tea or coffee in the morning. Pharaoh knew that the people in need did know where in the car to find money to take care of their need for breakfast, lunch, or dinner.

Now! It was a hot summer day when Pharaoh first noticed the African girl attending Morgan University with Pharaoh. She would always finish her classes before Pharaoh would finish his classes. The African girl, Wendy Sundae, would always ask Pharaoh if she could take his car and go for a ride and listen to W.H.U.R. on the car radio.

Wendy Sundae had to leave Morgan University to hear W.H.U.R. Morgan University also had a radio station that would not allow you to play another radio station on their campus. Not without so much static in the station, you were trying to play until it would not be worth your while to try and enjoy another radio station while on the grounds or campus of Morgan University.

Now! Pharaoh always wondered why Wendy Sundae never listened to the radio station that Baltimore's whole east side, south side, north side, and the west side was listening to.

Pharaoh just couldn't understand why Wendy Sundae had to listen to a radio station that wasn't even in Baltimore. Instead, the station was in Washington D.C.

She would also make sure she was home at night to listen to the "Quiet Storm" radio show that came on that radio station every night. She was always there from the first minute of the show to the last second. She was into that radio show with all her soul, heart, and every inch of her being.

One night, Wendy Sundae had asked Pharaoh to study and listen to the Quiet Storm radio show with her. Pharaoh told Wendy Sundae that he would study with her and listen to the radio show if she wore a dress that night.

Pharaoh had never seen Wendy Sundae in a dress. She was a woman with a great-looking body through her clothes, and Pharaoh had never seen her bare legs, and that was the reason why Pharaoh had asked her to wear a dress.

The night did come that Pharaoh did meet with Wendy Sundae, and they did studies from Morgan University while listening to the radio show. She wore a very impressive dress to Pharaoh mainly because Wendy did have hairy legs, which excited Pharaoh sexually, unbeknownst to him.

Pharaoh did get to know Wendy Sundae sexually but not before Wendy Sundae introduced Pharaoh to smoking a marijuana cigarette as they ended their study session.

They began a casual introduction to one another on a more personal and understanding level while they both enjoyed the Music on W.H.U.R.

Getting high was not a part of Pharaoh's character or personality. Pharaoh was against getting high, but he did take just two puffs off the marijuana cigarette while Wendy Sundae laid Pharaoh's head down to rest on her chest.

Even though Pharaoh was not a tittie man, he was impressed with her breasts. And as the Music played, Pharaoh understood why Wendy Sundae was so much into W.H.U.R. radio station on 96.3 FM, in Washington D.C. Pharaoh meditated wholeheartedly as he felt the vibes. He not only heard the Music but felt every beat and lyric, which provided an atmosphere of peace and heavenly thoughts and vibes.

Those moments in time laid a foundation of happiness and contentment with Wendy Sundae.

In future times, Pharaoh would take Wendy Sundae to New York with him for the company. The ride to New York Pharaoh did take quite frequently, and it was a ride that time after time, after time, became boring to him.

Wendy Sundae did help make the trip more exciting and less boring as she rode with Pharaoh more and more. They both began to know much more about each other. Pharaoh found out through conversations with Wendy Sundae that her goal in life, even before getting her degree in engineering, from Morgan University. Was to become a professional hitwoman, and she was not a woman to believe in God, which turned Pharaoh's heart away from her.

Pharaoh's God did turn his heart back towards Wendy Sundae so that Wendy Sundae would be exposed to the

Word of God, exposed to Christianity, and have a concern for the lives of others instead of the taking of life.

Pharaoh would have never taken Wendy Sundae to see Stokes or Stokes' mother. For in many ways, Pharaoh was ashamed of the fact that he was involved with a woman that did not worship or believe in God Almighty, the Creator of heaven and earth.

Nor did Pharaoh see Satan coming at him through Wendy Sundae. Wendy Sundae started becoming closer and closer to Pharaoh. She even started coming past Mama Grace's house and taking the little white baby who was the daughter of Cakes and the youngest of Pharaoh's children. So, Wendy Sundae got closer than close to Cake's daughter, Pharaoh's youngest female child.

Now! It came to pass that Pharaoh thought about Stokes and Stokes' mother so much until Pharaoh made a ritual. Every time he came to New York, he would stop past Stokes' old house where Pharaoh first met Stokes, Stokes' mother, and Stokes' wife.

Pharaoh would say a prayer for Stokes and his family, but it also seemed to be a ritual that was now always happening; Pharaoh and Wendy Sundae would get a hotel room and get high off of reefer. Pharaoh's limit was two puffs off the cigarette; he did not see Satan coming at him, trying to devour him in sin.

Satan tried to bring Pharaoh to bend down and accept some of Satan's evil ways and activities. Satan, Lucifer, or whatever name you would like to call him was scheming to bring Pharaoh to do sinful things—planning to get him to act in a very evil way and indulge in lies, perverseness, and worldly activities. Pharaoh now knew what getting high meant and felt like it was just starting with fun and laughter. Still, the monster of all highs would soon set in as the "highs" would elevate to different levels and become more profound, mature, intriguing, and dangerous. It came to be that every time that Pharaoh went to New York, he took Wendy Sundae with him. They smoked reefer and listened to Music, and then ate all kinds of goodies, foods, and nonalcoholic beverages. They would laugh until their sides were aching.

Pharaoh always brought along his Utz potato chips, Tastykake pies, and cakes from Baltimore. No one anywhere had potato chips like Utz potato chips in Baltimore, and no one had cakes and pies as good as Baltimore's Tastykake pies and cakes, either.

Now! It was 1976 and (Satan) had all types of new inventions to hold back, abuse, and misuse the Children of Jourmajesty. True, the latest technologies being developed had negativity that Satan could use against people to turn their faith in God to doubt.

Satan found that the churches were the best place for him to hide in. For where else would one *not* think Satan would be, as he upsets how to appreciate Music, for the words, lyrics, sound, rhythm, meaning and understanding, and what mental and physical relaxation Music had to offer spiritually, and even worldly.

Still, Pharaoh did not see Satan coming and trying to devour him in sin and being disobedient while not pleasing his God. Now Satan would sneak into the churches, which were the houses of Almighty God.

He brought his sinful ways onto the people of the churches that allowed Satan to take over their souls with promises. Promises of good fortune and chances to elevate themselves into higher positions in the church that would allow them to steal.

They became more prominent and authoritative as they showed off their new clothes and fancy automobiles. When they showed up *on time* Sunday morning for church after they had been out partying, cheating, lying, drinking, and using drugs. Along with other sinful things that occurred the night before they went to church the following day.

Pharaoh and Wendy Sundae were together during one of those times, getting high off reefer and enjoying music, eating, and sex. In New York, Pharaoh found a loaded magnum, a shoulder holster, and a small-caliber snub nose gun in some of Wendy Sundae's possessions.

It was in luggage that Wendy Sundae used as her overnight bag. When Pharaoh asked Wendy Sundae why she had it and its purpose for the guns, Wendy Sundae explained to Pharaoh that she was a professional hitwoman.

She wanted to know if she could be Pharaoh's protector, bodyguard, and hitwoman for whatever problems that might arouse in Pharaoh's businesses, both legal and illegitimate.

Pharaoh was astonished, super surprised, and amazed at what Wendy Sundae had just told him! Sitting down slowly on the bed and just holding his head in his hands, he then looked up at Wendy Sundae and said, "What makes you think that I need a bodyguard, and are you a hitwoman?"

"Do you go around killing people for money?" Pharaoh asked Wendy Sundae. Pharaoh was shouting and screaming when Wendy Sundae shouted back at Pharaoh, saying, "Pharaoh…You handle money! You have people working for you that always owe you money!"

"You have authority that people have to abide by whether they like it or not, and with that said, anyone that is in the position that you are in is powerful and needs people like me to serve out enforcement strategies from time to time!"

"I am a Christian by faith, and I don't need anyone to fight my battles, kill anyone, or enforce any situations that I am involved with!" Pharaoh shouted back at Wendy Sundae.

"And I have to answer to Almighty God for everything that I get involved with. So how can I tell Almighty God that I gave you permission to kill someone or hurt someone because they owe me money or did not follow my instructions? How Wendy Sundae could I possibly do that. How?"

"The same way you do when you sell cocaine. Do you ask your God can you do that, or is it just alright for you to do that?"

The tension was now set in the room after Wendy Sundae made that final remark to Pharaoh. The silence was the main factor with Wendy Sundae and Pharaoh.

It was the first argument and misunderstanding that Pharaoh and Wendy Sundae had in their relationship, and it was quite different. Pharaoh had been smoking reefer earlier, and now it had a different mental and physical effect on Pharaoh, which was disastrous.

Not too much more was said that evening between Pharaoh and Wendy Sundae, and it mentally bothered Pharaoh very much so. In the wee hours in the morning, Pharaoh decided to break this mental anguish that was standing between him and Wendy Sundae while in bed together.

Pharaoh wrapped Wendy Sundae in his arms and turned her over to face him while Pharaoh proceeded to kiss her, feel her private parts, and nibble on her breast, but to Pharaoh's surprise, something seemed wrong in this situation. Even though Wendy Sundae did settle into the sexual mood with Pharaoh, something seemed and felt wrong and out of place, and it was not right; it was peculiar and a downright turn-off.

Pharaoh was beginning to lose his desire for sex when Pharaoh realized that Wendy Sundae was soaked in sweat, maybe because she was a hairy woman all over her body, was to Pharaoh's opinion. Wendy Sundae felt like a giant wet fish, and Pharaoh confronted Wendy Sundae about the matter and asked what was wrong with her because this had never happened before.

It was then that Wendy Sundae told Pharaoh about her doctor's prescription concerning Wendy Sundae's medical condition whenever she became agitated. Then Pharaoh asked Wendy Sundae what the doctor's prescription for Wendy Sundae's drug was.

But Wendy Sundae asked Pharaoh why he was asking her all these questions. Was he the F.B.I. or some other agency with authority that needed to know other people's business? Disregarding Wendy Sundae's questions towards him, he continued the questioning towards Wendy Sundae. "What was the drug that the doctor prescribed for you to calm you down when you became over excited?"

"Heroin! Heroin!" Wendy Sundae screamed at Pharaoh.

"Heroin I sniff heroin. I am not a junkie, but I sniff heroin. And I know how you feel about anyone who uses heroin, and because I didn't want to lose you."

"I thought I could hide it from you. Pharaoh, you have changed my life around for the better, and if it had not been for you, I would still be trying to fool myself that it is alright to kill people for money regardless of how much I could get. And I feel as though you think you are better than anyone else because you don't use drugs, you don't drink alcohol, you don't smoke cigarettes, and you don't even smoke."

"Oh, and oh yeah, you love and worship your God, you to me are Mr. Goody Two Shoes, but one day you will know what it feels like to need something that is no good for you but something that you need. To function properly."

It was 4 am when Pharaoh woke Wendy Sundae up from her sleep and told her that a cab was waiting outside the hotel. Her bags were already packed, and 200 dollars for her cab fare and train ticket were on the desk by the telephone.

"And the train will be at the train station in one hour and fifteen minutes, which gives you plenty of time to get there, and there is no need for you to say any more than you have already said."

"And maybe even another time we might be sociable. You have way over bided your say so, your authority, respect, and manners towards me for this night.

Wendy Sundae was not stupid and nor was she foolish. She knew that there was nothing else, no apology or no forgiveness, that could have been worth trying. Wendy

Sundae did respect Pharaoh, and she cared for and about him. So, she dropped her head, bent down on her knees, and kissed both of Pharaoh's feet, in a gesture, trying to show Pharaoh how sorry she was for her negative comments and actions towards him, and without saying a word, picked up the money and left.

Now, of course, Pharaoh had already sent for Virginia. She was halfway to New York coming from Baltimore. She also would smoke some reefer with Pharaoh, enjoy eats while indulging in laughter, fun, and good meaningful conversation.

Wendy Sundae would always be the first female to have taken Pharaoh to his first indulgence of recreational highs of a reefer with food, fun, and sex, along with good meaningful music and inspiring conversation.

Virginia was a barmaid that worked for Pharaoh, and in fact, Virginia was the head barmaid in Pharaoh's nightclub. She was a beautiful woman with the God-given talent to attract men to her for conciliation of the soul and mind. She always had time, or instead took time, to hear one's problems. Virginia could drink and hold her liquor. She also kept tabs on all the bars and accounted for all the alcohol sold. She was not a thief nor a tattle tale of what was happening in the bar. Besides all that, she cared for Pharaoh, and Pharaoh cared for her very much.

Now! It happened to be that while Pharaoh was incarcerated, both Mr. Robinson, the numbers Mogul of West Baltimore, and Mr. Torain, the numbers Mogul of East Baltimore, both died. Mr. Robinson, the Numbers Mogul of West Baltimore, was also the owner of Robinson's crap house, Pharaoh's favorite gambling place. It was the most famous and well-known place in Baltimore to gamble and had closed down because of the death of Mr. Robinson. So, all the regular customers that always gambled in Robinson's crap house missed the action.

All the nightclub owners would get a call that night before the club would close on Friday and Saturday nights to inform the club owner which club the floating game would be held. That is how everyone that was a usual player of the high rolling crap games would know where to go and continue to gamble safely because no one could guarantee the kind of safety and honesty that Mr. Robinson could.

Pharaoh never got a chance to say hello, thank you, or goodbye to Mr. Torain, who was indeed the numbers Mogul of East Baltimore. He had been so very good to Pharaoh. He was the one who had gotten Pharaoh out on a fifty-thousand-dollar bail when Pharaoh's bail man could not put up the bail money, which was too large in that day and time.

Pharaoh missed them both, both Mr. Robinson and Mr. Torain were teachers and examples for Pharaoh as men and as special people in Pharaoh's life whom he respected, loved, and sort of patterned some of his ways, character, and intellect of the hustling world after.

Gambling was still Pharaoh's favorite pastime, and you could find him wherever the floating game was on the weekends and sometimes during the weekdays. Pharaoh now had a business of his own that dipped and dabbed all day with personal friends and associates buying cocaine for pleasure. The weekends were booming, especially from 12 am through

6 am; business was tremendous and gave Pharaoh little time to gamble. However, Pharaoh did not mind not gambling when he was making money.

It was 1976, and the narcotics squad had started and was in full force. From 1 am until around 5 am, there was little narcotic squad enforcement in Baltimore. So that was the time in which Pharaoh did almost all his business of selling cocaine.

Now all of a sudden, cocaine sales were in demand, and it seemed as if everyone was sniffing cocaine for fun to party with. So many times, Pharaoh was called to deliver some cocaine where he was asked if he would like to join in the sexual activities and have some fun.

So many times, when Pharaoh got to the destination to deliver the cocaine, Pharaoh knew the male or female participating in the sexual fun. Mostly the females would try to pull him to the side and ask him to please, not expose them for where they were or what they were doing or who they were with. Pharaoh made it his business to never indulge in any activities, be it be sexual or not, because Pharaoh was shy and very personal. He never participated in any activities with cocaine with anyone at any time.

While traveling from one hotel to another time after time, it was a fun time, and Pharaoh was invited to so many private houses where people party with the cocaine. During that time, Pharaoh's beeper went off, and when Pharaoh called his base number to find out who had called him. At that day and time, beepers were in style and use.

The beepers then had not yet become able to display the number of the person calling; it only just beeped. Pharaoh's set up with his beeper was that when his beeper would beep, he would then call his home base, and the lady answering the phone would tell Pharaoh who the person was and their phone number.

One of these calls that Pharaoh received from his base was that the lady working there for Pharaoh gave him the number to the person who called. It was a personal friend of Pharaoh's named {Big Head Moe}.

He was a major drug dealer and a pimp who took his whores out to steal expensive clothes and jewelry. When Pharaoh called the number given to him by his base, Big Head Moe told Pharaoh that he had just brought a new house and had some friends over, and he wanted to celebrate. He asked if Pharaoh could bring him over something that would cost a grand so they all could enjoy themselves.

Pharaoh knew that meant Big Head Moe wanted to spend a grand in cocaine. Big Head Moe gave Pharaoh the directions to the new house that he had just bought. In the same direction, Big Head Moe, Proposition Joe, and Pharaoh all three used to go towards the Night Races at Charlestown Horse Racing. When Pharaoh did reach Big Head Moe's house, he was excited to show Pharaoh the new house. In showing Pharaoh the new house, Pharaoh saw his best friend {Dapping Slim's} wife. Which was Pharaoh's other best friend {Sharkskin} brother. But this sight was something that Pharaoh was beginning to see quite regularly concerning people he knew when he delivered cocaine to hotels, houses, and rooms all across the whole City of Baltimore. Wives and husbands were cheating on each other, and those that weren't cheating on each other were doing sexual acts that were disgusting, embarrassing, and things to be ashamed of. It was then that Big Head Moe asked Pharaoh if he wanted sex with any female in the house. When Pharaoh said no, Big Head Moe called out Pharaoh's best friend, Dapping Slim's wife, and asked Pharaoh in front of her if Pharaoh wanted to have sex with her. Dapping Slim's wife and Pharaoh were best friends, and many times had Pharaoh and Dapping Slim been out together on dates with their female friends. And besides that, Pharaoh knew Dapping Slim's wife's family, and they were all respectful of each other and the best of friends. Pharaoh was not high off cocaine, but he looked into Dapping Slim's wife's eyes and saw the shame and embarrassment that she was confronted with, and Pharaoh simply said, "No, I'm cool, that's alright." It was at that moment that Pharaoh no longer respected Big Head Moe. And forever, Pharaoh would hold that against Big Head Moe. Pharaoh knew that Big Head Moe knew that Dapping Slim was Pharaoh's best friend. Big Head Moe knew that this was Pharaoh's best friend's wife and that what Big Head Moe had just done was disrespectful, animalistic, humiliating, and downright wrong! That incident and because of others incidents that were similar, Pharaoh never again took cocaine to anyone's house, hotel, or any place again. Instead, Pharaoh would pay a runner to make those trips for cocaine sales. It began to be that all the bars and nightclubs you went to always had someone in the bathrooms selling cocaine. The least one could spend twenty-five dollars, which bought you half of the smallest spoon on the ring, which was a quarter spoon. Which half of that quarter spoon would sell for twenty-five dollars, a half teaspoon would sell for fifty dollars, and a whole teaspoon would sell for one hundred dollars. No one was standing on corners selling cocaine as of yet but in all bars, nightclubs, and any place where adults would gather. Somewhere in that building, usually in the bathrooms, sitting on a barstool, or etc., you would find someone selling cocaine. The drugs were kept away from the children, while the cocaine was sold only in glassine bags or simple aluminum foil. The cocaine dealer always had some cocaine in a dollar bill so you could see, taste, and try his product before you brought it. At first, mainly hustlers and nightlife people were indulging in buying cocaine. Soon, people tried to outdo each other by selling the cocaine cheaper than the next man, and instead of having to pay twenty dollars for the price of cocaine, people started selling it for ten dollars. It made it much more able for many more people to afford it. It was like an epidemic that sped up, and the whole damn country got caught up in that cocaine epidemic in some way or another. Then, this cocaine thing began to be a menace, and the fault was blamed on so many people and so many situations. They were all wrong even though the white man and the cartels were the main sources of the cocaine blame. They all were wrong because this was a scheme that Satan had set forth over a generation before it happened. Satan destroyed hundreds of thousands of people who lost their lives, their souls, and their way as they got caught up in this great plan of destruction that only Satan himself could have created. As it is, Satan is responsible for all negativity on the planet earth. When it comes to the things humans are to blame for, Satan is always behind the scenes to create negativity for the human race. Especially for people that love and worship God. Satan had plans for the human race through the distribution of cocaine. The sale and use of the drug would come pretty soon, unbeknownst to the world. Through cocaine, Satan would make a monster of in the coming future, and through other drugs that Satan had not made up yet or even named. He will bend the backs of many nations and destroy millions of lives, and the people will blame everything and everyone but Satan. He will be the real cause and the creator and lord of evil, corruption, strife, and fear, which will majorly destroy the human race. Believing in God Almighty and His only begotten Son Jesus Christ is our way, the only way in which to maintain our share in salvation, and forever peace, and tranquility forever. {so believe the Christian faith}. The floating crap games that were now taking the place of the crap games that used to be in Mr. Robinson's crap house were having trouble surviving. The invasion of the cocaine epidemic was starting to show greed, unfairness, and low-down dirty schemes and tricks, and the after-effects were starting to show anywhere that money or cocaine was in play.

People were now stealing out the cocaine bags before they were sold. People were starting to make shady deals, and no one could be trusted anymore. The crap games had to continually keep floating around so the stick-up guys would not know where they had a game. Then all sorts of safety procedures had to be put in play to protect the players.

Pharaoh was now thirty-one years of age, and for the first time in his life, he started witnessing homeless people living in empty houses in Baltimore. There became more and more empty houses and more and more homeless people. They became homeless due to their own desire to choose to buy drugs with their money rather than to pay their bills. Some people would have rather lived in an empty house than pay their rent or mortgage. Then they could use their rent money to continually buy cocaine which was now smokeable by freebasing, which turned recreational cocaine into a monster as no one had ever seen before.

Now! There was a time when heroin was a threat to society. The community in which you lived. And a threat to the future of so many Americans. That lost their souls or their careers. And their futures. They even lost their health and strength, for the alcohol people drank, the cigarettes people smoked. The devious and evil thoughts that were a part of the lives of the people that did indulge in these things were all originated, created, initiated, and put into play by Satan. He is the mastermind and C.E.O. of negativity, sin, and destruction.

Especially destruction of one's soul, but because Satan is a spirit and cannot be seen with the naked eye unless he comes in the form of someone else or something else. Even then, it would redirect that seen image from being Satan. Therefore, he is invisible, out of sight, and overlooked as the original creator of all sin and destruction. And terrorizer of the human race. So, we as humans look for the closest thing, reason, or person that we can label as the actual cause of a problem caused by Satan. (SATAN), the only one we cannot see.

Now! It must be understood because you definitely can't see Satan with the naked or human eye; Satan must be included in figuring out how to deal with the problem. Satan is the problem, and Almighty God is the only being that can deal with Satan because God is the creator of Satan. Satan tried to be like God after God allowed Satan so much authority in heaven and many angels' overseer.

You must come to God first in prayer, so God can give you safe passage with Satan while God deals with Satan. But remember, God's days and nights are many more than your accumulated days and nights. To deal with Almighty God is first to have faith in what you are doing and have faith in your God. The only true and living God of all religions.

Now! The use of cocaine became monstrous after people started freebasing with cocaine, and the creators of this freebasing thing started mixing all sorts of animal tranquilizers, embalming fluid, and other abusive and unsafe things with the cocaine. The chemicals were all detrimental to the human body.

It seems to be the present time that people everywhere were preparing themselves for the coming of the worst.

The taxi cab drivers were being robbed and killed for as little as thirty-five dollars. The bus companies had long before stopped the bus drivers from carrying cash to change money for the bus customers.

The businesses were forced to get started to get the bulletproof glass installed all around their stores and other places of business. Because of so much new technology invented, one person working in the home could no more pay all the bills. New technology meant colored television compared to just black and white TV, and the remote-control device made everyone too lazy even to get up and change the TV station.

Then came the cell phones, and cable which were all additional bills for the household. All household bills increased while jobs were now hard to get.

Pretty soon, the street gangs were developing in Baltimore when there were none at one time. They were a menace to the streets of Baltimore. They sold drugs, intercepted our youth, and guided them in the wrong direction.

Besides the gangs came the stick-up boys.

They robbed the drug dealers who were seen as "soft. The soft drug dealers started retaliating, and the drive-by shootings began of the young kids killing one another over drug-related territories. They also killed over arguments where people were not paying for the drugs when given credit.

Or the ones that just fucked the money up by being their own best customers and having to pay with their lives. Sometimes being put in a wheelchair from bullet wounds that did not kill them but paralyzed them for life.

There were so many people being paralyzed that they had to use walkers or wheelchairs. Ramps and exits with handicap access had to be built. Now the people paralyzed and using walkers could participate in community activities. Even the City of Baltimore had to build entrances and exits for the sidewalks for the paralyzed and people riding bicycles. It was in the thoughts and minds of the City of Baltimore when they made available the entrances and exits of the sidewalks. So many people were paralyzed from violence from the war on drugs in Baltimore until that became the primary purpose of Baltimore's ramps and sidewalks, entrances, and exits.

Now! Satan was in existence before God even chartered out the earth. Satan has repeatedly used the same tactic since before the beginning of time on earth.

Two of Satan's most relied-on tactics on humans are fear and worry. Anxiety can cause one to destroy themselves by letting their imagination run away with thoughts of what could happen and endangering themselves by believing what they think is true even though it hasn't even become true yet.

Fearing that it might come true or that it is true when as a fact, it is not true. But just the thought of it being true keeps one up all night without the privilege of sleep, rest, or peace. It destroys the mind and body day after day until one of them breaks. When their mind or body, or both mind and body, give in, it opens the door for medical problems: strokes, heart attacks, high blood pressure, diabetes, and more. Fear brings death or destruction to the body.

It is a plus too (Satan) who hates and despises humans and cares not for his Creator, Almighty God. Who will one day destroy Satan because God has said He would destroy Satan in God's book, The Bible, which is the word of God. God indeed says that He will destroy Satan.

Now! Satan has always enjoyed creating chaos, confusion, and strife within the churches or religious institutions. It delights Satan so much to see one of God's people commit sin and have to face the whole congregation when they are caught in the act of embarrassment, humiliation, mental pain as they tear a hole in the structure both at home and in their church family.

Pharaoh saw all these things occur; he still did not recognize Satan coming at him. When Pharaoh saw people that he looked up to, trusted, and believed in indulging in the use of snorting cocaine, he did go straight to his health teacher. He had to inquire about what negative effects cocaine would have on you if and when one decided to indulge in sniffing the drug. What Pharaoh was more concerned about than anything else was would you and could you get hooked on cocaine, and become a junkie, and need to have cocaine constantly. Now! Pharaoh's health instructor, who was unknowing to Pharaoh, was himself a cocaine sniffer. Who told Pharaoh his version that sniffing cocaine was not detrimental to one's health and by no means was cocaine a habit-forming drug which might have been accurate at that present time. When you finished sniffing cocaine, the health instructor told Pharaoh, you have no problem stopping urges afterward for more cocaine, but you would have problems going to sleep if you sniffed too much cocaine. While having the enormous sex drive it gives you is beyond imagination.

Pharaoh was a man of two worlds: the worldly world and the Christian world, or the world of righteousness. He had heroes in each world. In the Christian world were Mama Grace and all her sisters of the Prayer Mob, Pharaoh's heroes of Christianity. In the righteous world were Daddy Grace, Mama Grace's husband, and the man who played the fatherly role to Pharaoh who provided food, shelter, comfort, and a righteous, Christian home for Pharaoh. That was one of Pharaoh's heroes of righteousness along with Mr. Gray, who provided the image of the other righteous heroes who was the father of Jazzy.

These men would forever stay in Pharaoh's life, mind, heart, and soul as Christian and righteous heroes. They both were men that Pharaoh would like to pattern his life after at another day and time, for they were providers for their families. They were both in the lives of the children who helped to cook food and had no problem minding, teaching, and being involved in their children's lives.

Another hero was Mr. Robinson, who ran the crap house that Pharaoh loved. He was the numbers mogul of West Baltimore. There was Mr. Torain, the mogul number backer of East Baltimore.

Both were Pharaoh's role models and heroes of the streets and the worldly people and men that Pharaoh would like to pattern his life after.

While being of the same character, morals, and principles as these men, Mr. Robinson and Mr. Torain were both respected, loved, and appreciated by many people.

They both provided help and concern while showing the way for generations to follow after. Showing images of successful business people who dominated, giving support, respect, and survival for not only themselves but for many other people at a time when black people were being held back, disrespected and abused with no place to turn.

They both used their money to help send people to college, pay bills or car payments. Also, pay gas and electric, water bills, food, and rent. And many other things to help people out in the neighborhoods.

Presently, Pharaoh did not like being himself, nor his job of delivering cocaine to people, because it had become downright disgusting.

Meeting and seeing the wives and girlfriends of the men Pharaoh knew well were cheating on their spouses. At first, it was fun or exciting, but now Pharaoh didn't like that job anymore and had someone else to make the cocaine deliveries.

He was tired of seeing the shame in people's eyes and the expressions on their faces when Pharaoh showed up as the delivery man for the cocaine.

When Pharaoh found out that his role model and friend Propositions Joe was also sniffing cocaine, it was a difficult task. Even though Proposition Joe did sniff cocaine, he never offered to buy any from Pharaoh. Maybe he didn't want Pharaoh to know that part of him. Pharaoh was surprised to find out that Proposition Joe did sniff cocaine. Half or more than half of the hustling world did sniff cocaine at that time, and many hustlers did sniff heroin also. Pharaoh was starting to look at sniffing cocaine as not being such a bad thing, and Pharaoh still did not see Satan coming.

It was the year 1976, and Pharaoh was thirty-one years of age. His first child Linda Lee Gold was now fifteen years of age, while Pharaoh's oldest son Gerard Lee Gold was ten years of age. Pharaoh's youngest son Avis Lee Gold was not quite ten years old. Gail Lee Gold, Pharaoh's second-oldest daughter, was six, and Pharaoh's baby girl at that time, who was Debra Lee Gold was five.

Now, cocaine and drug selling were still only done in bars or nightclubs and politely and smoothly, not outright bold about it. Pretty soon, the drugs and pills of all types would be sold on the street corners by the young, who would soon be selling drugs to the old.

Pharaoh was a well-known man around the city. He was also a man that was always involved in all his children's schoolwork. By attending their schools and talking to their teachers.

At that particular time, one could come and pay a visit to the school and talk with the teachers concerning your child's schoolwork, behavior, attendance, and respect towards the teachers. Parent visits were welcomed. They were met and greeted, giving ten or fifteen minutes dedicated to your questions and concerns with a great response to your visit to the school.

Pharaoh started to see some of the teachers in the classrooms as the same male and female people he had just left in the clubs and hotels and after-hour joints just three and four hours before.

Now it was late one night when Pharaoh was on his way to one of the floating crap games after being called at his club and given the location of the floating crap game.

He knew that he should bring along a couple of five hundred dollars packaged rounds of cocaine for his friends and associates that would take him in the bathroom to purchase them.

At the same time, Pharaoh was wondering how well and exciting it would be to experience the sexual feelings that the cocaine would bring upon his body after so much talk had been about experiencing sex while indulging in the use of cocaine.

It was then, at that moment, that Pharaoh put a small amount of cocaine on a playing card like he had watched so many other men and women do. He went over to the mirror in his home, and there he snorted the cocaine. There came to his nostril a sort of burning sensation. Pharaoh had to clear his throat afterward, but that was all that happened.

Pharaoh still did not see Satan coming. Days passed, and Pharaoh continued every day to snort some cocaine. Many years later, would find Pharaoh still sniffing cocaine every night. Never in the day, unless Pharaoh would sometimes be finishing up his cocaine action in the early morning from late the night before.

Satan was there, and Pharaoh knew then that Satan was there, but Pharaoh never saw Satan coming. God did bless Pharaoh with no desire to sniff cocaine in the daytime, which was a blessing in disguise for Pharaoh.

Pharaoh would sniff cocaine only at night, and Pharaoh never sniffed raw cocaine. Always cocaine that he had diluted with a cutting agent to make the drug less potent.

Now! True, Pharaoh was not a real smoker of cigarettes, but when Pharaoh was gambling, he would smoke a pack of cigarettes at night. When he finished smoking and gambling, he would not smoke any more cigarettes until the next night.

Pharaoh could not stand the smell of cigarette smoke unless he was gambling or sniffing cocaine. He found that when he would sniff cocaine, he had to smoke a cigarette only at night. Pharaoh only smoked cigarettes at night when he was gambling but now, when the night time came, and it was around ten or eleven o'clock at night, it started to be that Pharaoh would start sniffing cocaine by himself. The enjoyment was only that the cocaine gave Pharaoh an urge and knack for a cigarette, and the cigarette was enjoyable.

Pharaoh had to clear his throat by saying, "UMM It also lost Pharaoh's desire to sleep, but that was the limit of the effect the cocaine had on him. This was Pharaoh's introductory to cocaine and what it brought to the table for Pharaoh. He didn't realize it, but he did not see Satan coming to introduce him to get high. But now Pharaoh knew through the African girl Wendy Sundae what it meant to be high from the marijuana when he smoked reefer with her as they laughed, greeted their appetites, drank nonalcoholic beverages, and made conversation about many subjects. But the matter of fact was, Pharaoh now knew what getting high meant and felt like even though it was just reefer and with fun and laughter, the monster of all highs would soon set in as the "highs" would elevate to different levels. It would become more profound, mature, and intriguing, and dangerous. Now, as he found that sniffing cocaine had become a daily routine with him, even though this daily ritual only occurred at night, it would go on for hours before Pharaoh decided to end that cocaine session for that night.

The cocaine would eliminate his sleep from coming, which took him further and further into the wee hours. Pharaoh couldn't understand why he continued to sniff cocaine because he didn't get anything from it besides enjoying a cigarette and saying UMMM as he cleared his throat. But for some reason, cocaine was beginning to be a part of Pharaoh's daily new lifestyle.

Pharaoh had not seen Maria for a long time before the last time that Maria threatened Wendy Sundae for talking smart to Maria over the phone. Maria had called Mama Grace to say hello and asked to speak to Pharaoh. When Mama Grace called Pharaoh to the phone, Wendy Sundae heard some of the conversations between Maria and Pharaoh.

Wendy Sundae picked up the phone and told Maria not to call that number ever again for no reason, or Wendy Sundae would kick Maria's ass. Before the third hour had passed that the phone went dead in Wendy Sundae's ear, Maria was there and had broken into Wendy Sundae's car, in which Maria had heard Wendy Sundae tell Pharaoh where she had parked her car. Maria had sat in Wendy Sundae's car for another two hours. Before Wendy Sundae exited from Mama Grace's house to go home, Maria put a 45 automatic to Wendy Sundae's head and made Wendy Sundae drive six blocks away from Mama Grace's house. Then Maria made Wendy Sundae take off her shoes and clothes down to Wendy Sundae's bra and panties. Then Maria told Wendy Sundae that this was only the beginning of how she would embarrass Wendy Sundae if Wendy Sundae ever uttered another word to Maria. Whether it be a good night, good morning, or Goodbye, Maria would make Wendy Sundae wish that she was dead and had never been born.

"If you never believe anything or anyone in life before or ever again, believe me," Maria said, then taking Wendy Sundae's car keys and driving off in Wendy Sundae's car. She left Wendy Sundae standing there in her underwear! Maria drove back to her car, left Wendy Sundae's car up the street in Mama Grace's Block, and got out of Wendy Sundae's car. Then Maria got back in her car, leaving Wendy Sundae's car and keys, and drove back to New York without letting anyone but her and Wendy Sundae know what had happened between Wendy Sundae and Maria.

Now! It was quite a while before Pharaoh found out about what Maria had done to Wendy Sundae because Wendy Sundae thought that Pharaoh already knew about the unpleasant and embarrassing thing that Maria had done to her. When Wendy Sundae found out that Pharaoh did not know about that so embarrassing thing that Maria had done to her, Wendy Sundae was too embarrassed to tell Pharaoh about it.

Now! Maria had talked to Pharaoh a couple of times after that incident with Wendy Sundae but had never mentioned what she had done to Wendy Sundae. Now Pharaoh was looking into the beautiful face of Maria, and Pharaoh just had to smile. But it was a pleasing smile, a forgiving smile, and I still love you smile.

And the greeting hug between Maria and Pharaoh was like the first intriguing hug they used to give one another when they first met and were first dating. That is when Maria whispered in Pharaoh's ear and told Pharaoh that she had been diagnosed with throat cancer and was given less than sixty days to live.

The cancer had gone too far without being treated. And that she was on her way back to her country to visit her family and to die. Now! Pharaoh was furious with that sort of talk coming from Maria.

Pharaoh scolded Maria for not having faith, but Maria interrupted Pharaoh's conversation and scolding by putting her finger up to her lip in a hush-up position.

Then saying, "Pharaoh! I'm going to die. Please let it go." The conversation was briefly silent for a moment. Then Pharaoh smiled a very large smile and said, "I believe my God is testing your faith because he is going to make you a witness, a living, breathing witness. For no man can tell you your death date or the right time of your birth. He might be right one time, wrong ten times, or the wrong one time, and right ten times. For no one knows every time but Almighty God about one's calculations of another person's coming into the world or going out. Or even where they are going after leaving the earth."

It was then that Maria told Pharaoh that she thanks God every day of her life now for bringing Pharaoh into her life and teaching her of Almighty God and his begotten Son Jesus Christ our Lord and Savior.

At that very moment came a sudden downpour of rain, and Pharaoh hid his face in the long black and silver-streaked shiny hair of Maria as she promised to always and forever love Pharaoh.

Maria stayed with Pharaoh for two days and two nights before she left to go home to her country, never knowing that she would never see, hear from, or be in touch with Pharaoh again.

Maria would not die in sixty days as the doctors diagnosed her. Still, Maria would live another fifty years totaling well in her nineties in age, teaching Christianity to her people and especially the children, and becoming one that is a witness in truth and faith to testify for miracles that happened in her life, and about the one and only living God Almighty, besides His Son Jesus Christ who also is God.

Now! Pharaoh did tell Maria about him sniffing cocaine, and Pharaoh asked Maria's opinion on him sniffing cocaine. Pharaoh was very hesitant concerning Pharaoh sniffing cocaine, but Pharaoh did not want Maria to know that he had started to sniff cocaine for some odd reason.

Maria answered Pharaoh by explaining that it was something that she had done for almost twenty years and that it had never really hurt her in any way, except not allowing her to sleep sometimes.

"But when and if you ever become paranoid, then that is the sign of letting you know, most definitely, that it's past the time to quit."

"But cocaine affects different people in different ways, but cocaine is usually done for pleasure, but it can be abused."

"I am not one to tell another what to do or how to do it, but I don't think that your God would be pleased with you sniffing cocaine."

"But I have come to realize that you are still a young man with a lot to learn, experience, create, and live. Your own experience is the best way to learn about things that you are curious about or participating in."

Now Mama Grace did shed tears over Maria's fate that had been told to her by the doctors. Mama Grace did assemble her Prayer Mob to have prayer for Maria even though Maria had left to go back to her country.

The Prayer Mob did pray and pray and pray for Maria, her situation, and for God to allow her to have the strength and faith in God, That she needed to go through this trial and tribulation period of dedication. Most of all, the Prayer Mob headed by Sister Grace, mother, teacher, and advisor in Jesus Christ and Almighty God, prayed that Maria would have the strength and the faith to accept whatever God allowed her outcome to be.

Time was passing as it came to be that one night when Pharaoh received the phone call where the floating crap game would be.

Pharaoh decided to sniff a little cocaine before he got there, knowing that many people already there would have also had a little toot of cocaine.

Pharaoh did bring enough to sell a couple of five-hundred-dollar packs of cocaine to people participating in the game. To Pharaoh's surprise, the cocaine that Pharaoh had sniffed made him feel very uncomfortable, stupid, and not want to be around anyone at all.

Pharaoh could not concentrate on his gambling because he felt uncomfortable. Pharaoh made a decision right then and there to either stop gambling or stop sniffing cocaine. He knew that he would never do both of them again.

Pharaoh loved gambling more than anything that he had ever done before, and it was something that he had been doing all his life since he was around seven or eight years of age, and he was good at it.

Pharaoh could never see himself quitting gambling, but it was something about this cocaine that Pharaoh enjoyed. Even though Pharaoh could not explain it, he enjoyed sniffing cocaine and didn't even know why.

That was when Pharaoh decided not to gamble anymore with the floating games. The floating crap games were an extension of Mr. Robinson's crap games and were known from coast to coast. After the club closed, Pharaoh went home to sit down, smoke a joint, and sniff some cocaine. Pharaoh was thinking about some nights in the summer; when the kids were out of school or on the weekends when the kids were still in school, Pharaoh took his kids to all-night restaurants. They all enjoyed the wee hours in the morning together. But always after eating with the kid, all the kids were taken home to their different houses.

Pharaoh sat at home alone and enjoyed sniffing a little cocaine and taking a puff or two off a joint and then just relaxing and letting his mind meditate on his day that had just passed. What he did wrong and what he did right. How safe was his actions to put security on his freedom?

Pharaoh talked to God less and less to find out the approval rate of his actions and how well he was pleasing his God. Pharaoh began not to walk and talk with God much. Because he was in too much of a hurry to get home and indulge in getting high Off sniffing cocaine and smoking a joint, which had moved up from a hail or two off of a joint to smoking a half of a joint and from sniffing a little quarter spoon of cocaine to sniffing two little quarter spoons of cocaine.

Again, Pharaoh was not aware of Satan coming at him because it was all being camouflaged by the cocaine and reefer that Pharaoh was using to get high every day now. While also finding that after he was through relaxing and chilling, he would go upstairs in his bedroom and enjoy sexual activity with his female friend that seemed to be much better after he had participated in the use of cocaine and reefer. But, Pharaoh had to have time to let his body simmer down from all the excitement that the high was giving him.

The cocaine and reefer highs were becoming quite daily, but always after closing the nightclub.

True, it was that whenever Pharaoh indulged in using cocaine, that for a fact, Pharaoh was not a people person. In fact, besides choosing a very particular lady friend to be with sometimes whenever Pharaoh was getting high.

Then he chose to be alone because he could not stand to let anyone see him high or indulging in high material in any way, shape, or form.

Cocaine was most definitely not a good drug for Pharaoh because Pharaoh was already not a people person.

Life was good for Pharaoh, and for him to be a young black man, he was headed in the right direction. Or at least that is what Pharaoh thought because again, Pharaoh didn't see Satan coming.

Satan took Pharaoh from one level to the next, in climbing the ladder to identifying with the sinful activities of Satan. As one walks slowly away from the concern of pleasing God to Satan's sinful and harmful ways, even though one might not observe immediately ones changing methods of not pleasing God, but doing the will of Satan.

Satan deceives all by placing something that one needs, wants, and desires in front of them without the pressure of thinking that they are doing wrong. As one involves himself in the matter, then it is seen that it is wrong, but it is too late because one is already engaged in wrong or sinful activities brought on and tricked by Satan. So, one accepts his sinful and wrong ways and chalks it up as something that is not that bad and is beneficial to that individual.

Now! Pharaoh had not seen Wendy Sundae for a while and was surprised when she popped up at Pharaoh's night-club one night. Among the understandings that Pharaoh and Wendy Sundae had, Wendy Sundae was never to come looking for Pharaoh unless Pharaoh had asked Wendy Sundae to meet him someplace at some particular place and time.

Wendy Sundae was presently at the nightclub looking for Pharaoh, and to Pharaoh's surprise, Wendy Sundae was crying hysterically and could not be calmed by anyone.

Pharaoh's first thought was that Wendy Sundae was putting on an act so Pharaoh would not be angry with her for coming to the nightclub without getting an okay from Pharaoh, Or being told to come to the nightclub and what time to be there.

As soon as Wendy Sundae saw Pharaoh, she screamed out in her African broken English accent voice, "They killed them! They have killed my brothers Daniel and Egypt while they were a part of the {A.N.C.} in Africa, fighting for the release of an {African politician, and celebrities}."

"I have been summoned by my mother to come home without wasting or losing another day immediately."

"Because my mother and I are the sole survivors of our small family tree. I am the only one left to reproduce our family through my body."

"I'm the only one left to tell the story of Journajesty to my oncoming family and teach the young of my village of this great village superhero of our land that was much more ancient than the present ancient could ever mean."

"Compared to the era of time that Journajesty, our village superhero of ancient times. Ancient as we relate to as ancient times two thousand years before the Messiah came upon the earth to save humanity and bring the gift of eternal life to those who believed in the Creator and His Son. My direct bloodline is connected to this great Conqueror."

"I am the last one of his kindred besides my mother, who is too old. She is unable and unqualified to carry on Journmajesty, the ancient superstar's legacy. I am the one chosen to keep his legacy alive by telling this so wonderful, magnificent, and adventurous story and producing oncoming generations of this great and first-ever superhero."

"I remember and appreciate what he has given to humanity and how proud I am to be a blood relative of this long time ago superhero of his era of time. A time when dinosaurs roamed the earth, and the people of the earth accounted for only of thousands of people that lived upon the earth, and the average lifespan of a human was sometimes almost a thousand years old."

Now Wendy Sundae has told one person in America the story of the first superhero ever on Earth. The wonderful story of Journmajesty was told to Pharaoh.

Pharaoh was overwhelmed, superbly Impressed, and downright amazed at the story Wendy Sundae told Pharaoh. Of "The Great Warrior, Soldier and Conqueror, Journmajesty!" Who not only conquered every tribe upon the earth but battled and won against dinosaurs, dragons, and other beasts.

After he had climbed the highest mountain, he swam across rivers many times until coming to a place so high in altitude that he got dizzy for hours. He then heard this tremendous sound as he continued towards the sound until the earth spoke. The soil told Journmajesty that he was treading on Holy ground and that the earth in which Jour-

majesty was treading was taboo for him to continue walking where no human feet had ever touched. Nor would any
human feet would ever touch.

CHAPTER 11

Holy Ground and Rhythm

Journajesty turned around to leave, and it was then that the same sound that had been so relaxing, so mellow, yet so beautiful in his ear. Now the sound seemed encouraging, daring, and so dramatized, strong, and tempting as the melody called him by name. It offered peace, unity, tranquility, and happiness forever after bringing the gift of gifts to God's people if he could pay the price to become kindred to the wind in some small but truthful way.

With the understanding that once advanced any further, there would be no turning back, but I will be with you forever. I am never leaving you because I am willing to give up my position as Daughter of the Wind, a highly prestigious title and the only title of its kind. There is no more like my famous mother, who is very close to God. If we succeed in our journey and accomplish the goal I have set to reach, the joy we will give humankind will be one of the greatest feelings between a man and God that will be felt in man's very bones.

And while tingling man's soul with the pleasure of two ears full, as humanity, hears through his ears, the magic of my voice, as man feels the unity of him and God in harmony with one another. Because, through my melody, God will touch the soul of humanity.

Journajesty, with a push of gravity, pushed onward, trying desperately to hold back the advancement towards continuing that the mighty and strong Journajesty succeeded in doing until Journajesty stood there in the very presence of Rhythm, the only offspring of the wind.

While Rhythm sang, danced, and performed for the mountains, the trees, and the sky, Rhythm also performed for certain angels who were privileged to enjoy the performance of Rhythm as she had been steadily performing for her ordinance for 500 days straight.

Rhythm had witnessed Journajesty as he made his way across the rivers and up the mountains. Journajesty followed the sounds of Rhythm's beautiful sounds. That fed Journajesty's soul and touched his heart. With admiration, peace, joy, and the will to continue to reach Rhythm finally. For the first time, who was performing for a new audience or added one other viewer to her audience?

Rhythm performed diligently to supersede all of her other performances. Rhythm performed for Journajesty, who was the sole navigator and orchestrator for the route of Journajesty's journey to reach Rhythm, for Rhythm had finally seen a way to be as important to God Almighty as her mother, the Wind. By uniting humanity and the sound of Rhythm so humanity could worship, praise, honor, and feel the spirit of God through his bones by Rhythm's vibrations from society to God.

True, Rhythm's existence came with the magnificent label of being Daughter of the Wind through her birth.

But Rhythm's one desire was to one day earn her place in God's heart and the heart of her mother, the Wind. The Wind is more powerful, meaningful, and admired by God than many. And whose daughter inherited all respect and obedience from all automatically.

For Rhythm has her accomplishments as her mother had, and the Wind did earn respect and obedience from all and was smiled upon by God Almighty. Now, Rhythm was not human, but she felt so much less than the elements of the earth, mountains, rivers, and seas. Still, Rhythm was so much more than a human and was respected as just a tiny bit above the elements of the earth, but only because of her mother's power, knowledge, and closeness to God almighty.

Rhythm had orchestrated a plan that included her desire for the human Journajesty, whom Rhythm herself had seen many times while he was performing feats of the impossible. And had become attracted to his overwhelming persistence to serve God. By leaving his signature of always giving God the glory for any advancement or achievement that Journajesty made to let people know that the credit is to God, not him.

For man is only a tool for God to do his accomplishments through. Journajesty was a human symbol of one human created above the average human, blessed by God with the qualities of a supernatural hero, a mythical image.

One that is reality, truth, and the real deal. Now, Rhythm had orchestrated a plan to bring Journajesty over the rivers and through the sea, and on to climb the highest mountain and reach the Holy ground where no human has ever walked and never would.

Journmajesty stood there in front of the sun, the moon, the mountains, and the sky, they all were on leisure time from the planet earth. And while a few angels were there also to enjoy the performance of Rhythm, she performed for the elements of the earth along with the mountains, rivers, and seas. And some angels gathered to witness this outstanding performance by Rhythm, Daughter of the Wind. Who did this performance quite regularly to give leisure time to creations of God that were not human, But did at some time need recognition that they were in existence too, and not just for the needs and wants of the planet earth. Still, they also needed time to praise God and enjoy being created.

It was then noticed that an alien was in the midst of the performance. A human, an undesirable, who had to ignore the warnings from the earth itself. Who had to warn this human that this was Holy ground. It was not to be walked upon by any man or any feet that were not holy or created in the image of not being able to sin or do wrong, but created only to do the will of God.

The mountain spoke and said, "For what reason are you here? Were you not warned from the cries of the earth that your feet are upon Holy ground and not to go no further? How did you get here? And what do you want?"

Journmajesty replied, "I am Journmajesty. A superhero of my era of time upon the planet earth. A so-called bastard child born out of wedlock by two young children of only fourteen. Who deeply loved one another and worshiped the Creator God Almighty? Under cover of nightfall, under the darkness of a tree, did have sexual contact and produced me out of the power and bowels of love."

"They did produce me, and the people in the village condemned my parent's acts that made me into the world as a bastard child out of wedlock. It caused them to be put to death for their sins.

"As my mother burned in the fire, with her last breath, she cried out to God and asked Him"

"That If You didn't see any wrong with what we did out of love. Please take good care of my son Journajesty, and make his name great throughout all of Africa, the land in which he was born, and give him a great gift that will make up for all the things that his parents never had a chance to give him, and into your hands, I give my son Journajesty."

The mountain speaking said, "The question was not from whence have you come? Or who your parents were, but instead, why are you here? What do you want, and how did you get here? You were warned by the earth, herself, that this is holy ground. And taboo to you and feet that are not holy.

Now! Journajesty heard this voice speaking and knew it had to be the voice of the mountain, being that it was so heavy and thunderous, like in a human-like manner.

Rhythm stopped her performance, and it was so quiet that you could hear silence in the air. That is when the mountain says, "I am in charge here even though Rhythm has authority. I sentence this alien who has trespassed on Holy ground and calls himself Journajesty, the bastard child of the earth, born out of wedlock. And speaking for all who are here, I sentence you to 500 years in the sea without coming to the surface to breathe.

After that time, I declare the sea to wash your bones ashore, back to the land from which you have come. And to have warned your people of the coming of that day, that your bones will be free to wash back up on the shore to dry land. All will be waiting for the bones of the Great Journmajesty to wash back up to the beach. That all can see and bear witness to your arrival from the sea after 500 years in captivity.

Everyone has two stones in their hand, one stone for leaving and one stone for returning your bones to be remembered by. Remember that no one is allowed on the Holy ground of God. For this ground is sacred to the creations of God that are human. But our workplace of the inhuman, holy servants of God. Our rest place is here, designated for our private use of the real superheroes of existence. That is not to be disturbed by any unholy feet that might touch our Holy ground."

It took two days for Journmajesty to finally reach the water after being thrown off the mountain that it had taken him so long to climb.

As Journmajesty kept reaching for something to grab onto, he finally realized that there was nothing to hold onto but the air. From which he was falling from. Then he finally hit the sea with a tremendous big splash, as his body punctured deeper and deeper into the sea. The deeper Journmajesty plunged into the sea, the colder the water began to be. It was then in Journmajesty's life that he knew that he had finally met something that he could not overtake.

So Journmajesty closed his eyes, mentally called to his God, and asked God not to let him know or feel fear. Journmajesty had never before known fear or been afraid of anything, anyone, nothing, or nobody. While all this was going on with Journmajesty, Rhythm had approached her mother, the Wind, and asked her mother to ask God if she, Rhythm, could accompany Journajesty on his death sentence. In hopes that Rhythm might be able to get into Journajesty's soul and into his bones. Like she had done before when Rhythm had provided the strength and courage for Journajesty to get over the land, seas, and up the mountains to reach the Holy ground.

And be with him as he withstood his punishment, given to him by the mountain for being on Holy ground, that was a resting place and a workplace for some of the most potent and meaningful unhuman creations of God. That supplied the earth with all of its resources. And essential supplies of the planet earth. Like the rain, moon, stars, mountains, rivers, and trees that all took turns in watching Rhythm perform for God, with her magnificent rhythm, dance, and melody.

They were all a part of her performance as she performed for God Almighty.

Rhythm felt assured that if her mother {The Wind} would ask God this, then God would not turn {the Wind} down. Because {The Wind} had special privileges from God Almighty. And after Rhythm told her mother {The Wind} of the plan that Rhythm had to bring melody, harmony, and the sound of the base to the people of the earth, So they could feel the presence and the Spirit of God running through their bones, heart, and soul.

That was the plan of rhythm, ever since she had first seen Journajesty in the womb of his mother. Rhythm also heard the cries of Journajesty's mother to God concerning her son Journajesty and that she knew she had to leave behind.

Hearing rumors of Journajesty's defeats on so many tribes in war, tearing down governments and other institutions that opposed his God in his manhood. Hearing how most of all that Journajesty loved and worshiped God.

Rhythm knew that uniting with Journajesty, and becoming one in unity with Journajesty, that the two together could bring forth to the planet earth. A sound never heard before on the planet earth that would be known as {The Spirit of God} when heard. Which also would be felt from man's head to man's toes through movements of man's bones, as man's soul would be delighted to hear this new thing called *Music*.

Enjoyed by all nations through all different tongues, which would be heard and interpreted by the sound as a universal language. It would also understand and relate to the sound of Music.

It would be a universal language understood by all tongues that heard the sound, speaking all languages, related to, and by the sound heard from one's ear, which could even soothe the heart, and soul of the savage beast when heard by one, or something other than a human.

Today, at this present era of time, the sound of Music can make one determine where they were at a specific date in time. The Music that one hears brings back memories of what happened at that particular time, from the Music that one hears to remind them of the time. That one ventured through or came through at a specific time and place.

So be it true was the times that Journajesty was weak and in turmoil from stress and pain and needed to breathe the air of the universe when he heard the sound of the thunderous drum-like sound that truly caught his attention. At the same time, the soothing sound of gentleness provided strength for him to ride on throughout the night, forgetting where he was.

When then came the sound of the trumpet, to call his attention, to collect his thoughts, and once again get his ideas and strength together to proceed. Through another day, week, month, and year, for Rhythm once again, through year after year, after year, through Music, heard in the ear of Journajesty felt in the heart, soul, and spirit of Journajesty who did withstand the 500-year death sentence given to him by the mountain, which was overthrown and countered by a sentence of 500 years without the sum of death, so agreed by the Creator {God Almighty}.

The Creator accepted the request to allow Rhythm to accompany Journajesty through Journajesty's 500-hundred-year sentence. It was a glorious day that the sea did wash Journajesty back up upon the shores of Africa. All the people of the present 500-year population and the population of the past 500 years were there. They all each had two stones in their hands like the mountain had demanded, even though the mountain knew not then that Journajesty would be alive.

The mountain pronounced the demand of two stones for each pair of hands that would be there to greet Journajesty's s bones.

As Journajesty stood upon the seashore, he was no longer Journajesty. Nor was Rhythm any longer Rhythm, but they were united. They both together were one. And they together as one was called (Music). Thousands of people clapped their hands together to bring forth the first sound of Music, Which brought fascination, tears, triumph, and holiness to the people's hearts, souls, minds, and spirits. That everyone there that day did feel in their bones. The magnificent feeling from their head bones to their toe bones, the incredible sense of the spirit of God's love running through their bones.

So born that day was the introduction to Music upon the earth, which was Rhythm's gift to the human race to modify in worship, their worship to God as Rhythm united man with the spiritual feelings of God running through his bones, his heart, and man's soul.

Every time you hear the sound of Music in any sound, shape, fashion, or form, if you close your eyes, you will see Journajesty and Rhythm as the cornerstones, originators, and creators of Music.

And everyone alive this present day whose bones cannot keep still, be it your hand bone, knee bone, foot bone, shoulder bone, or backbone. You automatically feel them moving when Music is played, whether you be black, white, red, yellow, or any other color, race, or culture.

If your bones move automatically to Music or rhythm, then you are of inheritance of someone there when Journajesty and Rhythm emerged from the sea as Music or as one. And the sound of the two rocks in the hands of the people, waiting for the bones of this great warrior, conqueror, and worshiper of God Almighty to be washed ashore, as Music was born upon the earth. And Music's harmony, and rhythm, from the sound of the two rocks in the hands of the thousands of viewers, that had come to see the bones of Journajesty washed back home, upon the shores of Africa.

That sound did intertwine as Music was heard for the very first time upon the shores of Africa. The music was so loud and dramatizing that it was heard back to the mountain, Who smiled and thanked God for God's decision to grant Rhythm her wish and desire to present man with such a present. To hear something that would make them feel God throughout their bones from head to toe.

What a Glorious Day! Now Pharaoh was convinced that Wendy Sundae's story concerning her two brothers' death was true.

Pharaoh also believed Wendy Sundae's story of Journajesty, Rhythm, and Music. Pharaoh's heart was lifted a few days later when Wendy Sundae told Pharaoh that she was no longer interested in being a hitwoman or being an assassinator of black or white people.

Before Wendy Sundae could finish, Pharaoh smiled and said, "God has moved your heart from seeking revenge and the taking of life. To seek to rekindle your life and legend with your family while bringing back to life the legend of the great warrior and conqueror of your own bloodline. To be reintroduced to your people again. It should also be introduced to the world by you, Wendy Sundae."

Pharaoh also wondered about this great warrior, conqueror, legendary myth of a man, and did he live during the time of Enoch, father of Methuselah, who was the oldest man that ever lived on the planet earth. At that time, men lived between three hundred years of age, up to nine hundred and some years of age.

That was during the time before the flood that God sent against the earth because of the constant sinning of humanity.

After Wendy Sundae left to go back home, after Maria left to go back home, and Star was no longer in the picture, it came to be that Pharaoh was lonely.

Pharaoh hated starting new relationships that caused for the first time that two people kissed, had sex, and learned the favorite foods while learning each other's likes and would accept from his female friends. And together, they would have peaceful, understanding, exciting, and happy relationships for decades without negative interruptions without uncalled-for disagreements, and negative attitudes.

It just happened that way, but both Maria and Wendy Sundae was out of Pharaoh's life for a while. Pharaoh knew not how long it would be before he would be reunited with either Maria or Wendy Sundae but that same day, he would be feeling sexually aroused by a scene that he had seen while in the heart of the ghetto.

Seeing a little short big butt female ghetto female riding a bicycle and just pumping the bike peddles away, while that enormously perfect butt just kept dramatizing Pharaoh's imagination. Approaching this female close up, Pharaoh could see the top of her panties and their color halfway up her back just from standing behind her.

Now ghetto girls are different from most girls in the entire land of America. They have to learn how to survive, learn how to cope with stress, and be better than their competition. Whether in school, workplace, home or in the street, while their loyalty to you can be defended with their life.

Or, their loyalty can be destructive to whoever wrongs them.

{Beth} was her name, and she would be one of the females that made it possible for Pharaoh not to Miss Maria and Wendy Sundae, not like Pharaoh thought he would. Beth had just buried her boyfriend and was in mourning. And believing that no one could ever take her past friend's place who had just died.

Beth was young, pretty, with not too much education from school, but with a daughter who learned to love and appreciate Pharaoh. He did right and treated Beth and her daughter like they were blood family with a bond of truth and right between them. Even though Pharaoh had explained to Beth that he already had a girlfriend, they could also be friends. Beth was mentally strong even though she had a few skeletons in her closet dating back to when she had a nervous breakdown and was on medication that made her see shit that wasn't there sometimes. She was the best, dependable, loving, sincere baby of twelve children. She was a fighter, a tomboy; she played basketball, baseball ran track, and she was an excellent mother and a very good cook.

She was one to always put Pharaoh first in her life, and she was a good woman. Beth was awarded a house on section 8 or whatever the section was called then.

But Beth had four rooms of furniture in storage that belonged to her when she was keeping house with her boyfriend that died. After his death, Beth put her furniture in storage and went and lived back with her mother and father and three of her brothers until she met Pharaoh.

Pharaoh did become very good friends with Beth's family, even though Pharaoh was well acquainted with Beth's brothers, and one of Beth's brothers would become lifetime buddies with Pharaoh. He stayed in contact with Pharaoh through phone conversations from time to time even after Beth and Pharaoh's relationship seized.

After the acquaintance between Pharaoh and Beth was made, Beth was awarded the section 8 house. She had been waiting in line to get the section 8 house for two years. In which Beth and Pharaoh had enjoyed a relationship together. Along with Brown Eyes and Goldie, after Star, Pharaoh's son's mother.

Who had asked Pharaoh one day out of the clear blue sky to either marry her or leave her?

Pharaoh, not wanting to be told what to do and when to do it, did decide to leave. Pharaoh took nothing with him because he thought that Star, the mother of his two sons, was just blowing off steam. {So, to speak} And would stop acting like that when she would see that she couldn't make Pharaoh marry her until he was ready to marry her.

Pharaoh would have married her when he was ready for marriage if Star had continued to wait on him. Star had indeed been waiting for Pharaoh to marry her for twenty years.

Star had been the perfect girlfriend to Pharaoh, always putting him first before all things and anyone. Even though he respected, appreciated, and loved Star in his own genuine and sincere way, Pharaoh was not ready to give up his freedom as a bachelor and marry Star or anyone at that particular time.

Pharaoh had just walked out of the house. As Pharaoh walked out the door, he turned and said to Star, "I don't know what's wrong with you today. But maybe you know something that I don't know. By your actions, you are either super stupid or super smart. For you decision here today, and only time will tell whether you are super stupid or super smart."

While Pharaoh was leaving, his youngest son {Tony} said to him, "Take me with you?"

After leaving the house with Star and Pharaoh's two young sons, Pharaoh rented a room one block from the campus of Morgan University and went back to college. That is when he met Beth, who immediately took over the place of Star because those two Star and Beth were so much alike in loving and doing for Pharaoh above and beyond all others.

Beth never gave Pharaoh the chance to miss Star and Pharaoh used Beth's house as one of the places where he laid his head to sleep at night. In Beth's house were tens of thousands of dollars that Pharaoh would leave there at times for days and weeks. Never, not one dollar was missing.

Love, respect, appreciation, and trust lived in Beth's house with Beth, Beth's daughter, {Alecia} and Pharaoh when he stayed there.

Now Goldie was the little girl who lived down the street from Pharaoh when Pharaoh lived with Mama Grace. She had once rung the doorbell of Mama Grace's house and told Pharaoh that she loved him and would marry him.

Then Goldie jumped off the steps and ran home. On that very day, Goldie was seven years old when she told Pharaoh that she loved him and Pharaoh was twenty-two.

Eighteen years past and Goldie had two children before Pharaoh's youngest daughter Debra Lee Gold asked her father, Pharaoh. Ask Goldie if she would come and stay a few hours every evening to cook, clean up, wash, and iron clothes for Mama Grace. Mama Grace was now an old lady in years and short on remembering sometimes even who she was.

Pharaoh's youngest daughter Debra Lee Gold and Pharaoh who was not home or in town sometimes, and Goldie did agree. Pharaoh did pay her well, and Pharaoh felt comfortable when he was home. Also, when he was out of town because he trusted and believed in Goldie taking care of his house and his young daughter and Mama Grace while he was there and away.

Now! Mama Grace had become old and was beginning to be senile in her old age. Pharaoh had gotten a house for Mama Grace to live with him in which Pharaoh loved every day to see Mama Grace living with him and his youngest daughter Debra Lee Gold.

It was a great joy and blessing from God Almighty for Pharaoh to have gotten the gift from God, for Pharaoh to be able to take care of Mama Grace, whom he loved with all his heart. Mama Grace was the very one to have raised Pharaoh from the age of two months old until he was four years old.

Then Pharaoh found out that Mama Grace was not Pharaoh's biological mother. Pharaoh lived with Mama Grace until he was twenty-five years of age.

Mama Grace was the one who had first introduced Pharaoh to God and taught Pharaoh the Christian life and everything Pharaoh learned that was good and righteous.

Pharaoh learned from Mama Grace's Grace Memorial Baptist Church, which Mama Grace was a long-time member, and one of the founders of. She was also the treasurer, a singer in the church choir, and the leader of the church Prayer Mob. That practiced, prayed upon, prayed for, and witnessed all in Mama Grace's house. But that had been years ago, and now, Pharaoh had been allowed by God Almighty to take care of Mama Grace. Like Mama Grace once took care of Pharaoh and provided Pharaoh with a home, love, a Christian background, and righteous morals and principles.

Now! For a fact, Mama Grace loved Goldie and Beth, and even though Mama Grace knew Goldie all Goldie's life. Goldie and her whole family lived right down the street from Mama Grace before Goldie was even born.

Mama Grace knew and associated her family with Goldie's family for years before Goldie was born. Mama Grace knew and loved Beth because Beth was Pharaoh's girlfriend and was a good, respectful and loving woman.

Beth and Brown Eyes were Pharaoh's girlfriends after Star and Pharaoh had broken up their relationship for so many years because Pharaoh refused to marry Star at that particular time. Mama Grace loved, talked to, and respected Beth and Brown Eyes for being Pharaoh's girlfriends.

Now! Brown Eyes, like Paula, the female that used to be Pharaoh's everything, proved to be incapable, unreliable, and undependable when it boiled down to putting Pharaoh first and doing whatever Pharaoh asked to be done.

When Pharaoh did need her, but both Brown Eyes and Paula were two beautiful women with the intelligence of a college dean. And the nerve and balls of a true gangster, and even though Pharaoh, for a fact, never missed Paula.

Star had been there and performed for Pharaoh for twenty years. That is because Star stepped right in and ful-filled Pharaoh's every desire, need, and want that could be fulfilled. That is the same thing that Beth and Brown Eyes did together to make Pharaoh not miss Star.

Then Pharaoh never missed or needed Star, even though Pharaoh appreciated all Star had done for him.

Now! Brown Eyes was a beautiful light brown-skinned female who Pharaoh met while coming up on his brother Jonny's job to talk with him about a matter of importance. When Brown Eyes opened the office door and asked Pha-raoh, "Who would you like to speak to? And could she be of any help to him?"

At that moment, Pharaoh's brother Jonny Greeted Pha-raoh by shaking Pharaoh's hand and hugging Pharaoh.

Then introducing Pharaoh to Mrs. Marylyn by say-ing, "This is my manager and boss of the whole building, {Brown Eyes" {which was the name that Pharaoh had given her}. Because of her pretty Brown Eyes that sparkled beau-tifully brown, especially in the sun.

Brown Eyes was a beautiful female with pretty hair, teeth, and skin, while her intelligence was astonishing. Brown Eyes could get off from her daily professional and legiti-mate job, strap on a shoulder holster under her two-piece professional suit, and keep on her high heel shoes. She also wore it as part of her professional work code for her job. Her shoes fitted her big pretty legs that were perfect for her sort of tall height, and Brown Eyes had balls. She was not afraid to do anything that Pharaoh would do but asked her to do. Pharaoh feared nothing but God.

Brown Eyes loved Jesus and was the one to help Pharaoh get closer to Jesus when Pharaoh used to pray only to God. Even though Pharaoh believed in Jesus and knew Jesus as the begotten Son of God, Pharaoh did distinguish how Pharaoh worshiped God. By not giving Jesus the worship and praise through prayer, Pharaoh should have been giving Jesus, the begotten Son of God. With much prayer and faith, Pharaoh gave to God but did not do the same with Jesus until Brown Eyes showed Pharaoh the mistake he was making.

Now it was about this time that Dapping Slim, the brother of Shark Skin, was both the best friends of Pharaoh at that particular time.

Dapping Slim did know the many brothers of Beth and knew Beth as an excellent and respectful girl. Dapping Slim did know that Pharaoh and Beth now had a relationship, and he was proud and glad for Pharaoh to be in a relationship with someone like Beth. She was a neighborhood girl, a good girl, and a fine young mother to her daughter.

Now! At this time, Pharaoh was living in a room one block from the college campus he was then attending after he and Star had broken up for the first time in twenty years.

It was the first time that Pharaoh had taken a female to his room while attending college classes.

To Pharaoh's surprise, while he was taking a shower, Beth climbed down out the second-floor window by way of the drainpipe as Pharaoh was stepping out the shower through the bathroom window. Pharaoh did witness Beth reaching the ground from the second-floor window. Pharaoh called to Beth. Beth broke out in a track star move and ran home about three miles.

Pharaoh never forgot that episode from Beth and witnessed a few more odd similar situations. Still, never nothing harmful or in contrast of Beth's wonderfulness or goodness, and nothing never upset the beauty of the beautiful smile in which only Beth herself could display.

Now! Dapping Slim, the brother of Shark Skin, the two best friends of Pharaoh, did sometimes tease Pharaoh about which girl Pharaoh would end up with Between Star and Paula but had recently become a figment of one's imagination. Even though at one particular time, there could only be a question of which one of the two women between Star and Paula would still be with Pharaoh at the end.

It seems as if time waits for no one, and time has endings for all situations regardless of what one may think, believe, or elaborate on. Neither Paula nor Star was in the picture to be at Pharaoh's side or the one seen or related to as Pharaoh's woman. Both have been removed and replaced with others playing those roles and parts as Pharaoh's woman or Pharaoh's fiancé.

They are Beth and Brown Eyes, which unbeknownst to anyone, will soon be one that will replace all. Never be challenged or called out of her position as the second female to share Pharaoh's name, heart, love, or soul.

When asked the great question from Dapping Slim concerning who or what woman in Pharaoh's life did he love the most?

And not knowing how many women Pharaoh would have in his lifetime. Pharaoh's answer was that, at the time, and for all times, each person, he loved them all at the time it was, that was their time to deserve to be loved by Pharaoh. For love, they were giving up to Pharaoh by the standards that were only known by those giving themselves in pure love and devotion to Pharaoh without any demands, complications, or rules or regulations in return.

That lasted until the giving of true love and devotion seized from the giver to Pharaoh and found problems within the relationship that caused constant confusion, disbelief, static, and no satisfaction. Now! Pharaoh looked at love from a viewpoint seen seldom by people, for love was a gift that Almighty God had blessed Pharaoh with from the day when Pharaoh was but six weeks old. Mama Grace received the smile that Pharaoh, even as still an infant, gave to Mama Grace as a genuine token and symbol of his love for her.

She, in return, did take care of Pharaoh, teach Pharaoh the Christian way. Love Pharaoh and put into Pharaoh's arsenal for survival skills how one conducts himself as a righteous man. An honest man and a man of principles and character, but not only did God bless Pharaoh with the love and care of Mama Grace but also his birthright mother, his grandmother on his mother's side.

Mama Grace's husband provided for Pharaoh and played the father role in Pharaoh's life. A blood brother, a foster brother whom Pharaoh loved and who loved Pharaoh just as much as Pharaoh loved him.

A blood sister, Catrina, a foster sister, Carolyn, who Pharaoh always held close to his heart. A whole church and all the church members individually, a whole neighborhood where Pharaoh lived. His school and classmates, first love, wife, and forever friend.

All these people gave unconditional love to Pharaoh as a child. They filled his life with the joy of real love, which grew Pharaoh up into manhood as one that has known real love, and that Almighty God has given the pleasure of knowing the many strengths of having love to back you up. Which made Pharaoh look at love from a different viewpoint as to not being the type of person to care about who he loved because it matters to Pharaoh who loves him and how much they love him other than who Pharaoh loves.

You can't make someone love you because you love them. It is when someone loves you and proves to you by showing, telling, establishing, and continuously showing you love and always being there for you when everyone else is gone. Then you have to eventually love them back with an appreciative sort of love which is not just love, but a love from you that shows that you have not only learned to love them but that you appreciate them and their love for you.

Now! Time waited for no one, and time did pass, and Pharaoh was seventy-four years of age. While at the Y. M. C. A., Pharaoh had first walked around the lake for twenty minutes. Which was Pharaoh's secret way of making it still factual for his Johnson to still rise and be active maybe every three or four weeks at a time, it was Pharaoh's daily routine. It was then that Pharaoh noticed that the man across from him kept looking across and starring at Pharaoh. Pharaoh noticed something different about the man that was staring at him.

The man seemed to be not of the American culture in his clothes, and it was then that the man came over and spoke to Pharaoh.

His voice did carry an accent. "I know one that you call your friend," the man said to Pharaoh. "But let me introduce myself, my name is (123), and I am here to ask you a simple question so I won't have to spend half my life looking for something that you can tell me the answer to now."

Now Pharaoh had not even allowed himself to think of the days back when he ran a vendetta on the Brothers Three when he affiliated himself with (123) and the beautiful Maria. Which all was a lifestyle that Pharaoh was a part of over fifty years ago. Which he never missed since he married his second wife in 2000 even though Pharaoh was thirty years older than her. He had not been untrue to her in the twenty years they had been married.

She was the one who introduced Pharaoh to the brand-new world of business, which used credit cards, computers, debit cards, fax machines, emails, text messages, and a host of other new adventures to the world of business.

Pharaoh knew that he had better not say anything or ask anything until he found out who this person was. This person was now standing in front of him, saying he was (123). The man that said he was (123) stretched out his hand in a greetings posture, and in return, Pharaoh did shake his hand.

Pharaoh said to (123), you said you know a friend of mine. I am a man with some wrinkles, some gray, and much activity in my time. And I have always trusted in the Lord my God, who has never failed me. But most all my friends are dead or in the penitentiary. So, it would help if you meant that you know an associate of mine, not a friend. But what is it I can do for you? What is the reason that you are here?"

"I am here because my father spent over half his life looking for the hiding place or the whereabouts of your God. We all know that your God is here in America somewhere."

Pharaoh smiled and said to (123), "I once knew a (123). I believe I did mention it to some people who were about to rob the (123) that I knew. I did mention to the robbers that (123) was my friend, even though (123) would have probably killed them all before they would have been able to rob him."

"As for my God, well! God for certain is in America, but God is not standing around like a normal person. If you are truly looking for God, you have to clean out your heart and your soul. Receive Him into your heart and soul because He is to be found in the hearts and souls of all men that believe in Him and His Son, my Lord and Savior Jesus Christ, who also is God."

"You are one of the humans that follow Satan, who knows God better than any. But if you were to ask Satan of God, then Satan would destroy you for even asking him of God Almighty, who also created Satan."

"He found Satan sinful and kicked Satan out of heaven and also the followers of Satan. God lives in the hearts and souls of humankind that believe in Almighty God and Jesus Christ as the begotten Son of God, which are the people that keep America strong. By fighting for freedom, peace, justice, and equality for all Americans."

"I am sure that all I have said to you is in vain, for you are a follower of Satan and one who participates in hoping to be a part of the class that rules the world under the command of Satan," Pharaoh said to the stranger.

The man that said his name was (123) and thanked Pharaoh. He started to leave and turned halfway around to say, "I was told that you were a just man. A man of the God that you believe in. But speak of what you know, Pharaoh, and you know nothing of me."

"For some reason or another, I am interested in what you have been doing in your life for the past fifty years. Those are missing from the time you once knew my people. And my people knew only of you instead of knowing you. Do you know the whereabouts of Yaya's son?"

Maria has been completely converted into believing in your God and that Maria is still alive and teaching the Word of your God to the young people of her country.

Lastly, Pharaoh says, "I know nothing of or about Yaya's son, nor do I know anything about Maria. The fifty years of my life that you seem to be looking for are all there in the books, read them because there are two of them. *Righteousness In America* is the name of the books. Book 1, and Book 2."

Printed in the USA
CPSIA information can be obtained
at www.ICGtesting.com
CBHW071653230424
7244CB00006B/18

9 781685 156152